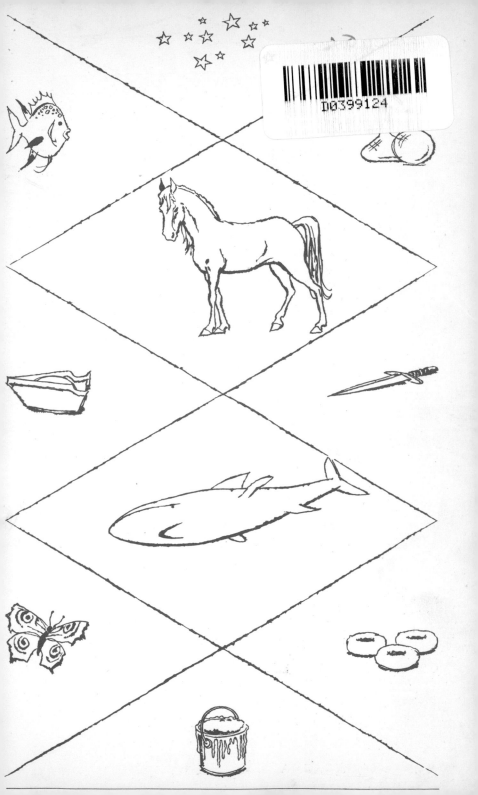

The Family
Treasury of
Children's Stories

Book Three

The Family Treasury of Children's Stories

edited by PAULINE RUSH EVANS

illustrated by DONALD SIBLEY

DOUBLEDAY & COMPANY, INC., *Garden City, New York*

Pauline Rush Evans has had wide experience in working with parents and children. After she received her M.A. in Child Psychology from Columbia, she joined the staff of the Child Study Association of America, where for nine years she edited the magazine CHILD STUDY and served as publications editor of the Association. From 1950 to 1954 she was an assistant editor at Doubleday and was the associated editor of the ENCYCLOPE-DIA OF CHILD CARE AND GUIDANCE. Mrs. Evans divides her time between New York City and a dairy farm in Danbury, Connecticut.

Don Sibley is a talented young artist who has had considerable success as a commercial illustrator and has also done work on children's books. He lives in Syosset, New York, and has three children—his most enthusiastic and severest critics.

Acknowledgments

George Allen & Unwin, Ltd. for "A Monster In the Pacific" from KON-TIKI: ACROSS THE PACIFIC IN A RAFT by Thor Heyerdahl. J. M. Dent & Sons, Ltd. for "A Serpent Mystery" from FAR AWAY AND LONG AGO by W. H. Hudson. Dodd, Mead & Company, Inc. for "The Great Peacock Moth" from THE INSECT WORLD OF J. HENRI FABRE by Edwin Way Teale. Copyright © 1916 by Dodd, Mead & Company, Inc. Renewal copyright by William Russell Geoffrey. Doubleday & Company, Inc. for "Four Years in a Shed" from MADAME CURIE by Eve Curie. Copyright 1937 by Doubleday & Company, Inc. Reprinted by permission of the publishers. E. P. Dutton & Co., Inc. for "The Summit" by Sir Edmund Hillary from THE CONQUEST OF EVEREST by Sir John Hunt. Copyright, 1953, by Sir John Hunt; "A Serpent Mystery" from FAR AWAY AND LONG AGO by W. H. Hudson. Copyright, 1918, E. P. Dutton & Co., Inc. Renewal, 1946, Royal Society for the Protection of Birds. Reprinted by permission of the publishers. Harper & Brothers for "The Cat and the Pain-Killer" from ADVENTURES OF TOM SAWYER by Mark Twain; THE NIGHT THE BED FELL by James Thurber. Copyright © 1933 The New Yorker Magazine, Inc. Reprinted by permission of the author. Harcourt, Brace and Company, Inc. for "George Washington, The Boy" from LEADER BY DESTINY by Jeanette Eaton, copyright 1938, by Harcourt, Brace and Company, Inc.; "Peculiarsome Abe" from ABE LINCOLN GROWS UP by Carl Sandburg 1926, 1928, by Harcourt, Brace and Company, Inc. Used by permission of the publishers. Hodder & Stoughton, Ltd. for "The Summit" by Sir Edmund Hillary from THE ASCENT OF EVEREST (The Conquest of Everest) by Sir John Hunt, based on the original despatches from Brigadier Sir John Hunt and other members of the Everest Expedition to The Times. Henry Holt and Company, Inc. for "Fog" from CHICAGO POEMS by Carl Sandburg. Copyright, 1916, by Henry Holt and Company, Inc. Copyright, 1944, by Carl Sandburg; "Silver" from COLLECTED POEMS by Walter de la Mare. Copyright, 1920, by Henry Holt and Company, Inc. Copyright, 1948, by Walter de la Mare; "Stopping by Woods on a Snowy Evening" from COMPLETE POEMS OF ROBERT FROST. Copyright, 1930, 1949, by Henry Holt and Company, Inc. Reprinted by permission of the publishers. J. B. Lippincott Company for "Trouble in the Calf Pasture" from MY FRIEND FLICKA by Mary O'Hara. Copyright 1941 by Mary O'Hara. Reprinted by permission of the author. "The Admiral's Ghost" from COLLECTED POEMS VOLUME II by Alfred Noyes. Copyright 1906, 1934 by Alfred Noyes. Reprinted by permission of J. B. Lippincott Company, the author, and Wm. Blackwood

Contents

A Glimpse into . . .

The Wide Wonderful World

A *Taste of* . . .

The Pleasures of Great Books

True and Could-be True . . .

Stories

of

Adventure

The Call of the Wild

by JACK LONDON

After John Thornton had saved the life of the big dog Buck, the strong affection between the two gives rise to many dramatic episodes, such as the testing of Buck's extraordinary strength described in this chapter. Jack London could write about the primitive days in the camps of Alaska with honest realism and genuine atmosphere because he had actually lived that life when he was prospecting for gold in the Klondike. The characters of Thornton's friends and enemies in the camp are sketched with great skill. But what you will remember always is the quality of the emotional bond and complete communication between master and heroic dog. This has never been better told in any animal story.

When John Thornton froze his feet in the previous December, his partners had made him comfortable and left him to get well, going on themselves up the river to get out a raft of saw logs for Dawson. He was still limping slightly at the time he rescued Buck, but with the continued warm weather even the slight limp left him. And here, lying by the river bank through the long spring days, watching the running water, listening lazily to the songs of birds and the hum of nature, Buck slowly won back his strength.

A rest comes very good after one has traveled three thousand miles, and it must be confessed that Buck waxed lazy as his wounds healed, his muscles swelled out, and the flesh came back to cover his bones. For that matter, they were all loafing—Buck, John Thornton, and Skeet and Nig—waiting for the raft to come that was to carry them down to Dawson. Skeet was a little Irish setter who early made friends with Buck who, in a dying condition, was unable to resent her first advances. She had the doctor trait which some dogs possess, and as a mother cat washes her kittens, so she washed and cleansed Buck's wounds. Regularly, each morning after he had finished his breakfast, she performed her self-appointed task, till he came to look for her ministrations as much as he did for Thornton's. Nig, equally friendly, though less demonstrative, was a huge black dog, half bloodhound and half deerhound, with eyes that laughed and a boundless good nature.

To Buck's surprise these dogs manifested no jealousy toward him. They seemed to share the kindliness and largeness of John Thornton. As Buck grew stronger they enticed him into all sorts of ridiculous games, in which Thornton himself could not forbear to join, and in this fashion Buck romped through his convalescence and into a new existence. Love, genuine passionate love, was his for the first time. This he had never experienced at Judge Miller's down in the sun-kissed Santa Clara Valley. With the Judge's sons, hunting and tramping, it had been a working partnership; with the Judge's grandsons, a sort of pompous guardianship; and with the Judge himself, a stately and dignified friendship. But love that was feverish and burning, that was adoration, that was madness, it had taken John Thornton to arouse.

This man had saved his life, which was something; but, further, he was the ideal master. Other men saw to the welfare of their dogs from a sense of duty and business expediency; he saw to the welfare of his as if they were his own children, because he could not help it. And he saw further. He never forgot a kindly greeting or a cheering word, and to sit down for a long talk with them ("gas" he called it) was as much his delight as theirs. He had a way of taking Buck's head roughly between his hands, and resting his own head upon Buck's, of shaking him back and forth, the while calling him ill names that to Buck were love names. Buck knew no greater joy than that rough embrace and the sound of murmured oaths, and at each jerk back and forth it seemed that his heart would be shaken out of his body so great was his ecstasy. And when, released, he sprang to his feet, his mouth laughing, his eyes eloquent, his throat vibrant with unuttered sound, and in that fashion remained without movement, John Thornton would reverently exclaim, "God! you can all but speak!"

Buck had a trick of love expression that was akin to hurt. He would often seize Thornton's hand in his mouth and close so fiercely that the flesh bore the impress of his teeth for some time afterward. And as Buck understood the oaths to be love words, so the man understood this feigned bite for a caress.

For the most part, however, Buck's love was expressed in adoration. While he went wild with happiness when Thornton touched him or spoke to him, he did not seek these tokens. Unlike Skeet, who was wont to shove her nose under Thornton's hand and nudge and nudge till petted, or Nig, who would stalk up and rest his great head on Thornton's knee, Buck was content to adore at a distance. He would lie by the hour, eager, alert, at Thornton's feet, looking up into his face, dwelling upon it, studying it, following with keenest interest each fleeting expression, every movement or change of feature. Or, as chance might have it, he would lie farther away, to the side or rear, watching the outlines of the man and the occasional movements of his body. And often, such was the communion in which they lived, the strength of Buck's gaze would draw John Thornton's head around, and he would return the gaze, without speech, his heart shining out of his eyes as Buck's heart shone out.

For a long time after his rescue, Buck did not like Thornton to get out of his sight. From the moment he left the tent to when he entered it again, Buck would follow at his heels. His transient masters since he had come into the Northland had bred in him a fear that no master could be permanent. He was afraid that Thornton would pass out of his life as Perrault and François and the Scotch half-breed had passed out. Even in the night, in his dreams, he was haunted by this fear. At such times he would shake off sleep and creep through the chill to the flap of the tent, where he would stand and listen to the sound of his master's breathing.

But in spite of this great love he bore John Thornton, which seemed to bespeak the soft civilizing influence, the strain of the primitive, which the Northland had aroused in him, remained alive and active. Faithfulness and devotion, things born of fire and roof, were his; yet he retained his wildness and wiliness. He was a thing of the wild, come in from the wild to sit by John Thornton's fire, rather than a dog of the soft Southland stamped with the marks of generations of civilization. Because of his very great love, he could not steal from this man, but from any other man, in any other camp, he did not hesitate an instant; while the cunning with which he stole enabled him to escape detection.

His face and body were scored by the teeth of many dogs, and he fought as fiercely as ever and more shrewdly. Skeet and Nig were too good-natured for quarrelling—besides, they belonged to John Thornton. But the strange dog, no matter what the breed or valor, swiftly acknowledged Buck's supremacy or found himself struggling for life with a terrible antagonist. And Buck was merciless. He had learned well the law of club and fang, and he never forewent an advantage or drew back from a foe he had started on the way to Death. He had lessoned from Spitz, and from the chief fighting dogs of the police and mail, and knew there was no middle course. He must master or be mastered; while to show mercy was a weakness. Mercy did not exist in the primordial life. It was misunderstood for fear, and such misunderstandings made for death. Kill or be killed, eat or be eaten, was the law; and this mandate, down out of the depths of Time, he obeyed.

He was older than the days he had seen and the breaths he had drawn. He linked the past with the present, and the eternity behind him throbbed through him in a mighty rhythm to which he swayed as the tides and seasons swayed. He sat by John Thornton's fire, a broad-breasted dog, white-fanged and long-furred; but behind him were the shades of all manner of dogs, half-wolves and wild wolves, urgent and prompting, tasting the savor of the meat he ate, thirsting for the water he drank, scenting the wind with him, listening with him and telling him the sounds made by the wild life in the forest, dictating his moods, directing his actions, lying down to sleep with him when he lay down, and dreaming with him and beyond him and becoming themselves the stuff of his dreams.

So peremptorily did these shades beckon him that each day mankind and the claims of mankind slipped farther from him. Deep in the forest a call was sounding, and as often as he heard this call, mysteriously thrilling and luring, he felt compelled to turn his back upon the fire and the beaten earth around it, and to plunge into the forest, and on and on, he knew not where or why; nor did he wonder where or why, the call sounding imperiously, deep in the forest. But as often as he gained the soft unbroken earth and the green shade, the love for John Thornton drew him back to the fire again.

Thornton alone held him. The rest of mankind was as nothing. Chance travelers might praise or pet him; but he was cold under it all, and from a too demonstrative man he would get up and walk away. When Thornton's partners, Hans and Pete, arrived on the long-expected raft, Buck refused to notice them till he learned they were close to Thornton; after that he tolerated them in a passive sort of way, accepting favors from them as though he favored them by accepting. They were of the same large type as Thornton, living close to the earth, thinking simply and seeing clearly; and ere they swung the raft into the big eddy by the sawmill at Dawson, they understood Buck and his ways, and did not insist upon an intimacy such as obtained with Skeet and Nig.

For Thornton, however, his love seemed to grow and grow. He, alone among men, could put a pack upon Buck's back in the summer traveling. Nothing was too great for Buck to do when Thornton commanded. One day (they had grub-staked themselves from the proceeds of the raft and left Dawson for the headwaters of the Tanana) the men and dogs were sitting on the crest of a cliff which fell away, straight down, to naked bed-rock three hundred feet below. John Thornton was sitting near the edge, Buck at his shoulder. A thoughtless whim seized Thornton, and he drew the attention of Hans and Pete to the experiment he had in mind. "Jump, Buck!" he commanded, sweeping his arm out and over the chasm. The next instant he was grappling with Buck on the extreme edge, while Hans and Pete were dragging them back into safety.

"It's uncanny," Pete said, after it was over and they had caught their speech.

Thornton shook his head. "No, it is splendid, and it is terrible, too. Do you know, it sometimes makes me afraid."

"I'm not hankering to be the man that lays hands on you while he's around," Pete announced conclusively, nodding his head toward Buck.

"Py jingo!" was Hans' contribution. "Not mineself either."

It was at Circle City, ere the year was out, that Pete's apprehensions were realized. "Black" Burton, a man evil-tempered and malicious, had been picking a quarrel with a tenderfoot at the bar, when Thornton stepped good-naturedly between. Buck, as was his custom, was lying in a corner, head on paws, watching his master's every action. Burton struck out, without warning, straight from the shoulder. Thornton was sent spinning, and saved himself from falling only by clutching the rail of the bar.

Those who were looking on heard what was neither bark nor yelp, but a something which is best described as a roar, and they saw Buck's body rise up in the air as he left the floor for Burton's throat. The man saved his life by instinctively throwing out his arm, but was hurled backward to the floor with Buck on top of him. Buck loosed his teeth from the flesh of the arm and drove in again for the throat. This time the man succeeded only in partly blocking, and his throat was torn open. Then the crowd was upon Buck, and he was driven off; while a surgeon checked the bleeding, he prowled up and down, growling furiously, attempting to rush in, and being forced back by an array of hostile clubs. A "miners' meeting," called on the spot, decided that the dog had sufficient provocation, and Buck was discharged. But his reputation was made, and from that day his name spread through every camp in Alaska.

Later on, in the fall of the year, he saved John Thornton's life in quite another fashion. The three partners were lining a long and narrow poling-boat down a bad stretch of rapids on the Forty-Mile Creek. Hans and Pete moved along the bank, snubbing with a thin Manila rope from tree to tree, while Thornton remained in the boat, helping its descent by means of a pole, and shouting directions to the shore. Buck, on the bank, worried and anxious, kept abreast of the boat, his eyes never off his master.

At a particularly bad spot, where a ledge of barely submerged rocks jutted out into the river, Hans cast off the rope, and, while Thornton poled the boat out into the stream, ran down the bank with the end in his hand to snub the boat when it had cleared the ledge. This it did, and was flying downstream in a current as swift as a millrace, when Hans checked it with the rope and checked too suddenly. The boat flirted over and snubbed in to the bank bottom up, while Thornton, flung sheer out of it, was carried downstream toward the worst part of the rapids, a stretch of wild water in which no swimmer could live.

Buck had sprung in on the instant, and at the end of three hundred yards, amid a mad swirl of water, he overhauled Thornton. When he felt him grasp his tail, Buck headed for the bank, swimming with all his splendid strength. But the progress shoreward was slow; the progress downstream amazingly rapid. From below came the fatal roaring where the wild current went wilder and was rent in shreds and spray by the rocks which thrust through like the teeth of an enormous comb. The suck of the water as it took the beginning of the last steep pitch was frightful, and Thornton knew that the shore was impossible. He scraped furiously over a rock, bruised across a second, and struck a third with crushing force. He clutched its slippery top with both hands, releasing Buck, and above the roar of the churning water shouted: "Go, Buck! Go!"

Buck could not hold his own, and swept on downstream, struggling desperately, but unable to win back. When he heard Thornton's command repeated, he partly reared out of the water, throwing his head high, as though for a last look, then turned obediently toward the bank. He swam powerfully and was dragged ashore by Pete and Hans at the very point where swimming ceased to be possible and destruction began.

They knew that the time a man could cling to a slippery rock in the face of that driving current was a matter of minutes, and they ran as fast as they could up the bank to a point far above where Thornton was hanging on. They attached the line with which they had been snubbing the boat to Buck's neck and shoulders, being careful that it should neither strangle him nor impede his swimming, and launched him into the stream. He struck out boldly, but not straight enough into the stream. He discovered the mistake too late, when Thornton was abreast of him and a bare half-dozen strokes away while he was being carried helplessly past.

Hans promptly snubbed with the rope, as though Buck were a boat. The rope thus tightening on him in the sweep of the current, he was jerked under the surface, and under the surface he remained till his body struck against the bank and he was hauled out. He was half drowned, and Hans and Pete threw themselves upon him, pounding the breath into him and the water out of him. He staggered to his feet and fell down. The faint sound of Thornton's voice came to them, and though they could not make out the words of it, they knew that he was in his extremity. His master's voice acted on Buck like an electric shock. He sprang to his feet and ran up the bank ahead of the men to the point of his previous departure.

Again the rope was attached and he was launched, and again he struck out, but this time straight into the stream. He had miscalculated once, but he would not be guilty of it a second time. Hans paid out the rope, permitting no slack, while Pete kept it clear of coils. Buck held on till he was on a line straight above Thornton; then he turned, and with the speed of an express train headed down upon him. Thornton saw him coming, and, as Buck struck him like a battering ram, with the whole force of the current behind him, he reached up and closed with both arms around the shaggy neck. Hans snubbed the rope around the tree, and Buck and Thornton were jerked under the water. Strangling, suffocating, sometimes one uppermost and sometimes the other, dragging over the jagged bottom, smashing against rocks and snags, they veered in to the bank.

Thornton came to, belly downward and being violently propelled back and forth across a drift log by Hans and Pete. His first glance was for Buck, over whose limp and apparently lifeless body Nig was setting up a howl, while Skeet was licking the wet face and closed eyes. Thornton was himself bruised and battered, and he went carefully over Buck's body, when he had been brought around, finding three broken ribs.

"That settles it," he announced. "We camp right here." And camp they did, till Buck's ribs knitted and he was able to travel.

That winter, at Dawson, Buck performed another exploit, not so heroic, perhaps, but one that put his name many notches higher on the totem pole of Alaskan fame. This exploit was particularly gratifying to the three men; for they stood in need of the outfit which it furnished and were enabled to make a long-desired trip into the virgin East, where miners had not yet appeared. It was brought about by a conversation in the Eldorado Saloon, in which men waxed boastful of their favorite dogs. Buck, because of his record, was the target for these men, and Thornton was driven stoutly to defend him. At the end of half an hour one man stated that his dog could start a sled with five hundred pounds and walk off with it; a second bragged six hundred for his dog; and a third seven hundred.

"Pooh!" said Thornton. "Buck can start a thousand pounds."

"And break it out and walk off with it for a hundred yards," demanded Matthewson, a Bonanza King, he of the seven hundred vaunt.

"And break it out and walk off with it for a hundred yards," John Thornton said coolly.

"Well," Matthewson said, slowly and deliberately, so that all could hear, "I've got a thousand dollars that says he can't. And there it is." So saying, he slammed a sack of gold dust of the size of a bologna sausage down upon the bar.

Nobody spoke. Thornton's bluff, if bluff it was, had been called. He could feel a flush of warm blood creeping up his face. His tongue had tricked him. He did not know whether Buck could start a thousand pounds. Half a ton! The enormousness of it appalled him. He had great faith in Buck's strength and had often thought him capable of starting such a load; but never, as now, had he faced the possibility of it, the eyes of a dozen men fixed upon him, silent and waiting. Further, he had no thousand dollars; nor had Hans or Pete.

"I've got a sled standing outside now, with twenty fifty-pound sacks of flour on it," Matthewson went on with brutal directness, "so don't let that hinder you."

Thornton did not reply. He did not know what to say. He glanced from face to face in the absent way of a man who has lost the power of thought and is seeking somewhere to find the thing that will start it going again. The face of Jim O'Brien, a Mastodon King and oldtime comrade, caught his eyes. It was as a cue to him, seeming to rouse him to do what he would never have dreamed of doing.

"Can you lend me a thousand?" he asked, almost in a whisper.

"Sure," answered O'Brien, thumping down a plethoric sack by the side of Matthewson's. "Though it's little faith I'm having, John, that the beast can do the trick."

The Eldorado emptied its occupants into the street to see the test. The tables were deserted, and the dealers and gamekeepers came forth to see the outcome of the wager and to lay odds. Several hundred men, furred and mittened, banked around the sled within easy distance. Matthewson's sled, loaded with a thousand pounds of flour, had been standing for a couple of hours, and in the intense cold (it was sixty below zero) the runners had frozen fast to the hard-packed snow. Men offered odds of two to one that Buck could not budge the sled. A quibble arose concerning the phrase "break out." O'Brien contended it was Thornton's privilege to knock the runners loose, leaving Buck to "break it out" from a dead standstill. Matthewson insisted that the phrase included breaking the runners from the frozen grip of the snow. A majority of the men who had witnessed the making of the bet decided in his favor, whereat the odds went up to three to one against Buck.

There were no takers. Not a man believed him capable of the feat. Thornton had been hurried into the wager, heavy with doubt; and now that he looked at the sled itself, the concrete fact, with the regular team of ten dogs curled up in the snow before it, the more impossible the task appeared. Matthewson waxed jubilant.

"Three to one!" he proclaimed. "I'll lay you another thousand at that figure, Thornton. What d'ye say?"

Thornton's doubt was strong in his face, but his fighting spirit was aroused—the fighting spirit that soars above odds, fails to recognize the impossible, and is deaf to all save the clamor for battle. He called Hans and Pete to him. Their sacks were slim, and with his own the three partners could rake together only two hundred dollars. In the ebb of their fortunes, this sum was their total capital; yet they laid it unhesitatingly against Matthewson's six hundred.

The team of ten dogs was unhitched, and Buck with his own harness, was put into the sled. He had caught the contagion of the excitement, and he felt that in some way he must do a great thing for John Thornton. Murmurs of admiration at his splendid appearance went up. He was in perfect condition, without an ounce of superfluous flesh, and the one hundred and fifty pounds that he weighed were so many pounds of grit and virility. His furry coat shone with the sheen of silk. Down the neck and across the shoulders, his mane, in repose as it was, half bristled and seemed to lift with every movement, as though excess of vigor made each particular hair alive and active. The great breast and heavy forelegs were no more than in proportion with the rest of the body, where the muscles showed in tight rolls underneath the skin. Men felt these muscles and proclaimed them hard as iron, and the odds went down to two to one.

"Gad, sir! Gad, sir!" stuttered a member of the latest dynasty, a king of the Skookum Benches. "I offer you eight hundred for him, sir, before the test, sir; eight hundred just as he stands."

Thornton shook his head and stepped to Buck's side.

"You must stand off from him," Matthewson protested. "Free play and plenty of room."

The crowd fell silent; only could be heard the voices of the gamblers vainly offering two to one. Everybody acknowledged Buck a magnificent animal, but twenty fifty-pound sacks of flour bulked too large in their eyes for them to loosen their pouch-strings.

Thornton knelt down by Buck's side. He took his head in his two hands and rested cheek on cheek. He did not playfully shake him, as was his wont, or murmur soft love curses; but he whispered in his ear. "As you love me, Buck. As you love me," was what he whispered. Buck whined with suppressed eagerness.

The crowd was watching curiously. The affair was growing mysterious. It seemed like a conjuration. As Thornton got to his feet, Buck seized his mittened hand between his jaws, pressing in with his teeth and releasing slowly, half-reluctantly. It was the answer, in terms, not of speech, but of love. Thornton stepped well back.

"Now, Buck," he said.

Buck tightened the traces, then slacked them for a matter of several inches. It was the way he had learned.

"Gee!" Thornton's voice rang out, sharp in the tense silence.

Buck swung to the right, ending the movement in a plunge that took up the slack and with a sudden jerk arrested his one hundred and fifty pounds. The load quivered, and from under the runners arose a crisp crackling.

"Haw!" Thornton commanded.

Buck duplicated the manœuvre, this time to the left. The crackling turned into a snapping, the sled pivoting and the runners slipping and grating several inches to the side. The sled was broken out. Men were holding their breaths, intensely unconscious of the fact.

"Now, MUSH!"

Thornton's command cracked out like a pistol shot. Buck threw himself forward, tightening the traces with a jarring lunge. His whole body was gathered compactly together in the tremendous effort, the muscles writhing and knotting like live things under the silky fur. His great chest was low to the ground, his head forward and down, while his feet were flying like mad, the claws scarring the hard-packed snow in parallel grooves. The sled swayed and trembled, half-started forward. One of his feet slipped, and one man groaned aloud. Then the sled lurched ahead in what appeared a rapid succession of jerks, though it never really came to a dead stop again . . . half an inch . . . an inch . . . two inches. . . . The jerks perceptibly diminished; as the sled gained momentum, he caught them up, till it was moving steadily along.

Men gasped and began to breathe again, unaware that for a moment they had ceased to breathe. Thornton was running behind, encouraging Buck with short, cheery words. The distance had been measured off, and as he neared the pile of firewood which marked the end of the hundred yards, a cheer began to grow and grow, which burst into a roar as he passed the firewood and halted at command. Every man was tearing himself loose, even Matthewson. Hats and mittens were flying in the air. Men were shaking hands, it did not matter with whom, and bubbling over in a general incoherent babel.

But Thornton fell on his knees beside Buck. Head was against head, and he was shaking him back and forth. Those who hurried up heard him cursing Buck, and he cursed him long and fervently, and softly and lovingly.

"Gad, sir! Gad, sir!" spluttered the Skookum Bench king. "I'll give you a thousand for him, sir, a thousand, sir—twelve hundred, sir."

Thornton rose to his feet. His eyes were wet. The tears were streaming frankly down his cheeks. "Sir," he said to the Skookum Bench king, "no, sir. You can go to hell, sir. It's the best I can do for you, sir."

Buck seized Thornton's hand in his teeth. Thornton shook him back and forth. As though animated by a common impulse, the onlookers drew back to a respectful distance; nor were they again indiscreet enough to interrupt.

My Friend Flicka

TROUBLE IN THE CALF PASTURE

by MARY O'HARA

When, out of all the horses on the large ranch, Ken Mc-Laughlin chooses the year-old filly Flicka to be his own horse, his brother Howard and his mother and father all try to make him change his mind. For Flicka seems to be tainted by a bad wild-horse strain and they are afraid that she might turn out to be "loco." But Ken sets his heart on having this beautiful and wild filly. After the scene described below, Mr. McLaughlin finds out that the reason Flicka is unable to stand up is not too serious; it involves only an infected leg. So Ken begins the patient and often painful business of gentling the spirited yearling to the saddle. How the boy finally trains fear out of Flicka and gets her to trust him; and how the responsibility and joy of winning the horse over changes Ken himself from a day-dreamer and shirker to a practical and skillful member of the ranch, all this makes an absorbing and moving story. It is written with an unusually fine understanding of the depth of a boy's love for his horse and also of the relation between Ken and his upright but demanding father.

Ken found a nicer place for the filly.

A fence ran from the corrals of the cowbarn, straight north, dividing the Calf Pasture from the practice field; a path led along this fence, and, about three hundred yards from the corrals, reached a spot where several cottonwood trees made a wall of foliage. Under the boughs of the trees, the path sloped sharply down for ten feet or so to a flat area of beautiful green turf, through which Lone Tree Creek ran.

When the creek was in flood, all this flat part was covered; but now, in summer, it was dry, and the grass such a vivid green that, coming upon it from the dryer land roundabout, it was startling to the eye. Golden sunlight lay upon part of it; part of it was dark and pleasant with the shade of the cottonwood trees that hung over the hill and sent their roots winding down its face to bore underground for water. Here, without having to hunt for it, Flicka had rich grass to eat and running water to drink; there was both sun and shade.

Ken called the place *Flicka's Nursery*, and each morning and evening he walked down the little path carrying a can of oats to empty into the wooden feed box which he had set near the roots of the cottonwoods.

Standing as tall as she could at the foot of the bank, Flicka could just see over the top of it and catch sight of Ken coming. He could see her too. It made him tingle all over, the first time he saw her head—just the pretty face, with the blond bang over her forehead and the dainty pricked ears framed in the down-hanging branches of the cottonwoods—and realized that she was looking for him and waiting for him.

Ken bragged about it that night at supper, but Howard said, "Nuts! She's lookin' for her oats, not for you."

McLaughlin answered sharply, "Oats, or the bringer-of-oats, in the long run it gets to be the same thing."

And Nell added dryly, "Are human beings any different?"

No doubt about it, Flicka did love her oats. As Ken stooped over to empty the can into the feed box, she would be close beside him reaching her nose in; but when he put out his hand to stroke her, she pulled back. She would not let him touch her.

Ken still had work to do; work in the corrals when the brood mares were brought in with their colts and the colts were branded; work on the fences when Tim was sent out with the small Ford service truck, full of fence posts that had been cut the summer before, dried, and dipped in an asphalt mixture to protect them against ground-rot; work on the ditches and the meadows which must be given every possible chance to grow hay in these last weeks before the cutting. Now that the Rodeo horses had been taken to town, the two boys were riding Cigarette and Highboy again, and every few days must ride the boundaries of the ranch to spot any breaks in the fence, any strange animals that had got in, any gates open that should be shut. Fishermen came in from the highway, opened the gates to drive their cars through so they could get down to the stream to fish, and sometimes drove out again without closing the gates. One day Ken and Howard found a hundred head of yearling steers that had got in on the Mc-Laughlin land and were gorging in the meadow and trampling the grass. The boys galloped home to give the alarm; McLaughlin and his men rode out, drove the steers off, and then McLaughlin, in a rage, wired up the gates and planted posts across so that they couldn't be opened again.

There was also the daily work of halter-breaking and training the four little spring colts. McLaughlin had taught Howard and Ken just how to do it, and for the first day or two he helped them himself.

First, the colt must be penned. The little one came running beside its dam, and the mare came for oats. Once in the small pen, the colt—not much frightened because it was standing by its mother—was held forcibly and the halter put on, and a long lead rope slipped into the halter ring.

Now the colt was hauled away from its dam out into the larger corral to the hitching post. The rope was looped several times around the post, one of the boys was given the end to hold and placed himself behind the post, so that the colt thought he was being held by the boy—not by the post.

Invariably, the colt pulled and fought against the rope. He shook his head from side to side, he braced all four feet out straight and stiff. Even grown horses did this, sometimes sitting down like big dogs. Occasionally this pulling and fighting went on for a long time, but as a rule, with a young colt, it was soon over. The sudden surrender was almost always expressed in the same manner.

The colt would rear straight up, paw the air a moment, then plunge forward to release the pull on his head. That plunge was a movement *toward* the master—a capitulation; and the colt never forgot it. At the moment of the plunge, when he approached most closely the one who was coercing him, there came the sudden physical easement of strain—a good feeling. If he stood there, trembling, close to his master, there was the comforting voice, the hand patting his head, and he began to feel safe. Sometimes there were tugs of war again, but never so long nor so determined. And in a day or two the habit was formed. At the slightest pull on the halter rope, the colt would follow.

From this point on, Howard and Ken needed no further assistance. The colts became as familiar with the boys as they were with their dams. They would sniff and nip at them, rear up and play, striking at them with their little forefeet.

The last week or so, all Ken and Howard had been doing with their colts was to lead them by the halter around the pasture, saying *Whoa* now and then, at the same time halting the colt; and making them go different speeds, from a slow walk up to a brisk trot. When they had walked them enough, they took them back into the pens, removed the lead ropes and played with them, patted and whacked them, waved blankets around them, leaned on their backs, fed them oats out of their hands.

Right over the fence from the Calf Pasture, where the boys worked with their colts, was the practice field, and here, for many hours a day, Ken's mother and father, and the bronco-buster worked with the four polo ponies, Rumba, Blazes, Don, and Gangway.

At last the day came when the work was done. The four ponies were loaded into the truck and McLaughlin drove them to the station to be shipped with Sargent's bunch.

Then the little bronco-buster left. They all gathered around his battered sedan, packed full of saddles and equipment, and said good-by to him and wished him luck at the Rodeo.

"Don't take chances," Nell McLaughlin said. "But I notice you're pretty careful."

Ross's steady blue eyes looked at her in his direct and respectful manner, and he answered, "A man that monkeys around wild horses don't kid himself any, Missus. It don't do no good."

Then he grinned, "I may be in hospital agin after the Rodeo, but if I ain't, I'll be back to see how Ken makes out with his filly." He grinned at Ken and Ken grinned back.

Then he took off his sombrero, shook hands all around, climbed into the driver's seat and rattled off.

And the next thing that happened was the Rodeo.

Ken was entirely alone on the ranch that day with Flicka, when suddenly she couldn't get up from the ground.

It was the last day of the Rodeo. The Studebaker had gone into Cheyenne on each of the four days of the big show, FRONTIER DAYS, called by Cheyenne boosters, *The Daddy of 'em All*.

Ken went the first day and saw Lady and Calico and Buck and Baldy in the parade, ridden by four of the City Fathers, all dressed up in ten gallon hats and fringed chaps. He saw the famous bucking horse, Midnight, throw every rider that mounted him. But Ken didn't go in again, not even on this last day when there was going to be the wild horse race, and it annoyed his father; but McLaughlin said it was up to him. If he'd rather be alone on the ranch than at the Rodeo with his family, why, he could suit himself. But one thing was certain, no one was going to stay with him—not Gus or Tim either, because they'd both been promised the day off. Gus would be back on the four o'clock bus to milk the cows, and until then Ken would be alone.

Ken said he didn't mind—he'd have Flicka.

Ken stood by the car to see them off, and, the last thing, his father stuck his head out the window and called to him, "All right, kid—leaving you in charge!—*it's all yours!*" And the Studebaker, carrying his mother and father and Howard and Gus and Tim slid down the hill, rattled over the cattle guard and bowled smoothly down the road.

Ken stood there, watching it until it disappeared. How different everything was now that they had gone. *All yours.* . . . He felt the responsibility his father had laid upon him . . . he was in charge. The two dogs, Kim, the collie who looked like a coyote, and Chaps, the black spaniel, were standing beside him. They too were watching the empty road. They were used to doing that, and they knew the difference—the road with the Studebaker on it, going or coming, the road empty, and silence all around.

Ken went up to his room and stood before his book shelf. He picked out the "Jungle Book," then ran downstairs and out, across the Green, into the Calf Pasture, and down the path by the fence to Flicka's Nursery. She was drinking at the brook when he came.

He greeted her with a stream of talk; he visited with her a while, standing as close to her as she would let him. Then he seated himself on the bank of the hill under the cottonwoods and began to read.

Flicka wandered around her nursery. Sometimes she wanted sunshine, and stood under the dappled golden light until she was warmed through, then a few steps took her into the shade of the trees. Ken, glancing up, saw her standing quite near, watching him. He began to read aloud to her, and her ears came forward sharply as if she was listening.

He read her the part that told about Rann, the Kite, seeing Mowgli, the wolf-boy, carried through the tree-tops by the flock of monkeys; and about Mowgli remembering the Master Word of the Jungle that Baloo, the brown bear who was his tutor, had taught him, and crying to Rann, the Kite, "We be of one blood, ye and I— Mark my trail! Carry word to Baloo of the Seeonee Wolf Pack, and Bagheera of the Council Rock! Mark my trai-ai-ail!"

Flicka's head turned. As Ken's voice went on, she moved over to the empty feed box, sniffed it, put out a long pink tongue and licked up a few stray grains left over from her breakfast. Then she stood quietly, broadside to Ken, switching her cream-colored tail to keep off the flies.

Now and then Ken stopped reading, put his book down and lay back on the hill with his arms under his head, looking up through the branches of the trees. He could see a patch of blue sky with a little vague half moon floating in it, the daytime moon, called the Children's Moon, because it is the only moon most children ever see. At first he thought it was a little soft cloud.

It was another hot day, but down here it was pleasant and shady. There wasn't a sound, except for the ripple of the stream where it ran over stones and shallow sandy places, now and then the splash of a trout that flipped out and in again, and, all the time, a faint hum, the buzzing of the racing flies that were always in the out-of-doors. It was a sound that went with summer —part of the silence.

Ken and Flicka were all alone in the Calf Pasture. The four colts that the boys had trained, and their dams, had been taken out to Banner on the Saddle Back, because the job was done—and well done, McLaughlin had said—the colts were perfectly halter-broke. It had taken about a month.

Flicka went down to the stream to drink and Ken's eye followed her. Flicka, of course, had never been halter-broke. It was a most important part of a colt's training and should be done as early as possible because it was the beginning of everything. But Flicka was a year and several months old, and she wouldn't even let him touch her. As for flirting blankets around her, or putting a rope on her—the very thought of such a thing made shivers run down his spine—he could imagine her fighting the rope—behaving as she had behaved up there in the corral and the stable—behaving like Rocket—*Loco*—

At this thought Ken drew up his knees, clasped his arms around them and put his head down on his arms, hugging himself against the dread—*he didn't know yet if she was or wasn't*. He *couldn't* know until he began the halter-breaking. He felt sickening tremors inside.

Just a little while ago he had found courage, somehow, to face the possibility of Flicka's being loco, but now his courage was gone—or at least, he could not easily find it. The hope and sweetness of the weeks of caring for her, and the little filly's tentative response to him, had pushed the dread out of the foreground of

his thoughts; had almost pushed it into one of those air-tight compartments of his mind. But the doors did not close as tightly as they had before. The boy knew what was behind them. Having faced the horror once, and righted himself after the shock, he would be able to do it again.

A vague sense of this came to Ken before he lifted his head from his knees, and it gave him strength to look forward to that day—and it was a day that was coming soon—when *Flicka would have to be halter-broken*.

Then he deliberately shoved away all these unpleasant thoughts, shut the door on them, and gave himself up to the rapture of contemplating his filly. The little animal was disclosing to him an odd, fascinating personality; whimsical, remote, temperamental. She moved a step or two at a time across the turf. In the sun, her glossy hide shone like gold, the long cream tail swinging to one side or the other. Now and then she stopped and stood motionless, her attention caught by some far sound or movement that Ken could not hear or see at all; and her statue-like pose, the graceful turn of her neck, the delicate, pointed ears, and every line of her body, instinct with life and intelligence, exerted on Ken the fascination that horses have always exerted upon human beings. He had fallen under her spell—a classic spell.

If she could only, *really* make friends with him! He had done his best to win her confidence. He had done all that his father had told him to do. Surely she knew that he loved her and he was there just to serve her and care for her, and still, when he came near, there was that alert turn of her head, the wary look in her eye, and the quick step away. Still—when the colts galloping on the upland were near enough to be heard, she turned to them, and yearned to them, and whinnied in longing. If she had four good legs, and her freedom, thought Ken, he'd never see her again— she'd be just a stream of power and speed—gold and pink— whipping over the range—

He sighed. Well—it was time to eat—he must go up to the house and get his lunch.

Flicka was still standing up when he left. When he came back, running down the path with the dogs at his heels, his eyes were fastened on the spot just over the brow of the hill where he so often saw Flicka's face watching for him, but it wasn't there.

He ran down the hill and saw that she was flat on her side.

As she heard him coming she made an effort to get up and fell back again.

It stopped Ken dead in his tracks. Then he ran to her and fell on his knees beside her. "Oh, Flicka," he cried, "what is the matter, Flicka? What's happened to you?"

She was dying . . . she had been dying all along—or, something had happened while he was away at lunch . . . perhaps she'd fallen and hurt herself again . . . perhaps her back was broken. . . .

Hardly knowing what he was doing, he patted her face and kissed it. He went behind her, crouched down, put his arms around her head and held it.

Flicka made another effort to get up. Lying on the left side, when a horse wants to get up, it rolls over on its belly, straightens the forelegs, pushes against them and against the right hind leg, and so gains its feet. The only leg that is not used in the process is the left hind leg upon which the horse is lying.

About to make the effort, lying on her belly with her legs gathered and her head up, Flicka neighed, ending in a few little grunts, and Ken had to smile because he understood just what she was saying. It was not exactly the neigh of nervous impatience of which his father had spoken, but it was a neigh of determination, and the grunts added on were from nervousness—she was going to do it but wasn't quite sure that she could.

Ken stood back to give her the chance. She started the scramble, then collapsed suddenly and dropped her head again.

"Oh, Flicka, Flicka!" he cried, almost certain now that something must be wrong with her back; and again he fell on his knees and took her head in his arms.

She heaved a deep sigh and half closed her eyes, completely relaxed, while Ken's little brown hands went all over her head and neck, smoothing the silken softness of her skin, patting the sensitive curves of her face, straightening her forelock.

She let him! Was it only because she couldn't help herself? Or was it perhaps what his father had said, that now, in her greater trouble and helplessness, the last shred of her fear had gone and she really wanted him and loved him? Whatever it was, it released all the boy's tenderness and longing. He pressed his hands upon her—he laid his head down on hers, and his breath was troubled.

At last he went back to the bank of the hill and sat down, wishing that the afternoon would hurry by and that Gus would come. The bus would drop him at four o'clock out on the highway. It would take him a half hour to walk to the house, change into his bluejeans (he'd be all dressed up in a tight shiny blue serge suit with a ten-gallon hat and fine shoes) and be ready to milk the cows. Ken was to bring the cows in and have them waiting in the corral, and he was to measure out the cow feed and put it in the feed boxes for the cows, so Gus would have nothing to do but drive them in and milk them.

Flicka seemed to have gone to sleep. Presently Ken lay down on the hillside and fell asleep too.

Lochinvar

by SIR WALTER SCOTT

O, Young Lochinvar is come out of the West—
Through all the wide Border his steed was the best;
And, save his good broadsword, he weapons had none—
He rode all unarmed and he rode all alone.
So faithful in love, and so dauntless in war,
There never was knight like the young Lockinvar.

He stayed not for brake, and he stopped not for stone,
He swam the Esk River, where ford there was none;
But ere he alighted at Netherby gate,
The bride had consented, the gallant came late:
For a laggard in love, and a dastard in war,
Was to wed the fair Ellen of brave Lochinvar.

So boldly he entered the Netherby hall,
'Mong bridesmen, and kinsmen, and brothers, and all:
Then spoke the bride's father, his hand on his sword
(For the poor, craven bridegroom said never a word),
"O, come ye in peace here, or come ye in war,
Or to dance at our bridal, young Lord Lochinvar?"

"I long wooed your daughter—my suit you denied;—
Love swells like the Solway, but ebbs like its tide;
And now I am come, with this lost love of mine,

To lead but one measure, drink one cup of wine.
There are maidens in Scotland more lovely by far,
That would gladly be bride to the young Lochinvar!"

The bride kissed the goblet; the knight took it up,
He quaffed off the wine, and he threw down the cup.
She looked down to blush, and she looked up to sigh,
With a smile on her lips, and a tear in her eye.
He took her soft hand, ere her mother could bar—
"Now tread we a measure!" said young Lochinvar.

So stately his form, and so lovely her face,
That never a hall such a galliard did grace;
While her mother did fret, and her father did fume,
And the bridegroom stood dangling his bonnet and plume,
And the bridemaidens whispered, " 'Twere better by far
To have matched our fair cousin with young Lochinvar."

One touch to her hand, and one word in her ear,
When they reached the hall door, and the charger stood near;
So light to the croupe the fair lady he swung,
So light to the saddle before her he sprung!
"She is won! we are gone, over bank, bush, and scaur;
They'll have fleet steeds that follow," quoth young Lochinvar.

There was mounting 'mong Graemes of the Netherby clan:
Forsters, Fenwicks, and Musgraves, they rode and they ran:
There was racing and chasing, on Cannobie Lee,
But the lost bride of Netherby ne'er did they see.
So daring in love, and so dauntless in war,
Have ye e'er heard of gallant like young Lochinvar?

Homer Price

THE DOUGHNUTS

by ROBERT MCCLOSKEY

The absurdly funny exploits of Homer and his friends— who are always involved with bits of electric wire and parts of old motors and radios—make an irresistibly attractive picture of American boyhood in a small town. He has been called a modern Tom Sawyer. But Homer is like no other boy in fiction. He is an original and most ingenious character to whom hilarious things, like the incident of the multiplying doughnuts, seem to keep happening naturally. It would be hard to think of any young person who would not relish Homer Price *because it is surely one of the most amusing stories of recent years.*

One Friday night in November Homer overheard his mother talking on the telephone to Aunt Agnes over in Centerburg. "I'll stop by with the car in about half an hour and we can go to the meeting together," she said, because tonight was the night the Ladies' Club was meeting to discuss plans for a box social and to knit and sew for the Red Cross.

"I think I'll come along and keep Uncle Ulysses company while you and Aunt Agnes are at the meeting," said Homer.

So after Homer had combed his hair and his mother had looked to see if she had her knitting instructions and the right size needles, they started for town.

Homer's Uncle Ulysses and Aunt Agnes have a very up and coming lunch room over in Centerburg, just across from the court house on the town square. Uncle Ulysses is a man with advanced ideas and a weakness for labor saving devices. He equipped the lunch room with automatic toasters, automatic coffee maker, automatic dish washer, and an automatic doughnut maker. All just the latest thing in labor saving devices. Aunt Agnes would throw up her hands and sigh every time Uncle Ulysses bought a new labor saving device. Sometimes she became unkindly disposed toward him for days and days. She was of the opinion that Uncle Ulysses just frittered away his spare time over at the barber shop with the sheriff and the boys, so, what was the good of a labor saving device that gave you more time to fritter?

When Homer and his mother got to Centerburg they stopped at the lunch room, and after Aunt Agnes had come out and said, "My, how that boy does grow!" which was what she always said, she went off with Homer's mother in the car. Homer went into the lunch room and said, "Howdy, Uncle Ulysses!"

"Oh, hello, Homer. You're just in time," said Uncle Ulysses. "I've been going over this automatic doughnut machine, oiling the machinery and cleaning the works . . . wonderful things, these labor saving devices."

"Yep," agreed Homer, and he picked up a cloth and started polishing the metal trimmings while Uncle Ulysses tinkered with the inside workings.

"Opfwo-oof!!" sighed Uncle Ulysses and, "Look here, Homer, you've got a mechanical mind. See if you can find where these two pieces fit in. I'm going across to the barber shop for a spell, 'cause there's somethin' I've got to talk to the sheriff about. There won't be much business here until the double feature is over and I'll be back before then."

Then as Uncle Ulysses went out the door he said, "Uh, Homer, after you get the pieces in place, would you mind mixing up a batch of doughnut batter and put it in the machine? You could turn the switch and make a few doughnuts to have on hand for the crowd after the movie . . . if you don't mind."

"O.K.," said Homer, "I'll take care of everything."

A few minutes later a customer came in and said, "Good evening, Bud."

Homer looked up from putting the last piece in the doughnut machine and said, "Good evening, Sir, what can I do for you?"

"Well, young feller, I'd like a cup o' coffee and some doughnuts," said the customer.

"I'm sorry, Mister, but we won't have any doughnuts for about half an hour, until I can mix some dough and start this machine. I could give you some very fine sugar rolls instead."

"Well, Bud, I'm in no real hurry so I'll just have a cup o' coffee and wait around a bit for the doughnuts. Fresh doughnuts are always worth waiting for is what I always say."

"O.K.," said Homer, and he drew a cup of coffee from Uncle Ulysses' super automatic coffee maker.

"Nice place you've got here," said the customer.

"Oh, yes," replied Homer, "this is a very up and coming lunch room with all the latest improvements."

"Yes," said the stranger, "must be a good business. I'm in business too. A traveling man in outdoor advertising. I'm a sandwich man, Mr. Gabby's my name."

"My name is Homer. I'm glad to meet you, Mr. Gabby. It must be a fine profession, traveling and advertising sandwiches."

"Oh no," said Mr. Gabby, "I don't advertise sandwiches, I just wear any kind of an ad, one sign on front and one sign on behind, this way. . . . Like a sandwich. Ya know what I mean?"

"Oh, I see. That must be fun, and you travel too?" asked Homer as he got out the flour and the baking powder.

"Yeah, I ride the rods between jobs, on freight trains, ya know what I mean?"

"Yes, but isn't that dangerous?" asked Homer.

"Of course there's a certain amount a risk, but you take any method a travel these days, it's all dangerous. Ya know what I mean? Now take airplanes for instance . . ."

Just then a large shiny black car stopped in front of the lunch room and a chauffeur helped a lady out of the rear door. They both came inside and the lady smiled at Homer and said, "We've stopped for a light snack. Some doughnuts and coffee would be simply marvelous."

Then Homer said, "I'm sorry, Ma'm, but the doughnuts won't be ready until I make this batter and start Uncle Ulysses' doughnut machine."

"Well now aren't you a clever young man to know how to make *doughnuts!*"

"Well," blushed Homer, "I've really never done it before but I've got a receipt to follow."

"Now, young man, you simply must allow me to help. You know, I haven't made doughnuts for years, but I know the best receipt for doughnuts. It's marvelous, and we really must use it."

"But, Ma'm . . ." said Homer.

"Now just *wait* till you taste these doughnuts," said the lady. "Do you have an apron?" she asked, as she took off her fur coat and her rings and her jewelry and rolled up her sleeves. "Charles," she said to the chauffeur, "hand me that baking powder, that's right, and, young man, we'll need some nutmeg."

So Homer and the chauffeur stood by and handed things and cracked the eggs while the lady mixed and stirred. Mr. Gabby sat on his stool, sipped his coffee, and looked on with great interest.

"There!" said the lady when all of the ingredients were mixed. "Just *wait* till you taste these doughnuts!"

"It looks like an awful lot of batter," said Homer as he stood on a chair and poured it into the doughnut machine with the help of the chauffeur. "It's about *ten* times as much as Uncle Ulysses ever makes."

"But wait till you taste them!" said the lady with an eager look and a smile.

Homer got down from the chair and pushed a button on the machine marked, "*Start*." Rings of batter started dropping into the hot fat. After a ring of batter was cooked on one side an automatic gadget turned it over and the other side would cook. Then another automatic gadget gave the doughnut a little push and it rolled neatly down a little chute, all ready to eat.

"That's a simply *fascinating* machine," said the lady as she waited for the first doughnut to roll out.

"Here, young man, *you* must have the first one. Now isn't that just *too* delicious!? Isn't it simply marvelous?"

"Yes, Ma'm, it's very good," replied Homer as the lady handed doughnuts to Charles and to Mr. Gabby and asked if they didn't think they were simply divine doughnuts.

"It's an old family receipt!" said the lady with pride.

Homer poured some coffee for the lady and her chauffeur and for Mr. Gabby, and a glass of milk for himself. Then they all sat down at the lunch counter to enjoy another few doughnuts apiece.

"I'm so glad you enjoy my doughnuts," said the lady. "But now, Charles, we really must be going. If you will just take this apron, Homer, and put two dozen doughnuts in a bag to take along, we'll be on our way. And, Charles, don't forget to pay the young man." She rolled down her sleeves and put on her jewelry, then Charles managed to get her into her big fur coat.

"Good night, young man, I haven't had so much fun in years. I *really* haven't!" said the lady, as she went out the door and into the big shiny car.

"Those are sure good doughnuts," said Mr. Gabby as the car moved off.

"You bet!" said Homer. Then he and Mr. Gabby stood and watched the automatic doughnut machine make doughnuts.

After a few dozen more doughnuts had rolled down the little chute, Homer said, "I guess that's about enough doughnuts to sell to the after theater customers. I'd better turn the machine off for a while."

Homer pushed the button marked "*Stop*" and there was a little click, but nothing happened. The rings of batter kept right on dropping into the hot fat, and an automatic gadget kept right on turning them over, and another automatic gadget kept right on giving them a little push, and the doughnuts kept right on rolling down the little chute, all ready to eat.

"That's funny," said Homer, "I'm sure that's the right button!" He pushed it again but the automatic doughnut maker kept right on making doughnuts.

"Well I guess I must have put one of those pieces in backwards," said Homer.

"Then it might stop if you pushed the button marked '*Start*,'" said Mr. Gabby.

Homer did, and the doughnuts still kept rolling down the little chute, just as regular as a clock can tick.

"I guess we could sell a few more doughnuts," said Homer, "but I'd better telephone Uncle Ulysses over at the barber shop." Homer gave the number and while he waited for someone to answer he counted thirty-seven doughnuts roll down the little chute.

Finally someone answered, "Hello! This is the sarber bhop, I mean the barber shop."

"Oh, hello, sheriff. This is Homer. Could I speak to Uncle Ulysses?"

"Well, he's playing pinochle right now," said the sheriff. "Anythin' I can tell 'im?"

"Yes," said Homer. "I pushed the button marked '*Stop*' on the doughnut machine but the rings of batter keep right on dropping into the hot fat, and an automatic gadget keeps right on turning them over, and another automatic gadget keeps giving them a little push, and the doughnuts keep right on rolling down the little chute! It won't stop!"

"O.K. Wold the hire, I mean, hold the wire and I'll tell 'im." Then Homer looked over his shoulder and counted another twenty-one doughnuts roll down the little chute, all ready to eat. Then the sheriff said, "He'll be right over. . . . Just gotta finish this hand."

"That's good," said Homer. "G'by, sheriff."

The window was full of doughnuts by now so Homer and Mr. Gabby had to hustle around and start stacking them on plates and trays and lining them up on the counter.

"Sure are a lot of doughnuts!" said Homer.

"You bet!" said Mr. Gabby. "I lost count at twelve hundred and two and that was quite a while back."

People had begun to gather outside the lunch room window, and someone was saying, "There are almost as many doughnuts as there are people in Centerburg, and I wonder how in tarnation Ulysses thinks he can sell all of 'em!"

Every once in a while somebody would come inside and buy some, but while somebody bought two to eat and a dozen to take home, the machine made three dozen more.

By the time Uncle Ulysses and the sheriff arrived and pushed through the crowd, the lunch room was a calamity of doughnuts! Doughnuts in the window, doughnuts piled high on the shelves, doughnuts stacked on plates, doughnuts lined up twelve deep all along the counter, and doughnuts still rolling down the little chute, just as regular as a clock can tick.

"Hello, sheriff, hello, Uncle Ulysses, we're having a little trouble here," said Homer.

"Well, I'll be dunked!!" said Uncle Ulysses.

"Dernd ef you won't be when Aggy gits home," said the sheriff. "Mighty fine doughnuts though. What'll you do with 'em all, Ulysses?"

Uncle Ulysses groaned and said, "What will Aggy say? We'll never sell 'em all."

Then Mr. Gabby, who hadn't said anything for a long time, stopped piling doughnuts and said, "What you need is an advertising man. Ya know what I mean? You got the doughnuts, ya gotta create a market . . . Understand? . . . It's balancing the demand with the supply . . . That sort of thing."

"Yep!" said Homer. "Mr. Gabby's right. We have to enlarge our market. He's an advertising sandwich man, so if we hire him, he can walk up and down in front of the theater and get the customers."

"You're hired, Mr. Gabby!" said Uncle Ulysses.

Then everybody pitched in to paint the signs and to get Mr. Gabby sandwiched between. They painted "SALE ON DOUGHNUTS" in big letters on the window too.

Meanwhile the rings of batter kept right on dropping into the hot fat, and an automatic gadget kept right on turning them over, and another automatic gadget kept right on giving them a little push, and the doughnuts kept right on rolling down the little chute, just as regular as a clock can tick.

"I certainly hope this advertising works," said Uncle Ulysses, wagging his head. "Aggy'll certainly throw a fit if it don't."

The sheriff went outside to keep order, because there was quite a crowd by now—all looking at the doughnuts and guessing how many thousand there were, and watching new ones roll down the little chute, just as regular as a clock can tick. Homer and Uncle Ulysses kept stacking doughnuts. Once in a while somebody bought a few, but not very often.

Then Mr. Gabby came back and said, "Say, you know there's not much use o' me advertisin' at the theater. The show's all over, and besides almost everybody in town is out front watching that machine make doughnuts!"

"Zeus!" said Uncle Ulysses. "We must get rid of these doughnuts before Aggy gets here!"

"Looks like you will have ta hire a truck ta waul 'em ahay, I mean haul 'em away!!" said the sheriff who had just come in. Just then there was a noise and a shoving out front and the lady from the shiny black car and her chauffeur came pushing through the crowd and into the lunch room.

"Oh, gracious!" she gasped, ignoring the doughnuts, "I've lost my diamond bracelet, and I know I left it here on the counter," she said, pointing to a place where the doughnuts were piled in stacks of two dozen.

"Yes, Ma'm, I guess you forgot it when you helped make the batter," said Homer.

Then they moved all the doughnuts around and looked for the diamond bracelet, but they couldn't find it anywhere. Meanwhile the doughnuts kept rolling down the little chute, just as regular as a clock can tick.

After they had looked all around the sheriff cast a suspicious eye on Mr. Gabby, but Homer said, "He's all right, sheriff, he didn't take it. He's a friend of mine."

Then the lady said, "I'll offer a reward of one hundred dollars for that bracelet! It really *must* be found! . . . it *really* must!"

"Now don't you worry, lady," said the sheriff. "I'll get your bracelet back!"

"Zeus! This is terrible!" said Uncle Ulysses. "First all of these doughnuts and then on top of all that, a lost diamond brace-let . . ."

Mr. Gabby tried to comfort him, and he said, "There's always a bright side. That machine'll probably run outta batter in an hour or two."

If Mr. Gabby hadn't been quick on his feet Uncle Ulysses would have knocked him down, sure as fate.

Then while the lady wrung her hands and said, "We must find it, we *must!*" and Uncle Ulysses was moaning about what Aunt Agnes would say, and the sheriff was eyeing Mr. Gabby, Homer sat down and thought hard.

Before twenty more doughnuts could roll down the little chute he shouted, "SAY! I know where the bracelet is! It was lying here on the counter and got mixed up in the batter by mistake! The bracelet is cooked inside one of these doughnuts!"

"Why . . . I really believe you're right," said the lady through her tears. "Isn't that *amazing?* Simply *amazing!*"

"I'll be durn'd!" said the sheriff.

"OhH-h!" moaned Uncle Ulysses. "Now we have to break up all of these doughnuts to find it. Think of the *pieces!* Think of the *crumbs!* Think of what *Aggy* will say!"

"Nope," said Homer. "We won't have to break them up. I've got a plan."

So Homer and the advertising man took some cardboard and some paint and printed another sign. They put this sign

FRESH DOUGHNUTS
2 for 5¢
WHILE THEY LAST
$100.00 PRIZE
FOR FINDING
A BRACELET
INSIDE A DOUGHNUT
P.S. You have to give the
bracelet back

in the window, and the sandwich man wore two more signs that said the same thing and walked around in the crowd out front.

Then . . . The doughnuts began to sell! *Everybody* wanted to buy doughnuts, *dozens* of doughnuts!

And that's not all. Everybody bought coffee to dunk the doughnuts in too. Those that didn't buy coffee bought milk or soda. It kept Homer and the lady and the chauffeur and Uncle Ulysses and the sheriff busy waiting on the people who wanted to buy doughnuts.

When all but the last couple of hundred doughnuts had been sold, Rupert Black shouted, "I GAWT IT!!" and sure enough . . . there was the diamond bracelet inside of his doughnut!

Then Rupert went home with a hundred dollars, the citizens of Centerburg went home full of doughnuts, the lady and her chauffeur drove off with the diamond bracelet, and Homer went home with his mother when she stopped by with Aunt Aggy.

As Homer went out of the door he heard Mr. Gabby say, "Neatest trick of merchandising I ever seen," and Aunt Aggy was looking sceptical while Uncle Ulysses was saying, "The rings of batter kept right on dropping into the hot fat, and the automatic gadget kept right on turning them over, and the other automatic gadget kept right on giving them a little push, and the doughnuts kept right on rolling down the little chute just as regular as a clock can tick—they just kept right on a comin', an' a comin', an' a comin', an' a comin'."

The Conquest of Everest

THE SUMMIT

by SIR EDMUND HILLARY

Why have men attempted to climb Mount Everest? The answer, "Because it is there," given by Mallary, the famous English mountaineer who disappeared on Everest in 1924, is not as simple as it appears. Obviously men don't enjoy climbing mole hills; what "is there" becomes an alluring magnet only when the problem is one that has long resisted the skill and persistence of others. Everest was the supreme example of such a challenge. During the past thirty years eleven major expeditions had tried to scale the mountain, and at least four times men had arrived within about a thousand feet of the peak, only to be forced back at the last moment. It was rumored that a spell had been cast over the final "keep," making it a barrier beyond which no human spirit could pass. The summit of Everest, the highest point of the earth's surface, became a symbol of the unattainable, the unknown, the supreme challenge to human endurance.

The day-by-day story of "The Conquest of Everest" is told mainly by Sir John Hunt, the organizer of the British expedition and the "gallant and determined" leader referred to at the end of this chapter. But he was not there at the final stage which was undertaken by two younger men, the Australian Hillary and the Sherpa guide Tenzing. And so it is Sir Edmund Hillary who writes his personal account of the final assault of the summit. His story, like Hunt's, is simply and modestly written, without frills, yet it is a deeply moving drama of the highest courage and teamwork,

*of the most painstaking preparation, and of man's victory over
what were probably the greatest human odds. The conquest of
Everest was announced on the day of the coronation of Queen
Elizabeth, and the whole world rejoiced with England over this
stirring event.*

Early on the morning of May 27th I awoke from an uneasy sleep
feeling very cold and miserable. We were on the South Col of
Everest. My companions in our Pyramid tent, Lowe, Gregory, and
Tenzing, were all tossing and turning in unsuccessful efforts to
gain relief from the bitter cold. The relentless wind was blowing
in all its fury and the constant loud drumming on the tent made
deep sleep impossible. Reluctantly removing my hand from my
sleeping bag, I looked at my watch. It was 4 A.M. In the flickering
light of a match, the thermometer lying against the tent wall read
−25° Centigrade [13 below zero].

We had hoped to establish a camp high on the southeast ridge
that day, but the force of the wind obviously made a start impossible. We must, however, be prepared to go on if the wind should
drop. I nudged the uncomplaining Tenzing with my elbow and
murmured a few words about food and drink, then callously snug-
gled my way back into my bag again. Soon the purring of the
Primus and the general warming of the atmosphere stirred us into
life and while we munched biscuits and drank hot water flavored
with lemon crystals and heaps of sugar, Lowe, Gregory, and I discussed rather pessimistically our plans for the day.

At 9 A.M. the wind was still blowing fiercely, and clad in all my
warm clothing I crawled out of the tent and crossed to the small
Meade tent housing John Hunt, Charles Evans, and Tom Bourdillon. Hunt agreed that any start under these conditions was
impossible. Ang Temba had become sick and was obviously incapable of carrying up any farther. So we decided to send him
down with Evans and Bourdillon when they left for Camp VII
about midday. Hunt decided at the last moment to accompany
this party, owing to Bourdillon's condition, and Lowe and I as-
sisted a very weary foursome to climb the slopes above the camp

and then watched them start off on their slow and exhausting trip down to Camp VII.

All day the wind blew furiously and it was in a somewhat desperate spirit that we organized the loads for the establishment of the ridge camp on the following day. Any delay in our departure from the South Col could only result in increased deterioration and consequent weakness. The violent wind gave us another unpleasant night, but we were all breathing oxygen at one liter per minute and this enabled us to doze uneasily for seven or eight hours.

Early in the morning the wind was still blowing strongly, but about 8 A.M. it eased considerably and we decided to leave. However, another blow had fallen—Pemba had been violently ill all night and was obviously not capable of going on. Only one Sherpa porter, Ang Nyima, was left to carry for us out of our original band of three. Our only alternative was to carry the camp ourselves, as to abandon the attempt was unthinkable. We repacked the loads, eliminating anything not vitally necessary and having no choice because of our reduced manpower but to cut down vital supplies of oxygen.

At 8.45 A.M. Lowe, Gregory, and Ang Nyima departed, all carrying over forty pounds each and breathing oxygen at four liters a minute. Tenzing and I were to leave later so that we could follow quickly up the steps made by the other party and so conserve energy and oxygen. We loaded all our personal clothing, sleeping bags, and air mattresses, together with some food, onto our oxygen sets and left at 10 A.M., carrying fifty pounds apiece.

We followed slowly up the long slopes to the foot of the great couloir and then climbed the veritable staircase hewn by Lowe in the firm steep snow of the couloir. As we moved slowly up the steps we were bombarded by a constant stream of ice chips falling from well above us where Lowe and Gregory were cutting steps across to the southeast ridge. We reached the ridge at midday and joined the other party. Nearby was the tattered ruin of the Swiss tent of the previous spring, and it added an air of loneliness and desolation to this remarkable viewpoint. From here Lambert and

Tenzing had made their gallant attempt to reach the summit after a night spent without sleeping bags.

It was a wonderful spot with tremendous views in every direction and we indulged in an orgy of photography. We were all feeling extremely well and felt confident of placing our camp high up on the southeast ridge. We heaved on our loads again and moved 150 feet up the ridge to the dump made by Hunt two days previously. The ridge was quite steep, but the upward-sloping strata of the rocks gave us quite good footholds and the climbing was not technically difficult, although loose snow over the steep rocks demanded care. The dump was at 27,350 feet, but we considered that this was still far too low for an effective summit camp, so somewhat reluctantly we added all this extra gear to our already large loads. Gregory took some more oxygen, Lowe some food and fuel, and I tied on a tent. Apart from Ang Nyima, who was carrying just over forty pounds, we all had loads of from fifty to sixty-three pounds. We continued on up the ridge at a somewhat reduced rate.

Despite our great burdens we were moving steadily, though very slowly. The ridge steepened onto a slope of firm snow and Lowe chipped steps up it for fifty feet. By 2 P.M. we were beginning to tire and started looking for a camp site. The ridge appeared to have no relief at all and continued upward in one unbroken sweep. We plugged slowly on, looking for a ledge without success. Again and again we hopefully labored up to a prospective site only to find that it was still at a 45-degree angle. We were getting a little desperate until Tenzing, remembering the ground from the previous year, suggested a traverse over steep slopes to the left, which finally landed us onto a relatively flat spot beneath a rock bluff.

It was 2.30 and we decided to camp here. All day the magnificent peak of Lhotse had commanded our attention, but now its summit was just below us. We estimated our height at 27,900 feet. Lowe, Gregory, and Ang Nyima dropped their loads on the site with relief. They were tired but well satisfied with the height gained, and to them must go a great deal of the credit for the successful climb of the following day. Wasting no time, they hurried off back to the South Col.

It was with a certain feeling of loneliness that we watched our cheerful companions slowly descending the ridge, but we had much to do. We removed our oxygen sets in order to conserve our supplies and set to work with our ice axes to clear the tiny platform. We scratched off all the snow to reveal a rock slope at an angle of some 30 degrees. The rocks were well frozen in, but by the end of a couple of hours' solid work we had managed to pry loose sufficient stones to level out two strips of ground a yard wide and six feet long, but almost a foot different in levels. Even though not breathing oxygen, we could still work quite hard, but rested every ten minutes or so in order to regain our breath and energy.

We pitched our tent on this double level and tied it down as best we could. There were no suitable rocks around which to hitch our tent guys, and the snow was far too soft to hold aluminum tent pegs. We sank several of our oxygen bottles in the soft snow and attached the guys to these as a somewhat unreliable anchor. Then while Tenzing began heating some soup I made a tally of our limited oxygen supplies. They were much less than we had hoped. For the assault we had only one and two-thirds bottles each. It was obvious that if we were to have sufficient endurance we would be unable to use the four liters per minute that we had originally planned, but I estimated that if we reduced our supplies to three liters per minute we might still have a chance. I prepared the sets and made the necessary adjustments. One thing in our favor was that Evans and Bourdillon had left two bottles of oxygen, still one-third full, some hundreds of feet above our camp. We were relying on this oxygen to get us back to the South Col.

As the sun set we crawled finally into our tent, put on all our warm clothing and wriggled into our sleeping bags. We drank vast quantities of liquid and had a satisfying meal out of our store of delicacies: sardines on biscuits, canned apricots, dates, and biscuits and jam and honey. The canned apricots were a great treat, but it was necessary first to thaw them out of their frozen state over our roaring Primus. In spite of the great height, our breathing was almost normal until a sudden exertion would cause us to pant a little. Tenzing laid his air mattress on the lower shelf half-overhanging the steep slope below and calmly settled down to sleep. I made myself as comfortable as possible half-sitting and half-reclining on the upper shelf with my feet braced on the lower shelf. This position, while not particularly comfortable, had decided advantages. We had been experiencing extremely strong gusts of wind every ten minutes, and whenever I received warning of the approach of such a gust by a shrilling whine high on the ridge above, I could brace my feet and shoulders and assist our meager anchors to hold the tent steady while it temporarily shook and flapped in a most alarming manner. We had sufficient oxygen for only four hours' sleep at one liter per minute. I decided to use this in two periods of two hours, from 9 to 11 P.M. and from 1 to 3 A.M. While wearing the oxygen we dozed and were reasonably comfortable, but as soon as the supply ran out we began to feel cold and miserable. During the night the thermometer read –27° Centigrade, but fortunately the wind had dropped almost entirely.

At 4 A.M. it was very still. I opened the tent door and looked far out across the dark and sleeping valleys of Nepal. The icy peaks below us were glowing clearly in the early morning light and Tenzing pointed out the monastery of Thyangboche, faintly visible on its dominant spur 16,000 feet below us. It was an encouraging thought to realize that even at this early hour the lamas of Thyangboche would be offering up devotions to their Buddhist gods for our safety and well-being.

We started up our cooker and in a determined effort to prevent the weaknesses arising from dehydration we drank large quantities of lemon juice and sugar, and followed this with our last can of sardines on biscuits. I dragged our oxygen sets into the tent, cleaned the ice off them and then completely rechecked and tested them. I had removed my boots, which had become a little wet the day before, and they were now frozen solid. Drastic measures were called for, so I cooked them over the fierce flame of the Primus and despite the very strong smell of burning leather managed to soften them up. Over our down clothing we donned our windproofs and onto our hands we pulled three pairs of gloves—silk, woolen, and windproof.

At 6.30 A.M. we crawled out of our tent into the snow, hoisted our thirty pounds of oxygen gear onto our backs, connected up our masks and turned on the valves to bring life-giving oxygen into our lungs. A few good deep breaths and we were ready to go. Still a little worried about my cold feet, I asked Tenzing to move off and he kicked a deep line of steps away from the rock bluff which protected our tent, out onto the steep powder snow slope to the left of the main ridge. The ridge was now all bathed in sunlight and we could see our first objective, the south summit, far above us. Tenzing, moving purposefully, kicked steps in a long traverse back toward the ridge and we reached its crest just where it forms a great distinctive snow bump at about 28,000 feet. From here the ridge narrowed to a knife-edge and as my feet were now warm I took over the lead.

We were moving slowly but steadily and had no need to stop in order to regain our breath, and I felt that we had plenty in reserve. The soft unstable snow made a route on top of the ridge both difficult and dangerous, so I moved a little down on the steep left side where the wind had produced a thin crust which sometimes held my weight but more often than not gave way with a sudden knock that was disastrous to both balance and morale. After several hundred feet of this rather trying ridge, we came to a tiny hollow and found there the two oxygen bottles left on the earlier attempt by Evans and Bourdillon. I scraped the ice off the gauges and was greatly relieved to find that they still contained several hundred liters of oxygen—sufficient to get us down to the South Col if used very sparingly. With the comforting thought of these oxygen bottles behind us, I continued making the trail on up the ridge, which soon steepened and broadened into the very formidable snow face leading up for the last 400 feet to the southern summit.

The snow conditions on this face were, we felt, distinctly dangerous, but as no alternative route seemed available, we persisted in our strenuous and uncomfortable efforts to beat a trail up it.

We made frequent changes of lead on this very trying section and on one occasion as I was stamping a trail in the deep snow a section around me gave way and I slipped back through three or four of my steps. I discussed with Tenzing the advisability of going on and he, although admitting that he felt very unhappy about the snow conditions, finished with his familiar phrase, "Just as you wish." I decided to go on.

It was with some relief that we finally reached some firmer snow higher up and then chipped steps up the last steep slopes and cramponed on to the South Peak. It was now 9 A.M. We looked with some interest at the virgin ridge ahead. Both Bourdillon and Evans had been depressingly definite about its problems and difficulties and we realized that it could form an almost insuperable barrier. At first glance it was certainly impressive and even rather frightening. On the right, great contorted cornices, overhanging masses of snow and ice, stuck out like twisted fingers over the 10,000-foot drop of the Kangshung Face. Any move onto these cornices could only bring disaster. From the cornices the ridge dropped steeply to the left until the snow merged with the great rock face sweeping up from the Western Cwm. Only one encouraging feature was apparent. The steep snow slope between the cornices and the rock precipices seemed to be composed of firm, hard snow. If the snow proved soft and unstable, our chances of getting along the ridge were few indeed. If we could cut a trail of steps along this slope, we could make some progress at least.

We cut a seat for ourselves just below the south summit and removed our oxygen. Once again I worked out the mental arithmetic that was one of my main preoccupations on the way up and down the mountain. As our first partly full bottle of oxygen was now exhausted, we had only one full bottle left. Eight hundred liters of oxygen at three liters per minute? How long could we last? I estimated that this should give us four and a half hours of going. Our apparatus was now much lighter, weighing just over twenty pounds, and as I cut steps down off the south summit I felt a distinct sense of freedom and well-being quite contrary to what I had expected at this great altitude.

As my ice ax bit into the first steep slope of the ridge, my highest hopes were realized. The snow was crystalline and firm. Two or three rhythmical blows of the ice ax produced a step large enough even for our oversized high-altitude boots and, the most encouraging feature of all, a firm thrust of the ice ax would sink it halfway up the shaft, giving a solid and comfortable belay. We moved one at a time. I realized that our margin of safety at this altitude was not great and that we must take every care and precaution. I would cut a forty-foot line of steps, Tenzing belaying me while I worked. Then in turn I would sink my shaft and put a few loops of the rope around it and Tenzing, protected against a breaking step, would move up to me. Then once again as he belayed me I would go on cutting. In a number of places the overhanging ice cornices were very large indeed and in order to escape them I cut a line of steps down to where the snow met the rocks on the west. It was a great thrill to look straight down this enormous rock face and to see, 8,000 feet below us, the tiny tents of Camp IV in the Western Cwm. Scrambling on the rocks and cutting handholds on the snow, we were able to shuffle past these difficult portions.

On one of these occasions I noted that Tenzing, who had been going quite well, had suddenly slowed up considerably and seemed to be breathing with difficulty. The Sherpas had little idea of the workings of an oxygen set and from past experience I immediately suspected his oxygen supply. I noticed that hanging from the exhaust tube of his oxygen mask were icicles, and on closer examination found that this tube, some two inches in diameter, was completely blocked with ice. I was able to clear it out and gave him much needed relief. On checking my own set I found that the same thing was occurring, though it had not reached the stage to have caused me any discomfort. From then on I kept a much closer check on this problem.

The weather for Everest seemed practically perfect. Insulated as we were in all our down clothing and windproofs, we suffered no discomfort from cold or wind. However, on one occasion I removed my sunglasses to examine more closely a difficult section of the ridge but was very soon blinded by the fine snow driven by the bitter wind and hastily replaced them. I went on cutting steps. To my surprise I was enjoying the climb as much as I had ever enjoyed a fine ridge in my own New Zealand Alps.

After an hour's steady going we reached the foot of the most formidable looking problem on the ridge—a rock step some forty feet high. We had known of the existence of this step from aerial photographs and had also seen it through our binoculars from Thyangboche. We realized that at this altitude it might well spell the difference between success and failure. The rock itself, smooth and almost holdless, might have been an interesting Sunday afternoon problem to a group of expert rock climbers in the Lake District, but here it was a barrier beyond our feeble strength to overcome.

I could see no way of turning it on the steep rock bluff on the west, but fortunately another possibility of tackling it still remained. On its east side was another great cornice and running up the full forty feet of the step was a narrow crack between the cornice and the rock. Leaving Tenzing to belay me as best he could, I jammed my way into this crack, then kicking backwards with my crampons I sank their spikes deep into the frozen snow behind me and levered myself off the ground. Taking advantage of every little rock hold and all the force of knee, shoulder, and arms I could muster, I literally cramponed backwards up the crack, with a fervent prayer that the cornice would remain attached to the rock. Despite the considerable effort involved, my progress although slow was steady, and as Tenzing paid out the rope I inched my way upward until I could finally reach over the top of the rock and drag myself out of the crack onto a wide ledge. For a few moments I lay regaining my breath and for the first time really felt the fierce determination that nothing now could stop our reaching the top. I took a firm stance on the ledge and signaled to Tenzing to come on up. As I heaved hard on the rope Tenzing wriggled his way up the crack and finally collapsed exhausted at the top like a giant fish when it has just been hauled from the sea after a terrible struggle.

I checked both our oxygen sets and roughly calculated our flow rates. Everything seemed to be going well. Probably owing to the strain imposed on him by the trouble with his oxygen set, Tenzing had been moving rather slowly but he was climbing safely, and this was the major consideration. His only comment on my inquiring of his condition was to smile and wave along the ridge. We were going so well at three liters per minute that I was determined now if necessary to cut down our flow rate to two liters per minute if the extra endurance was required.

The ridge continued as before. Giant cornices on the right, steep rock slopes on the left. I went on cutting steps on the narrow strip of snow. The ridge curved away to the right and we had no idea where the top was. As I cut around the back of one hump, another higher one would swing into view. Time was passing and the ridge seemed never-ending. In one place where the angle of the ridge had eased off, I tried cramponing without cutting steps, hoping this would save time, but I quickly realized that our margin of safety on these steep slopes at this altitude was too small, so I went on step cutting. I was beginning to tire a little now. I had been cutting steps continuously for two hours, and Tenzing, too, was moving very slowly. As I chipped steps around still another corner, I wondered rather dully just how long we could keep it up. Our original zest had now quite gone and it was turning more into a grim struggle.

I then realized that the ridge ahead, instead of still monotonously rising, now dropped sharply away, and far below I could see the North Col and the Rongbuk Glacier. I looked upward to see a narrow snow ridge running up to a snowy summit. A few more whacks of the ice ax in the firm snow and we stood on top.

My initial feelings were of relief—relief that there were no more steps to cut—no more ridges to traverse and no more humps to tantalize us with hopes of success. I looked at Tenzing and in spite of the balaclava, goggles, and oxygen mask all encrusted with long icicles that concealed his face, there was no disguising his infectious grin of pure delight as he looked all around him. We shook hands and then Tenzing threw his arm around my shoulders and we thumped each other on the back until we were almost breathless. It was 11.30 A.M. The ridge had taken us two and a half hours, but it seemed like a lifetime. I turned off the oxygen and removed my set. I had carried my camera, loaded with color film, inside my shirt to keep it warm, so I now produced it and got Tenzing to pose on top for me, waving his ax on which was a string of flags—British, Nepalese, United Nations, and Indian. Then I turned my attention to the great stretch of country lying below us in every direction.

To the east was our giant neighbor Makalu, unexplored and unclimbed, and even on top of Everest the mountaineering instinct was sufficiently strong to cause me to spend some moments conjecturing as to whether a route up that mountain might not exist. Far away across the clouds the great bulk of Kangchenjunga loomed on the horizon. To the west, Cho Oyu, our old adversary from 1952, dominated the scene and we could see the great unexplored ranges of Nepal stretching off into the distance. The most important photograph, I felt, was a shot down the north ridge, showing the North Col and the old route which had been made famous by the struggles of those great climbers of the 1920s and 1930s. I had little hope of the results being particularly successful, as I had a lot of difficulty in holding the camera steady in my clumsy gloves, but I felt that they would at least serve as a record. After some ten minutes of this, I realized that I was becoming rather clumsy-fingered and slow-moving, so I quickly replaced my oxygen set and experienced once more the stimulating effect of even a few liters of oxygen. Meanwhile, Tenzing had made a little hole in the snow and in it he placed various small articles of food —a bar of chocolate, a packet of biscuits, and a handful of candies. Small offerings, indeed, but at least a token gift to the gods that all devout Buddhists believe have their home on this lofty summit. While we were together on the South Col two days before, Hunt had given me a small crucifix which he had asked me to take to the top. I, too, made a hole in the snow and placed the crucifix beside Tenzing's gifts.

I checked our oxygen once again and worked out our endurance.

We would have to move fast in order to reach our life-saving reserve below the south summit. After fifteen minutes we turned to go. We had looked briefly for any signs of Mallory and Irvine, but had seen nothing. We both felt a little tired, for the reaction was setting in and we must get off the mountain quickly. I moved down off the summit onto our steps. Wasting no time, we cramponed along our tracks, spurred by the urgency of diminishing oxygen. Bump followed bump in rapid succession. In what seemed almost miraculous time, we reached the top of the rock step. Now, with the almost casual indifference of familiarity, we kicked and jammed our way down it again. We were tired, but not too tired to be careful. We scrambled cautiously over the rock traverse, moved one at a time over shaky snow sections and finally cramponed up our steps and back onto the South Peak.

Only one hour from the top! A swig of sweetened lemonade refreshed us and we turned down again. Throughout the climb we had a constant nagging fear of our return down the great snow slope, and as I led down I packed each step with as much care as if our lives depended on it, as well they might. The terrific impression of exposure as we looked straight down onto the Kangshung glacier, still 10,000 feet below us, made us move with the greatest caution, and every step down seemed a step nearer safety. When we finally moved off the slope onto the ridge below, we looked at each other and without speaking we both almost visibly shrugged off the sense of fear that had been with us all day.

We were now very tired but moved automatically down to the two reserve cylinders on the ridge. As we were only a short distance from camp and had a few liters of oxygen left in our own bottles, we carried the extra cylinders down our tracks and reached our tent on its crazy platform at 2 P.M. Already the moderate winds of the afternoon had wrenched the tent loose from some of its fastenings and it presented a forlorn sight. We had still to reach the South Col. While Tenzing lit the kerosene stove and began to make a lemonade drink heavily sweetened with sugar, I changed our oxygen sets onto the last partly filled bottles and cut down our flow rates to two liters per minute. In contrast to the previous day, when we were working vigorously without oxygen at this camp, we now felt very weak and exhausted. Far below on the South Col we could see minute figures moving and knew that Lowe and Noyce would be waiting for our descent. We had no extra sleeping bags and air mattresses on the South Col, so reluctantly tied our own onto our oxygen frames. Then with a last look at the camp that had served us so well we turned downward with dragging feet and set ourselves to the task of safely descending the ridge.

Our faculties seemed numbed and the time passed as in a dream, but finally we reached the site of the Swiss Ridge Camp and branched off on our last stage down onto the great couloir. There an unpleasant surprise greeted us. The strong wind which had been blowing in the latter part of our climb had completely wiped out all our steps and only a hard, steep, frozen slope lay before us. There was no alternative but to start cutting again. With a grunt of disgust I chipped steps laboriously downward for two hundred feet. Gusts of driving wind whirling down off the ridge tried to pluck us from our steps. Tenzing took over the lead and cut down another hundred feet, then moved into softer snow and kicked a track down the easier slopes at the bottom of the couloir. We cramponed wearily down the long slopes above the South Col.

A figure came toward us and met us a couple of hundred feet above the camp. It was George Lowe, laden with hot soup and emergency oxygen.

We were too tired to make any response to Lowe's enthusiastic acceptance of our news. We stumped down to the Col and slowly ground our way up the short rise to the camp. Just short of the tents my oxygen ran out. We had had enough to do the job, but by no means too much. We crawled into the tent and with a sigh of sheer delight collapsed into our sleeping bags, while the tents flapped and shook under the perpetual South Col gale. That night, our last on the South Col, was a restless one indeed. The bitter cold once again made any deep and restful sleep impossible and the stimulating effects of our success made us so mentally active that we lay there for half the night reliving all the exciting incidents and murmuring to each other between chattering teeth. Early the following morning we were all very weak and made slow but determined preparations for our departure.

The two-hundred-foot slope above the South Col was a great trial, and even when we commenced the long traverse down toward Camp VII we found it necessary to move very slowly and to have frequent rests. The upper part of the Lhotse glacier seemed very steep to us and as we came down the ice steps toward Camp VII our main wish was to rest. We were only thirty yards from the camp when a cheerful shout attracted our attention and there to greet us were Charles Wylie and several of the Sherpas, all looking fresh and strong and with the same question trembling on their lips. The hot drinks they pressed into our hands and their joyful acceptance of our news were a great stimulant in themselves and we continued on down the Lhotse glacier mentally if not physically refreshed.

As we approached Camp IV, tiny figures appeared from the tents and slowly drifted up the track. We made no signal to them but wearily moved down the track toward them. When only fifty yards away, Lowe with characteristic enthusiasm gave the "thumbs up" signal and waved his ice ax in the direction of the summit. Immediately the scene was galvanized into activity and our approaching companions, forgetting their weakness, ran up the snow toward us. As we greeted them all, perhaps a little emotionally, I felt more than ever before that very strong feeling of friendship and co-operation that had been the decisive factor throughout the expedition.

What a thrill it was to be able to tell them that all their efforts amongst the tottering chaos of the Icefall, the disheartening plunging up the snowy inferno of the Western Cwm, the difficult technical ice work on the Lhotse Face, and the grim and nerve-racking toil above the South Col had been fully rewarded and that we had reached the top.

To see the unashamed joy spread over the tired, strained face of our gallant and determined leader was to me reward enough in itself.

The Night the Bed Fell

by JAMES THURBER

I suppose that the high-water mark of my youth in Columbus, Ohio, was the night the bed fell on my father. It makes a better recitation (unless, as some friends of mine have said, one has heard it five or six times) than it does a piece of writing, for it is almost necessary to throw furniture around, shake doors, and bark like a dog, to lend the proper atmosphere and verisimilitude to what is admittedly a somewhat incredible tale. Still, it did take place.

It happened, then, that my father had decided to sleep in the attic one night, to be away where he could think. My mother opposed the notion strongly because, she said, the old wooden bed up there was unsafe: it was wobbly and the heavy headboard would crash down on my father's head in case the bed fell, and kill him. There was no dissuading him, however, and at a quarter past ten he closed the attic door behind him and went up the narrow twisting stairs. We later heard ominous creakings as he crawled into bed. Grandfather, who usually slept in the attic bed when he was with us, had disappeared some days before. (On these occasions he was usually gone six or eight days and returned growling and out of temper, with the news that the federal Union was run by a passel of blockheads and that the Army of the Potomac didn't have any more chance than a fiddler's bitch.)

We had visiting us at this time a nervous first cousin of mine named Briggs Beall, who believed that he was likely to cease breathing when he was asleep. It was his feeling that if he were not awakened every hour during the night, he might die of suffocation. He had been accustomed to setting an alarm clock to ring at intervals until morning, but I persuaded him to abandon this. He slept in my room and I told him that I was such a light sleeper that if anybody quit breathing in the same room with me, I would wake instantly. He tested me the first night—which I had suspected he would—by holding his breath after my regular breathing had convinced him I was asleep. I was not asleep, however, and called to him. This seemed to allay his fears a little, but he took the precaution of putting a glass of spirits of camphor on a little table at the head of his bed. In case I didn't arouse him until he was almost gone, he said, he would sniff the camphor, a powerful reviver. Briggs was not the only member of his family who had his crotchets. Old Aunt Melissa Beall (who could whistle like a man, with two fingers in her mouth) suffered under the premonition that she was destined to die on South High Street, because she had been born on South High Street and married on South High Street. Then there was Aunt Sarah Shoaf, who never went to bed at night without the fear that a burglar was going to get in and blow chloroform under her door through a tube. To avert this calamity—for she was in greater dread of anesthetics than of losing her household goods—she always piled her money, silverware, and other valuables in a neat stack just outside her bedroom, with a note reading: "This is all I have. Please take it and do not use your chloroform, as this is all I have." Aunt Gracie Shoaf also had a burglar phobia, but she met it with more fortitude. She was confident that burglars had been getting into her house every night for forty years. The fact that she never missed anything was to her no proof to the contrary. She always claimed that she scared them off before they could take anything, by throwing shoes down the hallway. When she went to bed she piled, where she could get at them handily, all the shoes there were about her house. Five minutes after she had turned off the light, she would sit up in bed and say "Hark!" Her husband, who had learned to ignore the whole situation as long ago as 1903, would either be sound asleep or pretend to be sound asleep. In either case he would not respond to her tugging and pulling, so that presently she would arise, tiptoe to the door, open it slightly and heave a shoe down the hall in one direction, and its mate down the hall in the other direction. Some nights she threw them all, some nights only a couple of pair.

But I am straying from the remarkable incidents that took place during the night that the bed fell on father. By midnight we were all in bed. The layout of the rooms and the disposition of their occupants is important to an understanding of what later occurred. In the front room upstairs (just under father's attic bedroom) were my mother and my brother Herman, who sometimes sang in his sleep, usually "Marching Through Georgia" or "Onward Christian Soldiers." Briggs Beall and myself were in a room adjoining this one. My brother Roy was in a room across the hall from ours. Our bull terrier, Rex, slept in the hall.

My bed was an army cot, one of those affairs which are made wide enough to sleep on comfortably only by putting up, flat with the middle section, the two sides which ordinarily hang down like the sideboards of a dropleaf table. When these sides are up, it is perilous to roll too far toward the edge, for then the cot is likely to tip completely over, bringing the whole bed down on top of one, with a tremendous banging crash. This, in fact, is precisely what happened, about two o'clock in the morning. (It was my mother who, in recalling the scene later, first referred to it as "the night the bed fell on your father.")

Always a deep sleeper, slow to arouse (I had lied to Briggs), I was at first unconscious of what had happened when the iron cot rolled me onto the floor and toppled over on me. It left me still warmly bundled up and unhurt, for the bed rested above me like a canopy. Hence I did not wake up, only reached the edge of consciousness and went back. The racket, however, instantly awakened my mother, in the next room, who came to the immediate conclusion that her worst dread was realized: the big wooden bed upstairs had fallen on father. She therefore screamed, "Let's go to your poor father!" It was this shout, rather than the noise of my cot falling, that awakened Herman, in the same room with her. He thought that mother had become, for no apparent reason, hysterical. "You're all right, Mamma!" he shouted, trying to calm her. They exchanged shout for shout for perhaps ten seconds: "Let's go to your poor father!" and "You're all right!" That woke up Briggs. By this time I was conscious of what was going on, in a vague way, but did not yet realize that I was under my bed instead of on it. Briggs, awakening in the midst of loud shouts of fear and apprehension, came to the quick conclusion that he was suffocating and that we were all trying to "bring him out." With a low moan, he grasped the glass of camphor at the head of his bed and instead of sniffing it poured it over himself. The room reeked of camphor. "Ugf, ahfg," choked Briggs, like a drowning man, for he had almost succeeded in stopping his breath under the deluge of pungent spirits. He leaped out of bed and groped toward the open window, but he came up against one that was closed. With his hand, he beat out the glass, and I could hear it crash and tinkle on the alleyway below. It was at this juncture that I, in trying to get up, had the uncanny sensation of feeling my bed above me! Foggy with sleep, I now suspected, in my turn, that the whole uproar was being made in a frantic endeavor to extricate me from what must be an unheard-of and perilous situation. "Get me out of this!" I bawled. "Get me out!" I think I had the nightmarish belief that I was entombed in a mine. "Gugh," gasped Briggs, floundering in his camphor.

By this time my mother, still shouting, pursued by Herman, still shouting, was trying to open the door to the attic, in order to go up and get my father's body out of the wreckage. The door was stuck, however, and wouldn't yield. Her frantic pulls on it only added to the general banging and confusion. Roy and the dog were now up, the one shouting questions, the other barking.

Father, farthest away and soundest sleeper of all, had by this time been awakened by the battering on the attic door. He decided that the house was on fire. "I'm coming, I'm coming!" he wailed in a slow, sleepy voice—it took him many minutes to regain full consciousness. My mother, still believing he was caught

under the bed, detected in his "I'm coming!" the mournful, resigned note of one who is preparing to meet his Maker. "He's dying!" she shouted.

"I'm all right!" Briggs yelled to reassure her. "I'm all right!" He still believed that it was his own closeness to death that was worrying mother. I found at last the light switch in my room, unlocked the door, and Briggs and I joined the others at the attic door. The dog, who never did like Briggs, jumped for him—assuming that he was the culprit in whatever was going on—and Roy had to throw Rex and hold him. We could hear father crawling out of bed upstairs. Roy pulled the attic door open, with a mighty jerk and father came down the stairs, sleepy and irritable but safe and sound. My mother began to weep when she saw him. Rex began to howl. "What in the name of God is going on here?" asked father.

The situation was finally put together like a gigantic jigsaw puzzle. Father caught a cold from prowling around in his bare feet but there were no other bad results. "I'm glad," said mother, who always looked on the bright side of things, "that your grandfather wasn't here."

"How They Brought the Good News from Ghent to Aix"

by ROBERT BROWNING

I sprang to the stirrup, and Joris, and he;
I galloped, Dirck galloped, we galloped all three;
"Good speed!" cried the watch, as the gatebolts undrew;
"Speed!" echoed the wall to us galloping through;
Behind shut the postern, the lights sank to rest,
And into the midnight we galloped abreast.

Not a word to each other; we kept the great pace
Neck by neck, stride by stride, never changing our place;
I turned in my saddle and made its girths tight,
Then shortened each stirrup, and set the pique right,
Rebuckled the cheek-strap, chained slacker the bit,
Nor galloped less steadily Roland a whit.

'Twas moonset at starting; but while we drew near
Lokeren, the cocks crew and twilight dawned clear;
At Boom, a great yellow star came out to see;
At Düffeld, 'twas morning as plain as could be;
And from Mecheln church-steeple we heard the half-chime,
So Joris broke silence with, "Yet there is time!"

At Aershot, up leaped of a sudden the sun,
And against him the cattle stood black every one,
To stare through the mist at us galloping past,
And I saw my stout galloper Roland at last,
With resolute shoulders, each butting away
The haze, as some bluff river headland its spray;

And his low head and crest, just one sharp ear bent back
For my voice, and the other pricked out on his track;
And one eye's black intelligence—ever that glance
O'er its white edge at me, his own master, askance!
And the thick heavy spume-flakes which aye and anon
His fierce lips shook upwards in galloping on.

By Hasselt, Dirck groaned; and cried Joris, "Stay spur!
Your Roos galloped bravely, the fault's not in her,
We'll remember at Aix"—for one heard the quick wheeze
Of her chest, saw the stretched neck and staggering knees,
And sunk tail, and horrible heave of the flank,
As down on her haunches she shuddered and sank.

So we were left galloping, Joris and I,
Past Looz and past Tongres, no cloud in the sky;
The broad sun above laughed a pitiless laugh,
'Neath our feet broke the brittle bright stubble like chaff;
Till over by Dalhem a dome-spire sprang white,
And "Gallop," gasped Joris, "for Aix is in sight!"

"How they'll greet us!"—and all in a moment his roan
Rolled neck and croup over, lay dead as a stone;
And there was my Roland to bear the whole weight
Of the news which alone could save Aix from her fate,
With his nostrils like pits full of blood to the brim,
And with circles of red for his eye-sockets' rim.

Then I cast loose my buffcoat, each holster let fall,
Shook off both my jack-boots, let go belt and all,
Stood up in the stirrup, leaned, patted his ear,
Called my Roland his pet-name, my horse without peer;
Clapped my hands, laughed and sang, any noise, bad or good,
Till at length into Aix Roland galloped and stood.

And all I remember is—friends flocking round
As I sat with his head 'twixt my knees on the ground;
And no voice but was praising this Roland of mine,
As I poured down his throat our last measure of wine,
Which (the burgesses voted by common consent)
Was no more than his due who brought good news from Ghent.

Kon-Tiki

A PACIFIC MONSTER

by THOR HEYERDAHL

Although anthropologists generally believed that in prehistoric times people had migrated eastward from Asia to the American continents, the author of this book held a different theory. He believed that some tribes had also moved in the opposite direction, that is, from South America westward to the Polynesian Islands. But how could they have got there, since it is known that they had no boats, only rafts? Thor Heyerdahl guessed that they could have done this without true sailing, by just drifting with the currents. To prove this theory, he and five brave companions set out on a balsa-wood raft, rigged only with primitive sail and in every other way built exactly as it would have been in prehistoric times. And in 101 days, they did succeed in drifting the 4,300 nautical miles from Peru to Tahiti.

Besides new scientific material, the voyage of the Kon-Tiki also produced a wonderful and true adventure story more absorbing than most fiction. The brush with the giant shark described here is only one of the many thrilling incidents that occurred on the raft almost every day. Kon-Tiki has generally been hailed as the greatest sea story of our time.

After a week or so the sea grew calmer, and we noticed that it became blue instead of green. We began to go west-northwest instead of due northwest and took this as the first faint sign that we had got out of the coastal current and had some hope of being carried out to sea.

The very first day we were left alone on the sea we had noticed fish round the raft, but we were too much occupied with the steering to think of fishing. The second day we went right into a thick shoal of sardines, and soon afterward an eight-foot blue shark came along and rolled over with its white belly uppermost as it rubbed against the raft's stern, where Herman and Bengt stood barelegged in the seas, steering. It played round us for a while but disappeared when we got the hand harpoon ready for action.

Next day we were visited by tunnies, bonitos, and dolphins, and when a big flying fish thudded on board we used it as bait and at once pulled in two large dolphins (dorados) weighing from twenty to thirty-five pounds each. This was food for several days. On steering watch we could see many fish we did not even know, and one day we came into a school of porpoises which seemed quite endless. The black backs tumbled about, packed close together, right in to the side of the raft, and sprang up here and there all over the sea as far as we could see from the masthead. And the nearer we came to the Equator, and the farther from the coast, the commoner flying fish became. When at last we came out into the blue water where the sea rolled by majestically, sunlit and serene, ruffled by gusts of wind, we could see them glittering like a rain of projectiles which shot from the water and flew in a straight line till their power of flight was exhausted and they vanished beneath the surface.

If we set the little paraffin lamp out at night, flying fish were attracted by the light and, large and small, shot over the raft. They often struck the bamboo cabin or the sail and tumbled helpless on the deck. Unable to get a take-off by swimming through the water, they just remained lying and kicking helplessly, like large-eyed herrings with long breast fins. It sometimes happened that we heard an outburst of strong language from a man on deck when a cold flying fish came unexpectedly, at a good speed, slap into his face. They always came at a good pace and snout first, and if they caught one full in the face they made it burn and tingle. But the unprovoked attack was quickly forgiven by the injured party, for, with all its drawbacks, we were in a maritime land of enchantment where delicious fish dishes came hurling through the air. We used to fry them for breakfast, and whether it was the fish, the cook, or our appetites, they reminded us of fried troutlings once we had scraped the scales off.

The cook's first duty, when he got up in the morning, was to go out on deck and collect all the flying fish that had landed on board in the course of the night. There were usually half a dozen or more, and once we found twenty-six fat flying fish on the raft. Knut was much upset one morning because, when he was standing operating with the frying pan, a flying fish struck him on the hand instead of landing right in the cooking fat.

Our neighborly intimacy with the sea was not fully realized by Torstein till he woke one morning and found a sardine on his pillow. There was so little room in the cabin that Torstein had to lie with his head in the doorway, and, if anyone inadvertently trod on his face when going out at night, he bit him in the leg. He grasped the sardine by the tail and confided to it understandingly that all sardines had his entire sympathy. We conscientiously drew in our legs so that Torstein should have more room the next night, but then something happened which caused Torstein to find himself a sleeping place on top of all the kitchen utensils in the radio corner.

It was a few nights later. It was overcast and pitch dark, and Torstein had placed the paraffin lamp close by his head, so that the night watches could see where they were treading when they crept in and out over his head. About four o'clock Torstein was awakened by the lamp tumbling over and something cold and wet flapping about his ears. "Flying fish," he thought and felt for it in the darkness to throw it away. He caught hold of something long and wet, which wriggled like a snake, and let go as if he had burned himself. The unseen visitor twisted itself away and over to Herman, while Torstein tried to get the lamp lighted again. Herman started up, too, and this made me wake, thinking of the octopus which came up at night in these waters.

When we got the lamp lighted, Herman was sitting in triumph with his hand gripping the neck of a long thin fish which wriggled in his hands like an eel. The fish was over three feet long, as slender as a snake, with dull black eyes and a long snout with a greedy jaw full of long sharp teeth. The teeth were as sharp as knives and could be folded back into the roof of the mouth to make way for what was swallowed. Under Herman's grip a large-eyed white fish, about eight inches long, was suddenly thrown up from the stomach and out of the mouth of the predatory fish, and soon after up came another like it. These were clearly two deep-water fish, much torn by the snakefish's teeth. The snake-fish's thin skin was bluish violet on the back and steel blue underneath, and it came loose in flakes when we took hold of it.

Bengt too was awakened at last by all the noise, and we held the lamp and the long fish under his nose. He sat up drowsily in his sleeping bag and said solemnly:

"No, fish like that don't exist."

With which he turned over quietly and fell asleep again.

Bengt was not far wrong. It appeared later that we six sitting round the lamp in the bamboo cabin were the first men to have seen this fish alive. Only the skeleton of a fish like this one had been found a few times on the coast of South America and the Galapagos Islands; ichthyologists called it *Gempylus*, or snake mackerel, and thought it lived at the bottom of the sea at a great depth because no one had ever seen it alive. But, if it lived at a great depth, it must have done so by day when the sun blinded its big eyes. For on dark nights *Gempylus* was abroad high over the surface of the sea; we on the raft had experience of that.

A week after the rare fish had landed on Torstein's sleeping bag, we had another visit. Again it was four in the morning, and the new moon had set so that it was dark but the stars were shining. The raft was steering easily, and when my watch was over I took a turn along the edge of the raft to see if everything was shipshape for the new watch. I had a rope round my waist, as the watch always had, and, with the paraffin lamp in my hand, I was walking carefully along the outermost log to get round the mast. The log was wet and slippery, and I was furious when someone quite unexpectedly caught hold of the rope behind me and jerked till I nearly lost my balance. I turned round wrathfully with the lantern, but not a soul was to be seen. There came a new tug at the rope, and I saw something shiny lying writhing on the deck. It was a fresh *Gempylus,* and this time it had got its teeth so deep into the rope that several of them broke before I got the rope loose. Presumably the light of the lantern had flashed along the curving white rope, and our visitor from the depths of the sea had caught hold in the hope of jumping up and snatching an extra long and tasty tidbit. It ended its days in a jar of Formalin.

The sea contains many surprises for him who has his floor on a level with the surface and drifts along slowly and noiselessly. A sportsman who breaks his way through the woods may come back and say that no wild life is to be seen. Another may sit down on a stump and wait, and often rustlings and cracklings will begin and curious eyes peer out. So it is on the sea, too. We usually plow across it with roaring engines and piston strokes, with the water foaming round our bow. Then we come back and say that there is nothing to see far out on the ocean.

Not a day passed but we, as we sat floating on the surface of the sea, were visited by inquisitive guests which wriggled and waggled about us, and a few of them, such as dolphins and pilot fish, grew so familiar that they accompanied the raft across the sea and kept round us day and night.

When night had fallen and the stars were twinkling in the dark tropical sky, a phosphorescence flashed around us in rivalry with the stars, and single glowing plankton resembled round live coals so vividly that we involuntarily drew in our bare legs when the glowing pellets were washed up round our feet at the raft's stern. When we caught them, we saw that they were little brightly shining species of shrimp. On such nights we were sometimes scared when two round shining eyes suddenly rose out of the sea right alongside the raft and glared at us with an unblinking hypnotic stare. The visitors were often big squids which came up and floated on the surface with their devilish green eyes shining in

the dark like phosphorus. But sometimes the shining eyes were those of deep-water fish which came up only at night and lay staring, fascinated by the glimmer of light before them. Several times, when the sea was calm, the black water round the raft was suddenly full of round heads two or three feet in diameter, lying motionless and staring at us with great glowing eyes. On other nights balls of light three feet and more in diameter would be visible down in the water, flashing at irregular intervals like electric lights turned on for a moment.

We gradually grew accustomed to having these subterranean or submarine creatures under the floor, but nevertheless we were just as surprised every time a new species appeared. About two o'clock on a cloudy night, when the man at the helm had difficulty in distinguishing black water from black sky, he caught sight of a faint illumination down in the water which slowly took the shape of a large animal. It was impossible to say whether it was plankton shining on its body, or whether the animal itself had a phosphorescent surface, but the glimmer down in the black water gave the ghostly creature obscure, wavering outlines. Sometimes it was roundish, sometimes oval, or triangular, and suddenly it split into two parts which swam to and fro under the raft independently of each other. Finally there were three of these large shining phantoms wandering round in slow circles under us.

They were real monsters, for the visible parts alone were some five fathoms long, and we all quickly collected on deck and followed the ghost dance. It went on for hour after hour, following the course of the raft. Mysterious and noiseless, our shining companions kept a good way beneath the surface, mostly on the starboard side where the light was, but often they were right under the raft or appeared on the port side. The glimmer of light on their backs revealed that the beasts were bigger than elephants but they were not whales, for they never came up to breathe. Were they giant ray fish which changed shape when they turned over on their sides? They took no notice at all if we held the light right down on the surface to lure them up, so that we might see what kind of creatures they were. And, like all proper goblins and ghosts, they had sunk into the depths when the dawn began to break.

We never got a proper explanation of this nocturnal visit from the three shining monsters, unless the solution was afforded by another visit we received a day and a half later in the full midday sunshine. It was May 24, and we were lying drifting on a leisurely swell in exactly 95° west by 7° south. It was about noon, and we had thrown overboard the guts of two big dolphins we had caught earlier in the morning. I was having a refreshing plunge overboard at the bow, lying in the water but keeping a good lookout and hanging on to a rope end, when I caught sight of a thick brown fish, six feet long, which came swimming inquisitively toward me through the crystal-clear sea water. I hopped quickly up on to the edge of the raft and sat in the hot sun looking at the fish as it passed quietly, when I heard a wild war whoop from Knut, who was sitting aft behind the bamboo cabin. He bellowed "Shark!" till his voice cracked in a falsetto, and, as we had sharks swimming alongside the raft almost daily without creating such excitement, we all realized that this must be something extra-special and flocked astern to Knut's assistance.

Knut had been squatting there, washing his pants in the swell, and when he looked up for a moment he was staring straight into the biggest and ugliest face any of us had ever seen in the whole of our lives. It was the head of a veritable sea monster, so huge and so hideous that, if the Old Man of the Sea himself had come up, he could not have made such an impression on us. The head was broad and flat like a frog's, with two small eyes right at the sides, and a toadlike jaw which was four or five feet wide and had long fringes drooping from the corners of the mouth. Behind the head was an enormous body ending in a long thin tail with a pointed tail fin which stood straight up and showed that this sea monster was not any kind of whale. The body looked brownish under the water, but both head and body were thickly covered with small white spots.

The monster came quietly, lazily swimming after us from astern. It grinned like a bulldog and lashed gently with its tail.

The large round dorsal fin projected clear of the water and sometimes the tail fin as well, and, when the creature was in the trough
of the swell, the water flowed about the broad back as though
washing round a submerged reef. In front of the broad jaws swam
a whole crowd of zebra-striped pilot fish in fan formation, and
large remora fish and other parasites sat firmly attached to the
huge body and traveled with it through the water, so that the
whole thing looked like a curious zoological collection crowded
round something that resembled a floating deep-water reef.

A twenty-five-pound dolphin, attached to six of our largest fish-
hooks, was hanging behind the raft as bait for sharks, and a swarm
of the pilot fish shot straight off, nosed the dolphin without
touching it, and then hurried back to their lord and master, the
sea king. Like a mechanical monster it set its machinery going and
came gliding at leisure toward the dolphin which lay, a beggarly
trifle, before its jaws. We tried to pull the dolphin in, and the sea
monster followed slowly, right up to the side of the raft. It did
not open its mouth but just let the dolphin bump against it, as
if to throw open the whole door for such an insignificant scrap
was not worth while. When the giant came close up to the raft, it
rubbed its back against the heavy steering oar, which was just
lifted up out of the water, and now we had ample opportunity of
studying the monster at the closest quarters—at such close
quarters that I thought we had all gone mad, for we roared
stupidly with laughter and shouted overexcitedly at the completely
fantastic sight we saw. Walt Disney himself, with all his powers of
imagination, could not have created a more hair-raising sea
monster than that which thus suddenly lay with its terrific jaws
along the raft's side.

The monster was a whale shark, the largest shark and the largest
fish known in the world today. It is exceedingly rare, but scattered specimens are observed here and there in the tropical oceans.
The whale shark has an average length of fifty feet, and according
to zoologists it weighs fifteen tons. It is said that large specimens
can attain a length of sixty feet; one harpooned baby had a liver

weighing six hundred pounds and a collection of three thousand teeth in each of its broad jaws.

Our monster was so large that, when it began to swim in circles round us and under the raft, its head was visible on one side while the whole of its tail stuck out on the other. And so incredibly grotesque, inert, and stupid did it appear when seen fullface that we could not help shouting with laughter, although we realized that it had strength enough in its tail to smash both balsa logs and ropes to pieces if it attacked us. Again and again it described narrower and narrower circles just under the raft, while all we could do was to wait and see what might happen. When it appeared on the other side, it glided amiably under the steering oar and lifted it up in the air, while the oar blade slid along the creature's back.

We stood round the raft with hand harpoons ready for action, but they seemed to us like toothpicks in relation to the mammoth beast we had to deal with. There was no indication that the whale shark ever thought of leaving us again; it circled round us and followed like a faithful dog, close up to the raft. None of us had ever experienced or thought we should experience anything like it; the whole adventure, with the sea monster swimming behind and under the raft, seemed to us so completely unnatural that we could not really take it seriously.

In reality the whale shark went on encircling us for barely an hour, but to us the visit seemed to last a whole day. At last it became too exciting for Erik, who was standing at the corner of the raft with an eight-foot hand harpoon, and, encouraged by ill-considered shouts, he raised the harpoon above his head. As the whale shark came gliding slowly toward him and its broad head moved right under the corner of the raft, Erik thrust the harpoon with all his giant strength down between his legs and deep into the whale shark's gristly head. It was a second or two before the giant understood properly what was happening. Then in a flash the placid half-wit was transformed into a mountain of steel m̶u̶s̶c̶l̶e

We heard a swishing noise as the harpoon line rus̶h̶e̶d̶ edge of the raft and saw a cascade of water as the gi̶a̶n̶t̶ its head and plunged down into the depths. The three men who were standing nearest were flung about the place, head over heels, and two of them were flayed and burned by the line as it rushed through the air. The thick line, strong enough to hold a boat, was caught up on the side of the raft but snapped at once like a piece of twine, and a few seconds later a broken-off harpoon shaft came up to the surface two hundred yards away. A shoal of frightened pilot fish shot off through the water in a desperate attempt to keep up with their old lord and master. We waited a long time for the monster to come racing back like an infuriated submarine, but we never saw anything more of him.

Stories from Great Lives . . .

Famous
Men
and Women

Joan of Arc

NEW FRIENDS

by NANCY WILSON ROSS

*For the French, Jeanne d'Arc is the great national heroine,
the saviour of France. But it is not so much her historical importance that has fascinated people of all nations. It is the fact
that a peasant girl who could not even read or write actually did
rally the defeated forces of France and lead them to victory against
the English. Joan was burned as a witch and later canonized as
a saint. Those who do not consider her one or the other still cannot explain—though there exist complete records of her trial in the
15th century—how this girl of 17 was able to plan military cam-
paigns with the wisdom of a general, or accomplish any other of
the things that it is recorded she did. Perhaps the miracle lay only
in Joan's complete faith in her heavenly voices and the confidence
she radiated to the war-weary people of France. In this biography
the author shows us Joan as she really appeared to those who lived
with her, and also tells us how different people have tried to explain the mystery of the Maid of Orleans.*

When Joan came for the second time into the presence of the
scornful captain, Robert de Baudricourt, he did not receive her
quite so rudely as he had the first time.

For one thing he was growing desperate about the state of affairs. His town, Vaucouleurs, was in peril. Every day he saw people deserting the seemingly hopeless cause of the Dauphin. Some
of de Baudricourt's best friends were trying to persuade him to

desert and cross over to the Burgundians, who were on the English side.

No wonder the captain was ready to listen to anyone—even an ignorant farm girl—who was on the Dauphin's side and who still had faith and courage!

There was something else that made de Baudricourt look on Joan with greater favor. Before she appeared for the second time, she had made a new and valuable friend who knew Robert de Baudricourt personally.

This new friend was a young nobleman named Jean de Metz. Since de Metz was to play such an important part in Joan's early career we must tell how she met him in the first place.

While Joan was waiting for Captain de Baudricourt to give her permission to visit him for the second time, she lived with some people in Vaucouleurs named de Royer. Who the de Royers were we do not know. Perhaps they were friends of the Lassois family. At any rate, Joan lived like a daughter in their household while she impatiently waited to see the captain. As she waited she made herself useful to Madame de Royer with spinning and other household tasks. Joan could never stay idle.

Word got around the town about the young girl from Domrémy who was staying with the de Royers. It was said she had seen visions. In these visions she had been told she was to save France. Perhaps she was the girl of whom the old prophecy had spoken!

Jean de Metz had heard these stories about Joan. Out of curiosity and a desperate hope that it might be true, he came to the house to see the strange girl from Lorraine.

He was a good young man, Jean de Metz, and though of noble birth he had no false pride. When he was ushered into the little dark room where Joan sat, spinning, he went straight up to her. He put out his hand and asked kindly, but bluntly, "What are you doing here anyway?"

Before Joan could reply, he demanded, "Are we all going to become English? Will the King be driven from his kingdom?"

Joan looked up at the tall, anxious young soldier and replied to his questions gravely in the order in which he put them.

"I have come here to ask Robert de Baudricourt to lead me, or to send me, with an escort to the Dauphin. He pays no attention to me. But none the less, before spring, I must be on my way to the Dauphin even"—and here her voice rose and became passionate with feeling—"even if I wear out my legs to the knees."

Then she added quite simply, "There is no one in all the world, neither king, nor duke, nor daughter of the King of Scotland, nor any other, who can regain the kingdom of France. There is no help for the kingdom but through me."

And then before he could speak—if indeed, he could have found a reply to such an astounding statement—she added that she would much rather be at home spinning beside her mother. Her voice broke as she said, "For these things do not belong to my station. Yet it is necessary that I go, since God wishes it."

Jean de Metz was deeply moved by this strange girl's faith and courage. He felt that no discouragement or delay could alter her belief in what she was meant to do. He took her hand again and swore that he believed her and would help her as much as he could.

In that very first meeting she was able to infect him with her own impatient desire to act quickly, while there was still time to save France.

Jean de Metz asked her, "When shall we start?"

And she replied, without hesitation, "Better today than tomorrow, better tomorrow than any later."

JOAN IS ON HER WAY AT LAST

Just two weeks after her first meeting with Jean de Metz, Joan, with de Baudricourt's permission, was on her way to the Dauphin.

Jean de Metz, well-known as a brave soldier and a sensible man, had used his influence with the captain to persuade him to let Joan go and to give her the escort she asked.

But still another event had helped to influence the captain to change his attitude toward Joan's mission. This was one of a number of strange events in Joan's life for which it is not easy to find an explanation.

It happened that one day, while still waiting for permission to travel to the Dauphin's court, Joan came hurrying to de Baudricourt's quarters very troubled.

When she was admitted to his presence, she cried in a disturbed and accusing voice, "You are too slow in sending me. This very day a great disaster has befallen the gentle Dauphin, and worse events are in store for him unless you send me to his aid."

De Baudricourt laughed and told her to run along back to her spinning like a good girl. How could she know something he didn't know?

A short time afterwards he received word that the French armies had been defeated a long distance away. What is stranger still, the disaster had been taking place just as Joan had entered the room to warn him. Even today we do not understand how Joan could have known this.

So at last de Baudricourt said she might go. But before she set forth he took one last precaution. He called in a priest and had him give Joan some tests to see if she was, or was not, a witch. The priest found her a "good, honest girl" and said so.

After that de Baudricourt put no further obstacles in her way. He even came to the gates of the town to see her off on her long journey to the court of Chinon.

Joan set off with an escort of five men. These were Jean de Metz and a friend of his—a nobleman named Bertrand de Poulengy—also their two servants, and a soldier called Richard the Archer. Judging from his name he must have been a specially fine marksman. He was probably taken along for added protection on the dangerous journey.

Joan had been given a horse, spurs and boots, and some hand-me-down armor. She had been outfitted by people of the town who believed in her cause and by her two new noble friends.

Jean de Metz had encouraged her to wear the clothes of a boy on the long and dangerous journey. Her Voices also had told her she was to do this. The suggestion was a very sensible one, but it was to cost her dear.

At his final parting, Robert de Baudricourt, the hardened commander, was deeply moved as he bade farewell to the strange farm girl who had first annoyed him with her persistence and finally won his respect. As the party reached the gate of the town, the captain himself put a sword in Joan's girlish hand and said, "Go—and let come what may!"

If his tone held any hint of doubts, Joan's voice did not echo it.

She replied in her usual calm manner, "The way is clear before me—for to do this deed I was born."

With a clatter of horses' hoofs on the stones of the courtyard, they made their way out of the gates of Vaucouleurs on the first lap of the long journey across France to the Dauphin.

JOAN'S JOURNEY TO THE PRINCE

At that time, the Dauphin was living in the town of Chinon. To reach him Joan had to ride nearly four hundred miles across France. Here, too, her determination pushed her onward, and she and her men covered between thirty and forty miles a day.

To add to their difficulties, they often had to travel at night, for the countryside was filled with bands of wandering soldiers. On these occasions, Joan's party would muffle their horses' hoofs with cloths to insure silence as they galloped over the echoing stones.

Joan seldom dared to go by way of the bridges because of the sentries who might report her passing. If she were stopped and questioned, and it was discovered that she came from Vaucouleurs, all the members of her party might be held prisoners.

Since they could not go over the bridges, they had to swim their horses across the rivers. At other times, they might have found shallow places or "fords" where the horses could walk from one bank to the other. Unfortunately, it was near the end of February, and the thawing snow had filled the rivers with deep and swiftly moving water. Swimming a horse across a stream under such conditions and at night was not an easy task.

Throughout the journey the moon was on the wane and there was very little light. In the many forests, after nightfall, as the party picked its way among the trees, the shadows must often have looked like enemies crouched and ready to spring.

Yet in spite of all the difficulties, Joan, though not accustomed to riding horseback, kept up with her escort all the way. She even urged the men to a faster pace, so great was her impatience to get to the Dauphin and to begin the work which her Voices had commanded her to do.

At last, on the eleventh day, they saw in the distance the shining towers of the great castle of Chinon, with the little village nestled near it.

Joan had her letter to the Dauphin ready for immediate delivery. She had stopped at an inn a short distance from Chinon to dictate a message to him. Since she could not write herself, one of her traveling companions had written for her. This message announced Joan's arrival and told the Dauphin what she had come to do.

As soon as they reached Chinon she sent off the message and then settled down to wait for a summons to court.

Joan waited three days. It was her first experience with the Dauphin's irritating habit of putting things off. If there was a choice between doing something today or tomorrow, he always chose tomorrow. Joan, as we have already seen, acted in just the opposite way.

During her three-day wait, Joan must have looked often in admiration, and even in fear, at the imposing castle of Chinon.

Joan had never seen anything to compare with this vast chateau that stretched its noble length along the banks of the river Vienne. Gray and massive it stood, with towers that overlooked the woods

and vineyards of Touraine. Inside the castle hundreds of rooms looked out upon formal gardens. Here at Chinon the Dauphin was enjoying a luxurious life among flatterers and favorites.

The Dauphin, though a weak man, was not a bad one. He might have been expected to scoff at a message from a peasant girl who wrote to tell him she had been sent to crown him King. But he did not. One reason was because gossip about this strange girl from Domrêmy had already reached his ears. He had been told that Joan claimed to be guided by mysterious Voices. Naturally he became curious, for he too had heard the old prophecy about the girl from Lorraine who was to save France.

After three days of asking everybody's advice, the Prince decided to see Joan. He sent a message summoning her to his presence.

Joan immediately obeyed, and on the way she gave another evidence of her strange powers. She had just walked up the hill across the drawbridge that led to the castle. As she was about to enter the main gate under the clock tower a common soldier reined his horse beside her. He looked Joan up and down in her boy's clothes and spoke to her in a way that was rude and insulting.

Joan paused only long enough to reply gravely, "You do wrong to speak thus, for you are very near your death."

A number of people heard her strange words. It was less than an hour later that the soldier fell into the river and was drowned.

But no one had yet heard this remarkable story when Joan entered the great hall of the Dauphin's castle.

Paul Revere's Ride

by HENRY WADSWORTH LONGFELLOW

Listen, my children, and you shall hear
Of the midnight ride of Paul Revere,
On the eighteenth of April, in seventy-five;
Hardly a man is now alive
Who remembers that famous day and year.
He said to his friend, "If the British march
By land or sea from the town tonight,
Hang a lantern aloft in the belfry arch
Of the North Church tower as a signal light,—
One, if by land, and two, if by sea;
And I on the opposite shore will be,
Ready to ride and spread the alarm
Through every Middlesex village and farm,
For the country folk to be up and to arm."

Then he said, "Good night!" and with muffled oar
Silently rowed to the Charleston shore,
Just as the moon rose over the bay,
Where swinging wide at her moorings lay
The *Somerset*, British man-of-war;
A phantom ship, with each mast and spar
Across the moon like a prison bar,
And a huge black hulk, that was magnified
By its own reflection in the tide.

Meanwhile, his friend, through alley and street,
Wanders and watches with eager ears,

Till in the silence around him he hears
The muster of men at the barrack door,
The sound of arms, and the tramp of feet,
And the measured tread of the grenadiers,
Marching down to their boats on the shore.

Then he climbed the tower of the Old North Church
By the wooden stairs, with stealthy tread,
To the belfry-chamber overhead,
And startled the pigeons from their perch
On the somber rafters, that round him made
Masses and moving shapes of shade,—
By the trembling ladder, steep and tall,
To the highest window in the wall,
Where he paused to listen and look down
A moment on the roofs of the town,
And the moonlight flowing over all.

Beneath in the churchyard, lay the dead,
In their night-encampment on the hill,
Wrapped in silence so deep and still
That he could hear, like a sentinel's tread,
The watchful night-wind, as it went
Creeping along from tent to tent,
And seeming to whisper, "All is Well!"
A moment only he feels the spell
Of the place and the hour, and the secret dread
Of the lonely belfry and the dead;
For suddenly all his thoughts are bent
On a shadowy something far away,
Where the river widens to meet the bay,—
A line of black that bends and floats
On the rising tide, like a bridge of boats.

Meanwhile, impatient to mount and ride,
Booted and spurred, with a heavy stride
On the opposite shore walked Paul Revere.
Now he patted his horse's side,

Now gazed at the landscape far and near,
Then, impetuous, stamped the earth,
And turned and tightened his saddle-girth;
But mostly he watched with eager search
The belfry-tower of the Old North Church,
As it rose above the graves on the hill,
Lonely and spectral and somber and still.
And lo! as he looks, on the belfry's height
A glimmer, and then a gleam of light!
He springs to the saddle, the bridle he turns,
But lingers and gazes, till full on his sight
A second lamp in the belfry burns!

A hurry of hoofs in a village street,
A shape in the moonlight, a bulk in the dark,
And beneath, from the pebbles, in passing, a spark
Struck out by a steed flying fearless and fleet:
That was all! And yet, through the gloom and the light,
The fate of a nation was riding that night;
And the spark struck out by that steed, in his flight
Kindled the land into flame with its heat.
He has left the village and mounted the steep,
And beneath him, tranquil and broad and deep,
Is the Mystic, meeting the ocean tides;
And under the alders that skirt its edge,
Now soft on the sand, now loud on the ledge,
Is heard the tramp of his steed as he rides.

It was twelve by the village clock,
When he crossed the bridge into Medford town:
He heard the crowing of the cock,
And the barking of the farmer's dog,
And felt the damp of the river fog,
That rises after the sun goes down.
It was one by the village clock,
When he galloped into Lexington.
He saw the gilded weathercock

Swim in the moonlight as he passed.
And the meeting-house windows, blank and bare,
Gaze at him with a spectral glare,
As if they already stood aghast
At the bloody work they would look upon.

It was two by the village clock,
When he came to the bridge in Concord town.
He heard the bleating of the flock,
And the twitter of birds among the trees,
And felt the breath of the morning breeze
Blowing over the meadows brown.
And one was safe and asleep in his bed
Who at the bridge would be first to fall,
Who that day would be lying dead,
Pierced by a British musket-ball.

You know the rest. In the books you have read,
How the British Regulars fired and fled,—
How the farmers gave them ball for ball,
From behind each fence and farmyard wall,
Chasing the red-coats down the lane,
Then crossing the fields to emerge again
Under the trees at the turn of the road,
And only pausing to fire and load.

So through the night rode Paul Revere;
And so through the night went his cry of alarm
To every Middlesex village and farm,—
A cry of defiance and not of fear,
A voice in the darkness, a knock at the door,
And a word that shall echo forevermore!
For, borne on the night-wind of the Past,
Through all our history, to the last,
In the hour of darkness and peril and need,
The people will waken and listen to hear
The hurrying hoof-beats of that steed,
And the midnight message of Paul Revere.

Paul Revere and the Minute Men

ON MOONLIT ROADS

by DOROTHY CANFIELD FISHER

For young people, Paul Revere has always been one of the most popular figures of the American Revolution, probably because of his enormous courage and energy and because of the appealing legend of his midnight ride. In this biography Dorothy Canfield Fisher imparts her fresh touch, as she does in all her writings, to make the Revolutionary hero come alive as a boy and as a leading New England silversmith and artist, as well as in his more familiar role as a patriot. This chapter shows us Paul Revere spreading the news of the British raid that will trigger the war. After his lucky escape from the British officers he goes on to give further service to the Revolutionary cause. For a dramatic description in poetry of his famous ride nothing has ever surpassed Longfellow's Paul Revere's Ride, *which precedes this story.*

The man on the horse fixed his mind on one thought: "I *must* see them first."

He must not ride so fast that he would run into an ambush. He must not ride so slowly that those red-coated troops now being landed could reach the first village before he did. For it would be enough, although not all he wanted, if he could reach even the first few farmhouses on the road to Lexington before the Regulars did. Just let him rouse two or three families, and tell them the British were on the way. The alarm would be passed along, to those beyond. The Minute Men would spring to their arms. The boys too young to carry a gun would be off on horseback to wake up people who lived on lanes and back roads and to get other big boys to go farther. The old men would start the drums beating so they could be heard for miles, would pull furiously on the ropes of the church bells to throw out their wild summons to fight. Yes, it would be enough if he could get through the empty wasteland back of Charlestown to the first cluster of houses, at a crossroads. Let him be shot down there—he would have done what he was out to do.

But what he wanted was to get through to Lexington. Two of the most important men on the American side—Samuel Adams and John Hancock—were in Lexington. The British hoped to take them by surprise. If they did, they'd be sent back to London to be hanged for treason—as Paul would be if he were caught. He felt that come what might, he *must* get through to the first settlement. If he possibly could, he must reach Lexington to make sure the two leaders of the Americans were safe. And it would be well if he could go on from there to Concord, although the alarm, if he could start it, might well have spread to that town without him.

That was what he intended to do. He knew he could do it—*if he could only see the British patrols before they saw him.*

As he rode out over the empty moorland back of Charlestown, there was not a sound except the hoofbeats of his horse, trotting cautiously when he came to a place where trees or bushes cast a shadow, let out to a full run on open stretches clear in the moonlight. The patrols would never show themselves in the open. They would hide in the shadows.

His keen black eyes ranged everywhere at once, searching the distance, focused intently on every dusky thicket beside the road. At any instant, just as in the boat, a shot might leap out at him. And now not only from one place on which he could keep his eyes. From anywhere. From either side of the road, behind him, from in front of him. But how much better this was, with something active he could do, than that dreadful passage on the water, sitting helpless, the hair on the back of his neck rising in suspense.

He checked his speed to peer sharply around a turn of the road, he loosened the reins, touched his mount's flanks with the spurs, and leaned forward over the mane as the horse broke into a run.

Nobody knows what thoughts went through his mind in that desperate race. Did he remember again that if he were caught he would be hanged? Did he remember his father's saying that all a brave man needs is a fighting chance, just one?

We don't know. But we do know, as though we were inside his mind, that one thought a man might have had never once occurred to him—the simple idea that all he had to do to be safe was just to turn his horse into the thick woods, anywhere. He could stay there, hidden, till everything was all over—whatever that night might bring. He was alone. Nobody was there to see what he did. Nobody would ever know. He could say the British patrols chased him into the woods and he lost his way.

He rode straight ahead, his quick eyes shifting from side to side of the road, his quick mind flashing over what he knew of British ways.

Any man of sense who had fought Indians, if he were set to guard a road on a moonlit night, would cover up anything on his clothes that might catch the light. But Revere thought of Braddock, of the British soldiers he had seen at Albany, of those he had watched drilling on the Common at Boston. He was sure that no British officer would ever spoil the looks of his uniform by covering up a well-polished buckle, a white strap or a cockade. So, as he rode on, trotting cautiously, or galloping wildly, he watched for anything that might show white or catch the light. *He must see them first.*

He did.

Under those trees, what was that white patch? Nothing natural was as white as that. And that gleam, as from something brightly polished? His quick hands drew his horse to a stop.

He saw them now. Two officers on horseback, almost invisible in the shadow cast by a tree. The white came from their ribbon cockades. The reflected gleam was from the pistol holsters kept so brilliantly shiny by the common soldiers who did the work for them.

Now the officers had seen him too, in spite of his dark coat, dark hair and pulled-down black hat. They had a plan to stop him. One of them launched his horse plunging straight at him. The other turned and dashed off up the road to head him off if the first one did not make the capture.

But Paul Revere had seen them first!

He swung his horse about, and struck in the spurs. In the instant of time since his eye had caught that first gleam of white, his ready mind had made a plan to fit that exact place. He would go straight cross-country at top speed, to another road.

As clearly as though it were before him on a map, he saw exactly what fields to cross, what stone walls to leap—and there was a pond, with clay banks that were slippery. He would know how to dodge that, with his little native-born horse. The Britisher on his great military charger would not.

He was off. The officer was taken aback at the idea of leaving the road, but spurred his handsome mount to follow. Again Paul Revere's back hairs crawled on his neck, as his taut body expected a shot from behind. But his mind knew no fear.

He kept his horse galloping at full speed, he watched the rough field over which they were racing, but he turned his head just enough so that he could see from the side of his eye where the British officer was. He was no nearer than in that instant on the road when he had sprung out to block the way. He was farther. Yes, he was dropping behind!

Paul leaned low over his horse's neck, put his weight well forward, kept his eyes fixed on the ground ahead rushing up towards them, dropping behind. Huckleberry bushes, great rocks, a clump of trees. There was the pond—its banks treacherously covered with grass. He swung his horse far to one side and felt, to his joy, a clatter of stony ground under those flying hooves. Behind him the British horse had gone straight ahead over what looked like grass land, had slipped when its feet struck the clay, was sliding down the bank, plunging and floundering wildly. His rider, thrown to one side of the saddle, struggled to get his balance.

Paul Revere shook out the bridle and gave his horse his head. He had almost come through to the Mystic River. Once there, he would find a wooden bridge into the first village on the road to Lexington. If he could only get as far as that.

Through the trees, he saw a road! It was a little country road. Did the British know about it? Would it be patrolled? Before leaving the woods, he drew rein to look up and down. The road was empty. He took his horse out on it in a run, raced down to the bridge and galloped across, the loose planks rattling under those flying feet.

He was in Medford. He had made it. He was alive.

The village lay dark and sleeping in the night just as it would have been—defenseless—a few hours later, if he had not come through.

None of us need ever hope to be happier than Paul Revere was as he galloped his horse down that dark village street and along the lane till he came to the home of the captain of the Medford Minute Men. He leaned from his saddle to hammer on the door with the handle of his whip. A window flew up. Through the dark came Paul Revere's shout, "*The Regulars are out!* On their way to Concord."

That was enough. Everyone knew what was meant by that cry. Knew what to do. Was ready to do it. Before Paul was even back on the road, one half-dressed boy was racing for the church to ring the tocsin bell, an old man with silvery hair had stepped from the next house, his drumsticks flying on his drum, another boy was in a barn saddling a horse. Lights came on in houses. Windows were flying up.

"The Regulars are out," shouted the dark rider to one side or the other, as he raced by. "Start a boy up to Cobble Hill to give the alarm there."

"The Regulars are out. On their way to Concord. Get somebody over the Menot Flats, to those houses."

"The Regulars are out."

A wave of hatred flowed over those country hearts at that name. "The Regulars are out." The village was flaming in excitement, the Minute Men were running from their houses, muskets in their hands, to form a line on the Common, ready to head for Lexington and Concord.

On the moonlit road beyond the village, the man on horseback rode hard. Sometimes before he reached a house, the swift beat of his horse's hooves, loud in the silent night, had wakened the people in a sleeping home. If a light showed in a window, if a head was thrust out, he did not draw rein, but shouted as he passed, *"The Regulars are out.* Give the alarm." If there was no sign of life, he rode up to the door and hammered on it fiercely till someone from inside called back. Then, "The Regulars are out. Get the alarm going," and he rode on, sure of what would follow.

House after house sprang from sleep to action. Mile after mile the rider covered at headlong speed. Then as he came to the top of a slope, there was the town of Lexington.

It was after midnight. The two American leaders were asleep in the minister's house where they were lodged. A sergeant's squad had been set to watch the house. When Revere came thundering in, they sprang up to stop him. Not a soul there yet knew what Paul Revere had come through to tell them.

"The Regulars are out," shouted Revere.

He was heard inside the house. His voice was known. John Hancock called out, "Come in, Revere." The door opened, he went in, and exploded his great bomb of news. Behind him one of the guard had run across to the church. As he told his story, the bell began to clang out its alarm. He raised his voice to be heard over its loud pealing.

"Over a thousand British troops are on the way. I saw them when I left Boston at ten o'clock tonight. Crossing the river in boats. They may arrive any moment now. The alarm has been given, all round about. The Minute Men are arming and gathering."

There was a wild hurry in the house as the two men, so vital to the American side, made ready to leave.

Half an hour later, William Dawes rode in. He had bribed his way past a sentry on the "Neck," shaken off one patrol and ridden the roundabout road through Roxbury. The two express riders were well satisfied with their night's work. They had a bite to eat, took a drink, and considered what to do next.

As his wife had reminded him, Paul had taken orders from the Committee of Safety to Concord only two days before. Most of their military stores were already hidden. And as for the alarm, that had already spread far and wide. Near and far they could hear bells tolling and muskets fired as warning signals. Just the same, they wanted to finish what they had started.

Paul and Dawes turned their horses towards Concord, and a young Dr. Prescott rode along with them. He lived in the district, knew everyone and all the lanes and byroads.

This time, halfway to Concord, there were not two, but four British officers suddenly blocking the way. The Americans were forced into a field where six more British were waiting. In the darkness and confusion Dawes slid off his horse and managed to hide in the bushes. Prescott jumped a stone wall and rode off. But Paul was squarely cornered with a pistol cold against his forehead.

"Who are you? Where do you come from?"

Paul thought quickly. Someone might recognize him. Boldness was his only hope. "My name's Revere," he said. "I left Boston about ten o'clock."

They could hardly believe him. It was only just past midnight. How could anyone have made such quick time? But at his name they broke out into angry words and threats.

Then a bell, quite near, started ringing. The British looked at one another, worried. They quieted down and one of them, remembering orders, tried to explain why they were here. "We're only out after deserters," he said.

Paul saw his chance. "I know better. I know what you're after. But you won't get it. The alarm has been given everywhere. And it's spreading."

The British put their heads together and talked in tones too low for Paul Revere to hear. Then they took the reins out of his hands and led his horse in their midst back along the road to Lexington. The major waved his pistol and said, "As for you, Paul Revere, don't try to escape or I'll blow your brains out. You go back with us. We'll send you to England to be tried and hanged for treason."

Paul answered briefly. "Do as you like about that. But what chance have you to get to Boston? There are only ten of you. Your troops are hours away. There are at least five hundred Minute Men heading here at this minute. In an hour there will be thousands more."

It was slow work leading Revere's horse. The road was dark and lonely. The Englishmen got uneasy and alarmed. With good reason. What chance did they have against a whole countryside swarming with armed men who hated them?

All at once a gun was fired. In the darkness, it rang out very loud. The officers drew their horses sharply to a halt.

"What was that?" the British major snapped out.

"Only another alarm gun. They're being fired like that everywhere from here to Connecticut. You've a mighty slim chance of getting back to Boston with whole skins." Revere spoke out boldly though he knew he was still in mortal danger.

The British officers had another short whispered talk. "Dismount," they told him. As Revere had hoped, they began to see that they had a better chance to escape without being burdened with a prisoner.

They mounted one of their sergeants on Paul's horse and, spurring their mounts to a run, vanished down the road.

Poor Richard

THE RUNAWAY APPRENTICE

by JAMES DAUGHERTY

Benjamin Franklin was possibly the greatest American of his time and certainly the most interesting. Yet this most civilized of Americans, who dazzled the courts of France by his wisdom and wit, began humbly enough as the youngest of 17 children of a candlemaker. After Ben had landed in Philadelphia with a few pennies, everything went well for the young printer's apprentice. The pretty girl who laughed at him munching his roll became his wife. It wasn't long before he had written Poor Richard's Almanac *whose common-sense philosophy and neatly turned phrases——"God helps those that help themselves," "A good example is the best sermon,"——soon were as well known as the Bible.*

Franklin went on to become the most versatile of men. He was the first real American statesman, a remarkable linguist and brilliant ambassador, a gifted and witty writer, a scientist whose experiments proved the identity of lightning and electricity, the organizer of our postal system and volunteer fire departments, the founder of the American Philosophical Society. Yet he never became stuffy or spoiled by fame, and never lost his sense of fun. His innumerable inventions, everything from the Franklin stove to the harmonica, were not patented, but given freely to the people. It was said of him that he invented "the hoax, the lightning-rod, and the Republic." James Daugherty has written the story of this many-sided man with simplicity and strength, and Ben Franklin emerges as the charming and lovable human being he was, as well as a great man.

After a fine three days' sail, they made New York. Out of the great emptiness of sea and sky the young man was suddenly dropped into the rushing hurly-burly of a busy morning on the New York waterfront. He walked under the long bowsprits and dolphin strikers of ships that overhung the waterfront street and found his way among rattling carts and straining stevedores moving mountains of scented cargo. The quick tempo of the vivid scene suited a Boston boy astride of high adventure, as he made his inquiring way to the printing shop of William Bradford. Old Mr. Bradford at first was gruff and suspicious of Benjamin's story but he soon succumbed to the Franklin charm and was figuring out some way to give the boy a hand. He could not use another apprentice himself and there was no other printer in the town, but there was his son in Philadelphia who had just lost his apprentice. There might be a chance for Ben if he would go. In the meantime he would put Benjamin up in his shop until he could get passage to Philadelphia.

As Ben blew out the candle in Mr. Bradford's attic that night and turned into the cool clean bed, he was thinking eagerly about another handful of adventure to be tossed in the lap of a young man on the way to Philadelphia in search of good fortune.

People of means traveled the hundred miles to Philadelphia from New York in a stuffy coach over the ruts and mire of a wilderness road or else posted leisurely on horseback with the added pleasure of air and exercise. But the printer's apprentice would take the economical way by water to Perth Amboy. Then after a fifty-mile hike across Jersey he would board a boat at Burlington for Philadelphia, thirty miles down the Delaware.

Ben sat in the stern curiously watching his fellow-passengers on board the sloop bound for Amboy. A drunken Dutchman was hanging over the bow crazily waving a stone gin bottle. As they came out of the narrows into the wild waters of the lower bay the rotten sail tore away. The craft rose and plunged like a wild horse, the Dutchman went overboard and out of sight in the rush of boiling water. When the bow lifted on the next wave Ben leaned far out and grabbed for the shock of hair as it rose and swept past. It was one chance in a thousand. They pulled the streaming figure over the rail and dumped him in the bottom of the boat.

The Dutchman wiped his dripping face on his sleeve, blew his nose with a thumb and forefinger, the bleary blue eyes looked up at Ben, and he grinned foolishly as he dragged a book out of the pocket of his leather jacket and handed it to the boy. Ben opened the book and forgot the rescue and the storm. It was the most beautiful book he had ever seen, a copy of Bunyan's *Pilgrim's Progress* printed in Dutch and illustrated with copper-plate engravings, a masterpiece of the printer's craft.

As darkness came on, the ship master said it would be impossible to make a safe landing in the fierce surf breaking on the rocky shore, so they threw over a couple of anchors to ride out the night. Waving figures on the shore signaled and shouted vainly into the screaming gale and then went away. Ben spent a storm-tossed night, wet and miserable, between the boatman and the drunken Dutchman. In the morning the storm abated and by night they made Amboy, after thirty hours without food or water.

Early next morning he started on his fifty-mile walk across Jersey. At least there was solid earth beneath his feet again. By afternoon he was thoroughly fagged and wet to the bone. Rain ran in a little stream from the brim of his hat. At every step the water sloshed in his shoes. He wished miserably he had never left Boston.

He stopped for the night at a wretched tavern where they took him for a runaway, an indentured servant with perhaps a reward on his head. If they notified the authorities there would be more trouble. Ben wasted no time the next morning; he paid his bill early and got clear for a hard day of steady tramping, eating up the long Jersey miles in his tireless Yankee stride.

By sundown he was still ten miles from Burlington. At the next inn he fell ravenously upon a fine hot supper. The innkeeper was chatty and talked about books. He had written a bit himself and had seen Europe as an itinerant doctor. Ben's talent for good talk and friendship revived. He could match the doctor for sharp wit and curious learning. They spent a rare evening which neither of them ever forgot.

The Philadelphia boat had gone when Ben came panting into Burlington-on-the-Delaware next morning. Well, no matter, he had a lifetime before him. He would go back and talk to the old lady at the gingerbread shop where he had stopped for food and thereby missed the boat. The little old lady clucked and cackled over him like a hen over a stray chick. She asked all about him and his folks. When he said he was a printer she urged him to stay in Burlington, as they had none. Anyway, he was to stay with her till the next boat. So the hungry boy listened to the grandmother's gossip as he stowed away her enormous dinner of ox-cheek and potatoes and gingerbread.

That evening walking along the bank of the river Ben hailed a large skiff rowing down stream. Yes, they were bound for Philadelphia and would take him on if he could pull a steady oar. So they rowed and sang through the still evening, winding down the yellow river between the burnished shores. Twilight and darkness fell, and still they pulled on through the slow hours till midnight. Had they passed the city? Where were they? They pulled into a little creek, made a fire of fence rails against the October chill, and shivered miserably in a half-doze till morning. They found they were still above the city and did not make the Market Street wharf till eight o'clock.

It was a fagged and hungry apprentice who trudged up deserted Market Street from the wharf that early Sunday morning. Would he perish of hunger in this uninhabited city? He wandered on until he suddenly met a baker's boy at a corner and was soon buying three huge rolls from the nearest baker. With one under each arm and the third fast disappearing, he strolled contentedly on through the Sabbath stillness.

He was nearing a house where a girl was sweeping the white stone steps. As she passed she turned, hearing his step in the quiet street. He looked up shyly with his mouth full of roll, and for a moment stood still. She stared at him in amazement and then turned away, her shoulders shaking with laughter. He glanced

back in embarrassment and she waved to him gaily and vanished behind the white door.

He walked on idly kicking a pebble and retaining in his mind the image of beauty and coquetry. It was his welcome to Philadelphia. He was going to like this "city of brotherly love." It seemed that with the vision of the laughing girl he heard voices saying: "This is to be your city and she shall take you and make you her wise and darling son, and her name and fame with yours shall go throughout the wide world."

He went back to the wharf and gave his other two rolls to a woman and child who had been passengers on the journey of the night before. He was utterly fagged from his five days of strenuous travel. He saw people in their Sunday clothes going into a plain-looking building. It was a Quaker meeting house. He went in, sat down in a dark corner, and slept until he was awakened by the gentle nudging of one of the kindly Friends. He came out rubbing his eyes, hailed an honest-looking lad, and asked where he could find a decent lodging. "There are plenty of ill repute, but thee will find the Crooked Billet despite its rough name a comfortable and decent place."

So at the Crooked Billet he ate, slept in his clothes all afternoon, ate again, tumbled into a deep feather bed and a dreamless sleep. As he closed his eyes he felt vaguely that the city of brotherly love was a most agreeable place.

Leader by Destiny

GEORGE WASHINGTON, THE BOY

by JEANETTE EATON

We all know something about George Washington as a most noble, wise, and great man who led his country to independence. But because his personality is not as colorful as other famous people, like Franklin or Lincoln, we are not so familiar with his more human side. Jeanette Eaton in this fictionalized biography skillfully uses conversation and incidents to create a living portrait of the great leader. Yet it is an authentic picture based on the most careful research; the author has explored every place where Washington ever stayed, so as to provide the right atmosphere. In this opening chapter about his boyhood days, you can catch a vivid glimpse of the kind of man he was to become. His love of horses— he grew into the best horseman of his time—and his quick temper are clearly marked. Much later Thomas Jefferson could still notice that "his temper was naturally irritable and high toned; but reflection and resolution had obtained a firm and habitual ascendancy over it." Indeed he learned to have such good control over his temper that in a crisis no man of his time could be trusted to exercise greater calmness or fairer judgment than Washington.

Through the long grass sopping wet with dew a tall boy came walking. It was half an hour before sunrise, but already light enough to show the outline of his broad-shouldered figure and fine head. After a swift glance back at the solid brick house behind him as if he were expecting someone, he climbed down the bank of the

creek. He could see across it now to its border of willows and
the jutting boulders against which the current rippled. Beyond the
marshes lay the wide river, a tarnished mirror framed in lush
foliage.

Suddenly a mockingbird from an ancient hemlock splashed the
stillness with his sweet, whistling carol. And as the song ceased, a
small boy scrambled between the low branches of an old willow
tree. Jumping down on the bank above his elder brother, he cried
reproachfully, "Why did you not awaken me before you were
dressed and ready?"

Chuckling, the other said, "You were so tight asleep, Jacky, it
seemed a pity." Then he added, "My traps are empty and there's
nothing to see here. But there'd be time to swim before breakfast
is set out."

With one joyous look of agreement the two boys leaped up the
bank and started along the path past the slave quarters. Because of
the deep mud bottom, dangerous as quicksand, the creek was impossible for swimming. There was nothing for it but a walk of a
mile and a half down the plantation road to the shipping wharf
on the Potomac. It was a well-made road for those days, running
between great blue-green fields of tobacco. The long strides of the
elder boy kept Jacky trotting, but at last the pair reached the little
strip of sandy beach washed by the waters of the wide river. Instantly they began slipping off their jackets.

Suddenly the tall boy pounced upon his brother and snatched
him high in his arms. His deep laugh, the scream of the victim,
and an enormous splash far out in deep water followed in swift
succession. As a dark head came up for air and a hand waved,
George swung himself to the wharf, ran down its length and dove.
After a long swim under water he came up beyond the spot where
Jacky was kicking and splashing in delightful contortions.

A little while later the boys sat on the edge of the wharf lacing
their boots and buttoning their vests. Jacky twisted his wet hair
into the pigtail which the fashion of the times required. He
grunted with impatience and glanced at his companion, wishing
he would talk more. Then he began a conversation himself.

"I wish you were coming home with me when I leave Wakefield, George, or that I might stay longer here. Austin and his lady allow more pleasuring than our mother does." Receiving only a nod, he added: "Betty is lonely for you, too, at the Ferry Farm. When are you coming back, George?"

Rising to his feet, the other said: "Likely when full summer is here. I promised Cousin Robin to stay with him at Chotank a bit. But first Mr. Williams would have me complete certain studies he has laid out for me." He made a wry face at the thought.

As they started down the road, the elder boy suddenly caught hold of his brother's arm and blurted out shyly, "Look, Jacky, here is something worth more than the Latin my teacher would push upon me." He jerked from his pocket a somewhat battered notebook.

"Hmm! What have you copied here? Is it poetry?"

"No. These are principles of doing the right thing at table or of meeting persons of distinction. Read the title!" He bent over his brother's shoulder, " 'Rules of Civility and Decent Behaviour in Company and Conversation.' I find them of great benefit."

But Jack was interested in something else. "How fine you have learned to write!" he exclaimed. "There is a handsome tail to your signature in this book."

Pleased, the other looked down upon the name written there. Vigorously and with a lively flourish it stood out upon the page—

Young John returned the book to its owner. "Shall you go to school in England as Lawrence and Augustine did?"

George shook his head. "I am not good at lessons—except accounting. Also, there is no money now. You know father left me but a few acres of land besides the Ferry Farm which mother has while she lives. I must fend for myself soon."

They had been walking swiftly and were nearing the spot where a grassy lane led off like an aisle between pines and cedars to a distant patch of cleared ground. Instinctively the boys glanced that way with sobered faces. Beyond view there in a peaceful semicircle lay the graves of their ancestors, and one stone, recently marked, which bore the name of Augustine Washington, their father, who had died four years before.

What the boys remembered about him was his enormous energy. Whether he was galloping around the plantation or merely talking, he was a man of force. He never tired telling his children about the Washington clan which from 1657 on had been establishing plantations through that section of Virginia, called the Northern Neck, which lies between the broad Potomac and the narrow Rappahannock rivers. Now the Washingtons were still further intermarried and scattered. Augustine had left to his seven children and his wife some five thousand acres of land in four different counties. His best properties were willed to his two oldest sons by his first wife, Lawrence and Augustine. Mary Ball Washington, the second wife, lived at the Ferry Farm on the Rappahannock with her daughter Betty and her three younger sons.

George, Mary Washington's eldest son, spent most of his time at Wakefield with his half-brother Augustine, called Austin for short. But the boy, who was rather a favorite in the family, stayed part of each year with his mother and went for long visits to his other half-brother, Lawrence, at his place called Mount Vernon. Now and then one of George's younger brothers would be invited by Augustine to come and stay at Wakefield also. George was always glad when it was John's turn, for he liked him better than either Charles or Samuel.

"We must hurry!" shouted Jack, suddenly breaking into a run. "We shall be late for breakfast!"

They could see the house now, and presently pushed open the rustic gate and went clattering down the box-bordered flag walk. This was the rear of the house and from the small brick kitchen inside the gate—always a separate building in these Virginia places —a turbaned Negress emerged carrying a tray with covered dishes. The wide door of the mansion house stood open and from the threshold one could see through the front door opposite, at the end of the hall, the lovely green vista straight down to the edge of the creek. The hungry boys hastened into the pine-paneled dining room.

Mrs. Anne Aylette Washington, seated alone before the silver teapot, glanced up smiling to say good morning. Dazzling sunlight fell upon the bare table set with sparkling silver, with pewter pitchers of milk and cream, a plate of cheese, a dish of preserves, and a great Spode bowl of strawberries.

Sipping her tea, their sister-in-law chatted at unheeding ears. She said her little boy was feverish from teething, reported an early morning quarrel in the slave quarters, and lamented the delay of the post from Williamsburg—doubtless due, she thought, to the fact that Mr. Franklin in Philadelphia had too many irons in the fire to attend to his duties as Deputy Postmaster. At last, however, she made an announcement of interest. "Augustine is expecting his brother Lawrence today," she said.

George looked up with eager surprise. "Really, m'am! What brings him here?"

"I believe he is on his way to Williamsburg a little in advance of the Assembly session. I expect him for dinner." As her husband entered the room at that moment, Anne turned to him, half-petulantly, "Augustine, I've just told George that Lawrence arrives today, and look at his face! I think he would leave us tomorrow for Lawrence and Mount Vernon!"

Seating himself in an armchair at the head of the table, Augustine Washington cast a bantering glance at his half-brother. But before he could speak, a Negro servant entered with a great plate of smoking corn cakes and a platter of bacon and fried fish. At once everyone's attention was fixed on making way with breakfast.

As he ate, George reflected that his sister-in-law had spoken with some justice. Although he had been born here at Wakefield and enjoyed the place, it was not so dear to him as Mount Vernon.

Neither was the Ferry Farm across the river from the hamlet of Fredericksburg. Indeed, no estate he had ever seen could compare with his eldest brother's home one hundred and fifty miles north on the Potomac. Besides—he glanced at Augustine—certainly Austin was kind and a man of affairs, too. But Lawrence! He had been off to the Spanish wars in the West Indies. And—well—Lawrence was different.

Jack broke the long silence. Pushing back his empty plate with a sigh of satisfaction, he asked, "Shall we sail the small boat today? Or are we riding?"

Laughing, Augustine arose. "If you think to have George idle away the morning with you, John, it cannot be. He gave me his word yesterday he would help break in my colt, Phoebus. Come, let us go out to the stable and look him over."

Through the garden filed the three brothers. There gillyflowers and heart's-ease and early yellow roses bloomed between low hedges of privet. Before the stable door several Negroes were lounging about in low-voiced chatter. But on sight of the master they hurriedly made a pretense of activity. Augustine gave an order, and presently a big, deep-chested two-year-old of mottled gray was led out by a halter. He flung up his head nervously, rolled his eyes at the newcomers, and danced about as if defying anyone to tame him.

Shrinking back a little, Jack watched proceedings with admiring interest. Calmly George drew from his pocket a barley sugarstick, offered it to Phoebus on the palm of his hand, stroked nose and neck, and murmured soothing sounds into the restless ears. Stealthily the boy took a bridle from the groom. With one swift motion he slipped it on and adjusted the bit. There was a longer struggle to buckle the saddle girth. But once it was secure, George put a foot in the stirrup and vaulted to his seat.

In a quiet voice he said, "Now let go the bridle and mind his heels." For an instant he sat stroking the twisting neck.

Suddenly Phoebus sprang forward and bolted through the barnyard gate out to the grassy pasture. The battle between horse and rider had begun. Jack, clambering to the top rail of the fence, was

just in time to see the first firm pull on the reins which checked the wild flight and brought the straining animal to a slower pace. Time and again the gray horse made a dash for liberty. Time and again, feeling thwarted, he plunged, reared, flung out his heels, and tried to shake off the hateful bridle.

Augustine came to stand against the fence behind his little brother. Near them gathered the grooms to watch and exclaim: "Law-see, dat boy kin stick!" "Seem jes' lak he grow on de saddle!" Suddenly in the distant field horse and rider disappeared behind a rise of ground.

Half an hour passed with no further view of them. At last, Augustine in dismay voiced the fear that they had dashed into the woods where it was all too easy to meet with an accident. Then beyond a distant clump of cedar trees the horse and rider reappeared. Into the stable yard they whirled. Quivering, snorting, covered with lather, Phoebus came to a dead stop.

Augustine waved his hat in air, crying, "Good boy!" The grooms clapped their hands and shouted. Jacky leaped off the fence to legs trembling with excitement and relief. But the horseman seemed to pay no attention to the fuss. With one swing he dismounted, pulled the head of his horse around, and rubbed his nose.

"He's a good mount," he remarked in a matter-of-fact tone. "A few more trials of this kind will teach him, I'll warrant."

There might have been more praise for George, but at that instant a man in shirt-sleeves came galloping through the paddock on a small black mare. It was the overseer of the Wakefield plantation. Leaning from his saddle, he spoke to his employer in a tone of some excitement.

"Mr. Washington, a small boat has just put in from *The Heron*. The Captain sends word he has space to carry twelve hogsheads of tobacco, if we have them ready. He means to weigh anchor at high tide. Is there time to load?"

Augustine had already swung himself into the saddle. Over his pleasant face had come the shrewd look of the business executive. "Then we have but two hours!" he shouted. "Call all hands to the warehouse!" Digging his heels into the flanks of his horse, he dashed away.

Slowly George and John followed on foot through the paddock out to the grassy, uncut stretch which served as lawn from house to creek. George looked thoughtful. "A dozen hogsheads!" he mused. "What price will that fetch in the English market now, I wonder. The last load Austin shipped brought so little that he swore he meant to choose another London merchant."

His small brother looked at him in disgust. He couldn't bear the fearless horse-tamer to talk in that dull grown-up fashion about tobacco prices. Hastily he suggested, "We might practice wrestling under the trees here."

After a pause George answered slowly. "I had thought to paddle out to look at this merchant ship *Heron*. Would you like that?" He laughed then at Jack's joyous whoop.

By the time the boys edged the canoe between the boulders of the inlet and out on the river, they could hear the faraway creak of ox-carts on their slow way down to the wharf. Through the trees they caught glimpses of figures busy about the drying shed and heard Negro voices chanting in minor cadence. Out on the water, however, it was very still. The boys dipped their paddles noiselessly, Indian fashion.

"Look!" cried George presently. "There's *The Heron* swinging at anchor. Ship ahoy!"

The boatswain leaning over the stern looked up and shouted back a greeting. Presently as the canoe drew close, he was answering with great good humor George's questions about the number of the crew and the amount of cargo aboard.

"We left a packet of goods for Colonel Thomas Lee of Stratford this morning," he said. "His sons must be great young gallants to judge by the amount of lace frills and velvet waistcoats and Russia leather boots we brought over for them from London-town."

An expression of intense interest lit up the listening face of George. Then he let go the rope of the vessel and, as it shot forward, sang out, "Good voyage to you!"

"Some day," George remarked to his brother, "I also will order satin coats and breeches from the London shops."

Unhurriedly they pushed against the current for some time. But suddenly Jack felt the canoe shoot forward and looked around to see his brother paddling for dear life. "What is it? A squall?" he asked in surprise.

George laughed. "No. Lawrence! I'd almost forgot he was coming."

There was need for haste. Hardly had the pair reached the house when they heard far down the crossroad leading to the highway the clop-clop of hoofs and the jingle of bridle rings. Anne Washington, with several house servants, was already at the gate. Standing close behind her, George watched the beautiful chestnut mare bring Lawrence closer. Behind him rode two Negro servants with rolls of luggage strapped to their saddles. At the gate Lawrence dismounted, flung his bridle to a black boy, snatched off his three-cornered hat, and in a gay voice cried, "Greetings!"

He was a young man of good height, very slender, and perfectly turned out in the fashion of the day. Flinging a smile at George, he bent low over the hand of his sister-in-law. With his powdered hair and his grace of movement, he had the air of a courtier. George thought Augustine, who came hurrying up from the warehouse to join in the welcome, looked far more the commonplace planter. He was glad when half an hour later he went into the drawing-room that only Austin was there with the visitor. Perhaps he would get a special word with his favorite brother.

"How is it with you, boy?" asked Lawrence, with a look of affection. "How go the studies? Can you read a bit of Latin now?" Receiving a shy nod from George, he said, "Good. Now translate this—what Tiberius said about taxing the provinces, '*Boni pastoris est tondere pecus, non deglubere.*'"

George blushed, dropped his head, and pondered in glum silence. At last, catching the two young men exchanging winks, he muttered, in a sulky tone, "It signifies something about a good shepherd and his sheep."

Lawrence and Augustine laughed with the easy superiority of

men who had studied the classics at English universities. "Fie!" teased the visitor. "That is a thick piece of wood you wear on your shoulders."

With a look of fury George sprang to his feet. "It is not fair to mock me thus!" he cried with blazing eyes. "I've not been at it long. Nor am I born clever—like you both! Have I had tutors and schools as you had?"

Lawrence had ceased laughing at once and leaned forward with sympathy in his sensitive face. But Augustine said sharply, "Tut, tut! Mind that temper of yours or it will get the best of you!"

Clenching his hands and breathing hard, the boy mastered his rage. "I can do some—some things well enough. I can figure and copy maps. Latin is not the whole of useful learning, is it?" Observing the kindly look bent upon him by his eldest brother, he cried out: "Lawrence, let me learn surveying. I would do something active and useful. I'm wearied of books!"

At this moment Augustine's wife entered the room to summon them to dinner and the men rose from their chairs. Lawrence placed his hand on the arm of the agitated youngster. "I understand and will see what I can do."

For this he received a look of profound gratitude, and with every trace of anger gone George took his place at the dinner table. Presently, as the platter of ham and greens went around, he asked, "Pray tell me how are your neighbors, Mr. Fairfax and his lady and the boy Bryan?"

His brother looked pleased. "They often inquire about you. Mrs. Fairfax has been ailing. But in spite of that the house at Belvoir has been very lively. Young George, the eldest son, is back from school in England, and Lord Fairfax, Mr. William's cousin, has come to stay with him until he decides where he means to settle."

Anne Washington put down her fork with a click. "Settle? Here in America? You mean a great lord like that will stay and not go back to London?"

Lawrence suppressed a little smile. "He is a rather sad and bitter gentleman who has lost his illusions in the world of fashion.

He has come here to escape it and is looking about his vast estate to find a place suitable for building a residence." Suddenly looking at George, the speaker added, "When you come next to visit me, boy, he will doubtless take you fox-hunting. For that sport he has a passion."

George flushed with shy pleasure and put into the eyes he fixed on his brother the cry of his heart. "And when am I to come to Mount Vernon?" Reading that plea, Lawrence nodded thoughtfully.

Then the talk between the two men turned on a topic dear to them—the possibility of developing the lands beyond the Allegheny Mountains. As he spoke of the western wilderness the face of Lawrence glowed with enthusiasm. "They say that beyond the mountain range are fertile valleys ready for tilling. We should be sending settlers out to hold what was given Virginia by the Royal Charter. We should be pushing the fur trade with the Indians—not the Pennsylvanians. As for the French, they have even less right in that territory."

George watched Augustine nod a vigorous agreement. All the boy had ever heard about that unknown land west of the mountains fascinated him. But at this point his thoughts drifted off to the possibility of his own future. How he wished that Lawrence would take him and give him a chance! No one could do so much for him, that he knew. Lawrence was the best of all the Washingtons.

That was probably true. After he had returned from the British expedition against Cartagena in the West Indies, Lawrence had received from his father a piece of land on the upper Potomac. There he had built a house and named the place after his commander in the war, General Vernon. With his marriage to Anne Fairfax, Lawrence had become a person of importance—an Adjutant General in the Virginia Militia and a member of the House of Burgesses. Yet for all his twenty-five hundred acres, his slaves and his many interests, Lawrence had two griefs. Since the war his health had been very uncertain and the children his wife had borne all died in infancy.

After dinner, when George had finished his lessons for the day, he went down to pitch quoits with Jack on the grass in front of the house. But he was thinking too much about Lawrence to make a good score. George had been with his brother when he took off his coat and vest in the downstairs bedroom and had been shocked at the thin frame so often shaken by coughing spells. How he wished he could help his brother! Certainly he could manage the stable. And as for farming, he knew something about it already and could master such problems. For that was the kind of learning he loved.

"I've won every game!" crowed Jacky. "You pitch too far to-day."

George stretched himself and yawned, then straightened up quickly at the sight of Augustine striding down from the house.

"Boy, I have news you'll like. Lawrence wants to tell you about the talk he and I had concerning your future. Go in and see him now. Tomorrow he leaves at daybreak and will have no time."

George ran up the slope and hurried into the house. For a long moment he paused in the cool hall. His mind tossed together all the fascinating bits which Lawrence had flung in air that day like confetti—the gay dinner parties at Belvoir, the meetings of the militia, fox-hunting, plans to explore the western lands, Governor Gooch's ball at Williamsburg. Here was life, adventure, glamor! That was what he wanted—to be part of it at Mount Vernon. Would Lawrence ask him to stay there? As he tapped on the bedroom door, he felt as if he were knocking at the Wish Gate itself.

Nor did he knock in vain. Lawrence asked him to make his future home in Mount Vernon and put the invitation in a way to warm the heart of any younger brother. "I agree with what you said, George, that it would be well to have you learn surveying. I mean to have you taught fencing, also, and military tactics as a preparation for the future. You might survey my lands after a bit. For truly I am convinced that you could assist me in many ways."

So the die was cast. Late summer and fall were to be spent at the Ferry Farm and after that Lawrence would welcome his brother. This momentous conversation took place in May, 1747, when George Washington was just fifteen years and two months old. Before another spring came around he had started on his first significant adventure.

Thomas Jefferson 1743–1826

by ROSEMARY *and* STEPHEN VINCENT BENÉT

Thomas Jefferson,
What do you say
Under the gravestone
Hidden away?

"I was a giver,
I was a molder,
I was a builder
With a strong shoulder."

Six feet and over,
Large-boned and ruddy,
The eyes grey-hazel
But bright with study.

The big hands clever
With pen and fiddle
And ready, ever,
For any riddle.

From buying empires
To planting 'taters,
From Declarations
To trick dumb-waiters.

"I liked the people,
The sweat and crowd of them,
Trusted them always
And spoke aloud of them.

"I liked all learning
And wished to share it
Abroad like pollen
For all who merit.

"I liked fine houses
With Greek pilasters,
And built them surely,
My touch a master's.

"I liked queer gadgets
And secret shelves,
And helping nations
To rule themselves.

"Jealous of others?
Not always candid?
But huge of vision
And open-handed.

"A wild-goose-chaser?
Now and again,
Build Monticello,
You little men!

"Design my plow, sirs,
They use it still,
Or found my college
At Charlottesville.

"And still go questing
New things and thinkers,
And keep as busy
As twenty tinkers.

"While always guarding
The people's freedom—
You need more hands, sir?
I didn't need 'em.

"They call you rascal?
They called me worse,
You'd do grand things, sir,
But lack the purse?

"I got no riches.
I died a debtor.
I died free-hearted
And that was better.

"For life was freakish
But life was fervent,
And I was always
Life's willing servant.

"Life, life's too weighty?
Too long a haul, sir?
I lived past eighty.
I liked it all, sir."

From A *Book of Americans* by Rosemary and Stephen Vincent Benét

Daniel Boone

CAPTURED BY THE SHAWNEES

by JOHN MASON BROWN

Boone was the most skillful and most famous of all the pioneer scouts in colonial America. The account of his explorations into the Kentucky wilderness, his gallant fights with the Indians, his opening of new frontiers, makes one of the most thrilling tales in American history. He was always looking for new trails to blaze, because for Daniel Boone, any neighborhood was too crowded when he could see more than a few cabins in the clearing. All the dramatic details of his rich and colorful life are authentically portrayed in this biography.

After he had been captured by the Shawnees and adopted into their tribe as a son of their chief, Boone fooled the Indians into believing that he would convince the other white settlers to surrender before the spring raid. Instead, he managed to escape and reached Boonesborough in time to prepare the settlers for the planned raid, and to save the village when the Indians attacked.

A year and a half after Jemima's capture, Daniel was to have his own experiences as a prisoner of the Indians. In the bitter cold of a freezing January he and twenty-nine men had left Boonesborough for the Lower Blue Licks.

They had important work to do. The settlements were in desperate need of salt. In the past it had been sent to them by the seaboard colonies, but the Revolution made the sending of such supplies inconvenient, if not impossible. Fortunately, there was plenty of salt in Kentucky's salt springs or "licks." To prepare it for human use, these waters had to be boiled down in large iron kettles. The pioneers had lacked such kettles until Virginia sent some by pack horse across the mountains. It was with this newly arrived equipment that Daniel and his men went to work.

They had been at the Lower Blue Licks for a month during which, as they worked undisturbed, they had made quantities of salt. They thought their task almost done, and were looking forward to being relieved by another group of salt-makers, when disaster abruptly overtook them.

Towards sundown on the 7th of February Daniel was struggling in a snowstorm to return to camp. He had been out hunting and the horse he led was carrying fresh buffalo meat for himself and his men. Although the horse shied nervously on approaching a fallen tree, Daniel blamed the blinding snow for this. Within a few seconds he knew better. Four Shawnee braves jumped from behind the tree and, though Daniel tried to run away, soon captured him.

The four braves forced Daniel to go with them to their nearby camp. On reaching it he realized at once how serious his situation was. A hundred and twenty warriors were gathered there under Chief Blackfish. With them, dressed and painted like Indians, were James and George Girty, those white traitors to the American cause. Their brother, the even more infamous Simon Girty, would figure darkly in Daniel's life in the coming years.

All the men at the Indian camp had heard of Daniel, all knew the importance of their prisoner. They gave him a loud welcome, shook hands with him, and pretended to greet him as a friend. Among those most pleased to see him were some of the very braves from whom he had escaped eight years before after they had warned him to beware of the stings of the "wasps and yellow jackets." These braves were so delighted to have him in their power again that they could not help laughing. Daniel, knowing the ways of Indians, fooled them all into thinking he was as happy to be with them as they were to have him.

They soon told him their plans. They announced they were go-

ing to attack Boonesborough and wished him to guide them there. When they added that they expected Daniel to persuade his group of salt-makers to give themselves up before the expedition started, they presented Daniel with one of the most difficult decisions he ever had to reach. To make a choice affecting his own life was easy enough; to make one which affected so many other lives was a terrible responsibility.

As he listened to the Indians, the beat of Daniel's heart may have quickened but the expression of his face remained unchanged. He thought of Rebecca and the children. He thought of the men with him and their families. He remembered that the stockade at Boonesborough was finished only on one side. He realized that, without his twenty-nine companions and those who might be coming to relieve them, the defenders of Boonesborough would be hopelessly outnumbered by their attackers.

How he could save Boonesborough was Daniel's only concern. To save it, he knew he must delay the threatened attack, trust to luck, and sacrifice the few for the many. To gain time, he went so far as to promise the Indians that he and his party of salt-makers would give themselves up and go with them peacefully to their Ohio villages. The Indians in return promised not to hurt their captives.

Daniel pointed out that without attacking Boonesborough they would already have collected a large number of prisoners. He argued that, if the Shawnees went north and stayed there until the snow was gone, their expedition would be far simpler to carry out. It would be better equipped too, because they could buy more arms with the twenty pounds which Governor Hamilton would pay for each American captive delivered alive in Detroit. Daniel, who could play the Indian game as well as any Indian, added as a final inducement that if the Shawnees waited for the spring he would himself guide them to Boonesborough and persuade the settlement to surrender.

The Indians were won over by Daniel's arguments; so were Daniel's men. Though some of the settlers protested sullenly, they admitted the wisdom, both for themselves and their families, of laying down their rifles and going north with the Shawnees.

The red men showed at once how unreliable their promises were. They had guaranteed not to hurt their captives but, now that the white men were helpless, many of the braves were eager to kill them. A council, at which Daniel was allowed to speak, was held to determine their fate.

It lasted for two hours and was presided over by Blackfish, a kindly chief and a man of character who wanted to live up to the agreement. The vote was close—frighteningly close—but it was accepted as binding. In spite of Blackfish's eloquence, only sixty-one warriors were in favor of sparing the prisoners, while fifty-nine voted to murder them all except Daniel.

After this council the journey to Ohio began. On the way, Daniel was the first to be forced to run the gauntlet. Running the gauntlet was the odd ritual of torture with which Indians welcomed their prisoners. To red men it was at once a test and a game. It was their way of learning which were the weaklings and which the strong.

They would stand in two rows on either side of a line, and, armed with sticks, stones, antlers, or tomahawks, beat the man who ran between them. Only the hardiest survived, and often these suffered permanent injuries. Since the Indians considered this a sport, they were as willing to cheer their victims as to destroy them. Daniel won their admiration by zigzagging down the course at great speed, using his head as a mallet and knocking over several braves, to the delight of the others, and coming out of the ordeal with only a few bruises.

Dr. George Washington Carver, Scientist

SALVAGING SCRAP

by SHIRLEY GRAHAM *and* GEORGE D. LIPSCOMB

Nobody could have had a more discouraging beginning than George Washington Carver. Born of slave parents, orphaned as a baby, then bought by the poor farmer Carver for the price of a horse, little George grew up a sickly child with a serious speech defect. Yet against great odds of poverty and being a Negro, his perseverance saw him through college and graduate studies to become one of America's most ingenious scientists. His philosophy was "Throw away nothing, everything can be used." And he produced paints and stains out of common clay, 118 products from the sweet potato, over 300 from peanuts, and many other products from waste material. He won international fame for his work in soil improvement and is said to have invented the science of ersatz or substitutes, in which field he accomplished miracles. And the character of this gentle and truly religious man was such that he never thought of making money out of these things, only of giving service to mankind. Dr. Carver gave all his savings to Tuskegee Institute to be used for research.

The two men met on the steps of the Administration Building at Tuskegee and for a few minutes stood talking. They were often to stand thus together in the years to come and always they made a striking contrast. Tall, broad-shouldered, robust, deep-voiced Booker T. Washington, with his leonine head, strong features, and tawny complexion, and George Washington Carver, slender figure poised lightly on his feet, narrow, slightly sloping shoulders, delicate features, high-pitched voice, and eyes the burning center of his dusky face. This was the fall of 1896 and, as he looked out over the school grounds, Carver later confessed that he was appalled, almost bewildered.

"I had never seen anything like it. There was yellow soil and red and purple and brown and riveted and banded, and all sorts of things, except grass or plants. There were erosion gullies in which an ox could get lost!"

Yet a few miles away, beside the railroad tracks at Chehaw, he discovered Neviusia, a rare deciduous shrub which he had been taught grew only under the most careful cultivation.

At the time of Doctor Carver's arrival, Doctor Washington apologized that the carriage had not been at Chehaw when his train arrived.

"I'd forgotten that you might not know about the short line on to Tuskegee. Conductors don't always inform our visitors," he explained.

"The boys told me you sent your fine surrey and best horses to meet all 'big folks.' " Carver's eyes twinkled. "They wondered why you bothered today!"

Washington laughed and regarded this young scientist with keen appreciation. His lack of ostentation, quiet, simple dignity delighted him. But he was puzzled also. Who was this man? Where had he come from?

Carver did not consume the time talking about himself. He asked a dozen keen and searching questions which made Washington wonder even more. Then he said he'd like to see the laboratory.

Washington replied at once: "We'll go to the Agricultural Hall. It's our newest building, put up by the students. They," he added, "are mighty proud of it."

"But, the laboratory," began Carver. Washington held up his hand.

"Also—it has plenty of space."

Carver regarded him with a quizzical expression around his eyes.

"I see. You mean you're giving me the space and——"

"God has given you the brains!" finished Doctor Washington.

"Well," said Carver, dryly, "I guess, together, we ought to manage a laboratory." And then they both chuckled.

They looked at each other, the chuckle grew to laughter, and the two great souls knit as one. Never in the close companionship, ending only with Booker T. Washington's death, did their understanding, loyalty, or faith in one another waver. Not even death changed that. For when the offers came from round the world, with gold and fame and everything men seek, Carver said simply:

"I promised Doctor Washington I'd work at Tuskegee. He's gone, but Tuskegee and work and needs remain."

No laboratory, no greenhouses, no gardens! Carver did not voice his dismay, and if he thought with longing of all he'd left behind, no one knew. Quietly he rounded up the few students in Agriculture.

It did not take him long to discover that "farming" was the most unpopular subject in the curriculum. Most of the boys had come to Tuskegee to get away from farm work. They wanted to learn a "trade" or "skill." Anybody could farm! Their frankly expressed attitude is told by T. M. Campbell in his delightful little book, *The Movable School Goes to the Negro Farmer.*

"Custom and environment in my home community had schooled me in the idea that all work other than farming could be done only by white people. But when I reached Tuskegee and observed such activities as saw-milling, brick-making, the construction of houses, carriages, wagons, and buggies and the making of tin utensils, harness, mattresses, brooms, clothes, shoes—all done by Negroes—it was to me like entering a new Heaven. I could scarcely believe such things were possible."

To make the subject of Agriculture even more undesirable, some teachers in other departments sought to punish students by assigning them to "the farm." But among the students whom Doctor Carver first met were Jacob Jones, now a lawyer in Oklahoma, and Walter Keys, who engaged himself to this new teacher as helper, J. H. Palmer, who served all the remainder of his life at Tuskegee, and some time later, Thomas Monroe Campbell, first Negro to be appointed Field Agent in the United States Department of Agriculture, and Sanford Lee, County Agricultural Agent in the State of Georgia.

How was he best to reach these boys who, with no elementary background, no knowledge of general science or even books as taught in Northern high schools, wanted to know how to make things grow? Sanford H. Lee has described something of Doctor Carver's method:

"My very first recollection of him was my first morning in his class. As he always did, before going right into the subject at hand, he gave us about ten minutes' general talk. I remember his words so well—'To him, who in the love of Nature holds communion with her visible forms, she speaks a various language!' All of us stared at this strange man from 'up North.' What on earth was he talking about? Then, looking hard at us, he continued: 'Young people, I want to beg of you always keep your eyes and ears open to what Mother Nature has to teach you. By so doing you will learn many valuable things every day of your life.' How many times have I heard him quote Bryant's *Thanatopsis* both to his classes and on other occasions. In fact, it was rather difficult for him to begin the discussion of any lesson without quoting some favorite author, or from the Psalms. 'O Lord, how manifold are Thy works, in wisdom hast Thou made them all.' This was one of his favorites.

"To this day, I seldom begin a day without thinking of that familiar Bryant quotation—'To him who in the love of nature——' As a county agent, every year, I learn much more from my chickens and orchard and flowers than I do from books. They 'tell' me something every time I walk among them—just as Doctor Carver told us they would."

The word went out among the students that the new teacher was "different." Students who had been sent to "farming" for punishment decided to remain. The first campaign to salvage waste was being organized!

One morning the new teacher closed his talk with a little poem. He said it was called "Things not Done Before." Whether he wrote the lines himself or found them somewhere is not known. The final verses are:

> "The few who strike out without map or chart
> Where never a man has been,
> From the beaten path they draw apart
> To see what no man has seen.
> Their deeds they hunger alone to do,
> Though battered and bruised and sore,
> They blaze the trail for the many who
> Do nothing not done before.

> "The things that haven't been done before
> Are the tasks worth while today;
> Are you one of the flock that follows, or
> Are you one who will lead the way?
> Are you one of the timid souls that quail
> At the jeers of a doubting crew,
> Or dare you, whether you win or fail,
> Strike out for the goal that's new?"

His voice lilted on the question and raising his eyes he looked into the faces of his students. They smiled back at him and he said:

"Today, we're going to do something which has never been done before. We're going out and find the things we need for our laboratory. We're going into town and look through every scrap heap. We'll go to the back doors and ask the lady of the house for old kitchen utensils she can't use. We need containers of all kinds, and lamps, and pans in which to cook."

He showed them pictures of crucibles, and beakers, distilling apparatus and extracting apparatus. From his box he took out tubes and small glass cases. "These are the kind of things we need. God knows our need. He will direct us! Shall we go?"

"Yes, sir!" they said, and followed him.

It was an exciting hunt. The students had caught his crusading spirit. They searched up and down alleys, raked through trash and dump heaps, politely but firmly accosted housewives, gathered hollow reeds from the swamp, which "teacher" said could be used for pipettes. When evening came, they met with all their findings. Carver praised each one. What he could not use at once, he set aside, saying, "There is no waste, save of time. All of these things can be used again." Thus spoke the first and pioneer chemurgist. Only now is the country awakening to the truth of his words.

You may see that first laboratory equipment today preserved in the Carver Museum: a large lantern, its chimney still shining bright; jugs, large and small—one of them marked "Vinegar"; a bent skillet, saucepans, broken bottles, tops of cans, an oil lamp, pieces of rubber. With this discarded scrap Carver began to rebuild Alabama.

A twenty-acre patch of ground was assigned to him—"no-good" ground. Hogs rooted among the weeds and rubbish on it. He and his students first cleaned it off and then he asked for a two-horse plow. No one down that way had ever seen a two-horse plow, but Doctor Washington okayed his request and one was sent for. When it arrived and Carver hitched it up and began to turn the soil, observers slapped their thighs and rocked with laughter. The idea of a professor plowing! Even his students were a bit chagrined. But he was good-natured about it, even joking with the farmers who gathered round. Their mirth changed to pity, then.

At his bidding, the students brought back muck from the swamps and leaf-mold from the woods. He plowed these under, then told them to clean the barns and bring the "drippings." The farmers were appalled when after all this work, instead of planting cotton, he planted cowpeas!

When the students harvested the spindly cowpeas with a miserable pea in each stalk, they were disgusted. All this for something to throw to the hogs! But the teacher surprised them by saying,

"Now I'll show you how to cook them!"

Well, Northerners were a bit crazy anyhow! But one evening

they all sat down to a delicious meal prepared by their professor. Never had they tasted such food. Afterward, he explained each dish—prepared from cowpeas! The word got around and other students asked to join his classes. People began to talk.

When he planted sweet potatoes on his tract, they simply looked on, saying nothing. But when the tract yielded eighty bushels to an acre, their eyes opened. In the spring he said to his now greatly augmented class:

"Now, we shall see. I've been *rotating crops* on this land. It has been *rested, refreshed,* and *enriched.* Now, we'll try cotton."

This they could understand. Long before the cotton was picked, farmers came from near and far to gaze in wonder at the perfect stalks, and when he harvested a five-hundred-pound bale of cotton from one acre, whites and blacks regarded him with deep respect. Never had such a thing been done in that vicinity!

Meanwhile, Carver was acquainting himself with the neighborhood. Each morning at four he arose and went to woods or swamp. To the discouraged people of Alabama, he began to say and to write that all around them was untold wealth; that the state had more varieties of trees than could be found in all of Europe— twenty-two species of oak, pine trees, the longleaf, shortleaf, upland spruce, lowland spruce, slash, yellow—all valuable hard woods. The yellow poplar, with its yellowish-green blossoms, often reached a height of one hundred and twenty feet. There were twenty varieties of the white-blooming haw tree, magnificent evergreen trees, rare yellow-blooming magnolias. And that spring he found more wild flowers than he had ever known existed!

When the country people saw him gathering plants and scooping up different kinds of soil, they said, "This man's a root-doctor!"

And they came to Carver with their aches and pains. He, recognizing that most of them were suffering from the hidden hunger of pellagra, began to prescribe wild grasses and weeds which, tested, proved rich in vitamins. He showed them how to brew teas from certain roots, and cooked and let them taste weeds which grew beside the road. They sang his praises, bowed, and called him "Doctor."

They came to him for more advice. He gave it freely and went among them demonstrating how to apply fertilizer. He put into children's language explanations of the interlocked relations of plants and animals and soil and rain and air and sun.

He tested many soils, and because he never threw anything away, the jars and jugs full of clay accumulated and even piled in heaps upon the trays. One bright Saturday morning, Walter Keys, in a burst of energy, decided to clean up for the professor.

He first tackled the dirt in the corner—dumping it all into a large basket. He was just about to carry it out when Carver entered the laboratory. With his hand still on the door, he asked,

"What are you doing?"

"Gonna clean up this place, wash all the tubes, and get everything in order for you, sir."

Walter waited expectantly for his teacher's customary expression of appreciation. Instead, he asked sharply,

"Where are you taking that clay?"

"You've finished with this." Walter was positive. "All of it's been tested, so I'm throwing it out."

"Oh, no," Carver protested, "I——"

What on earth did he want with the clay? He himself wasn't sure, except that—— Leaning over the basket, he ran his fingers through the gritty stuff. Slowly, he asked,

"Walter, what do you see there?"

Now Walter had been with him long enough to know that his teacher expected him really "to see." He didn't want to disappoint him, but—— He frowned and studied the basket of dirt. All he could see was hard, lumpy, gritty clay of various hues.

"Well, sir—it's—it's got some grit in it, and some's lumpy and some's sort of sandy—— Oh, yes"—his voice brightened—"there's a few weeds and roots."

"But—the colors—the colors, boy, don't you see them—yellow and red and purple and brown? Why so many colors?"

Walter shrugged his shoulders. He had been looking at similar clay all his life.

"Oh, that! That's just the way clay *is!*"

"But—why?" Carver insisted.

Walter was stumped!

"No," said Carver, waving his hand, "don't throw it out. There *is* a reason. I'll have to talk to God about this."

Walter pushed the basket into the corner. Like Farmer Carver, so many years ago, he was a little shocked. He knew about praying. He knew you should fall on your knees, close your eyes, and choose the very best words while you asked God to "forgive your sins," "redeem your soul," and "save" you from "the devil and all his works." He'd heard lots of praying. But he certainly couldn't imagine God, "up on His great white throne, bending His ear" to listen to anybody "talking" about clay—not even the Professor!

The Professor had gone out quietly. He was in deep thought. He turned his footsteps toward the swamp and soon the spreading branches of sweet gum trees linked with Spanish moss shut out the sun. The marshy ground tangled with muscadine vines and mosses slushed beneath his feet. But he went on, his eyes catching a glimpse of wild hydrangea, with its spikes of thickly clustered white flowers. How lovely they were! Just then his foot caught and he fell flat into a mud hole. He was not hurt, but scrambled up quickly. Poisonous snakes inhabited such places and, as he wiped away the sticky, oozy mud with his handkerchief, he kept sharp watch. He rubbed hard, but though the mud came off, the stains remained. This was a pretty pickle, he thought ruefully. He looked down at the handkerchief. It was a brilliant blue! He shook the mud off, even rinsed the cloth out in the muddy water. Grit and sand were removed, but the blue remained. For a while he studied it and then said aloud:

"Thanks, Mr. Creator! Thank you very much. At last, I see!"

He hurried back to the laboratory. Walter had gone. Trays and test tubes were clean and shining. Forgetting all about his grimy appearance, Carver pulled out the basket of clay and after arranging a tray dumped a handful of the red clay on it, smoothing it out

with his palm. Then, tilting the tray a little, he held a dipper of water above it and allowed the water to slowly drip over the clay. Small rocks and grit began to wash away. He emptied the dipper, and tilting the tray in the opposite direction repeated the process. This he did until there remained on the tray only a thin, pasty coating of red. He touched this lightly with his finger and smeared the finger across a sheet of paper. Holding the paper close to the window he studied it a long time. Then he nodded his head.

"Paint! The people down here are walking on paint—good paint —durable paint!"

For several days and nights he worked alone. He carefully separated his clays according to their colors and washed them clean. Then with intense heat he reduced the clay to finest powder, mixed the powder with oils, with water, hot and then cold, tested them on woods, on canvas, with brush and with fingers. Finally, he told his students.

Shortly after this, a group of white farmers asked Carver to come to their church and tell the people of their community something about soil improvement. The place was some distance away, near Montgomery, but Carver gladly agreed to go.

Walter drove him over, after carefully cleaning and shining the buggy. They found the church with little trouble, since it had been described as new and still unpainted. Carver's talk was well received. Many of the farmers came up to shake his hand. One of them said,

"We're poor folks over here and sure needed your talk!"

"I hope I've been some help."

"Our cotton's been falling off steady. We got this church up, and haven't even been able to raise enough money to paint it."

"Now, that's too bad," said Carver sympathetically.

"Yes, 'tis," joined in another man, "weather's going to come down and our nice building's going to be ruined."

"Is paint so expensive?" Carver was thinking rapidly.

"Down this way it costs a heap. If crops are good this season, I reckon we'll have a rally and raise the money. That'll be after the spring rains, though," the man added regretfully.

Carver smiled at him.

"This is God's house, and it deserves the best. I'll give you paint, good paint."

Several people turned around and stared at the shabby, dark-faced professor. They had heard a great deal about Tuskegee. And they knew the school was always needing money. Yet here was one of its teachers offering to give them enough paint to paint their church. Well! But Carver was speaking gently:

"Lift up your eyes, good people, to the hills of God. See all the gorgeous colors with which he has decked them? We'll take just a little from his bounteous store of pure and lasting coloring, and with it paint your church!"

They really couldn't believe him. But a few days later a little wagon drew up in front of the church. Carver and several students climbed down. From the back they took pails of blue paint, Carver directing everything. And the next Sunday morning the people worshiped in a church which matched the sky in color, its steeple pointing upward proudly. The rains fell and the paint neither cracked nor peeled.

God's good earth gives freely of itself. Nothing is wasted and God's colors do not fade.

Abraham Lincoln 1809–1865

by ROSEMARY *and* STEPHEN VINCENT BENÉT

Lincoln was a long man.
He liked out of doors.
He liked the wind blowing
And the talk in country stores.

He liked telling stories,
He liked telling jokes.
"Abe's quite a character,"
Said quite a lot of folks.

Lots of folks in Springfield
Saw him every day,
Walking down the street
In his gaunt, long way.

Shawl around his shoulders,
Letters in his hat.
"That's Abe Lincoln."
They thought no more than that.

Knew that he was honest,
Guessed that he was odd,
Knew he had a cross wife
Though she was a Todd.

Knew he had three little boys
Who liked to shout and play,
Knew he had a lot of debts
It took him years to pay.

Knew his clothes and knew his house.
"That's his office, here.
Blame good lawyer, on the whole,
Though he's sort of queer.

"Sure, he went to Congress, once,
But he didn't stay.
Can't expect us all to be
Smart as Henry Clay.

"Need a man for troubled times?
Well, I guess we do.
Wonder who we'll ever find?
Yes—I wonder who."

That is how they met and talked,
Knowing and unknowing.
Lincoln was the green pine.
Lincoln kept on growing.

From *A Book of Americans* by Rosemary and Stephen Vincent Benét

Abe Lincoln Grows Up

"PECULIARSOME" ABE

by CARL SANDBURG

You might think that you have already been told so much about Abraham Lincoln that it is hardly worthwhile to read any-thing more. Yet the magnificent biography by Carl Sandburg is so original and full of insight into the great man that it is bound to give you a new slant on him. Out of the boyhood chapters of the first volume the author has made a separate book for young people called Abe Lincoln Grows Up. *The selection given here shows the young Lincoln as a boy, with only about a year of schooling and hungry for learning, reading over and over again his precious little store of books. Abraham Lincoln has been more written about than any other American figure. Probably not only because he has become a symbol of the backwoods lad who becomes president, but also because writers are challenged by his complicated and great-hearted character. Carl Sandburg's study of him is that rare combination of scholarly wisdom, fine writing, and a deep sympathy for his subject that makes a book not only great biog-raphy, but great literature.*

The farm boys in their evenings at Jones's store in Gentryville talked about how Abe Lincoln was always reading, digging into books, stretching out flat on his stomach in front of the fireplace, studying till midnight and past midnight, picking a piece of char-coal to write on the fire shovel, shaving off what he wrote, and then writing more—till midnight and past midnight. The next thing Abe would be reading books between the plow handles, it seemed to them. And once trying to speak a last word, Dennis Hanks said, "There's suthin' peculiarsome about Abe."

He wanted to learn, to know, to live, to reach out; he wanted to satisfy hungers and thirsts he couldn't tell about, this big boy of the backwoods. And some of what he wanted so much, so deep down, seemed to be in the books. Maybe in books he would find the answers to dark questions pushing around in the pools of his thoughts and the drifts of his mind. He told Dennis and other people, "The things I want to know are in books; my best friend is the man who'll git me a book I ain't read." And sometimes friends answered, "Well, books ain't as plenty as wildcats in these parts o' Indianny."

This was one thing meant by Dennis when he said there was "suthin' peculiarsome" about Abe. It seemed that Abe made the books tell him more than they told other people. All the other farm boys had gone to school and read "The Kentucky Preceptor," but Abe picked out questions from it, such as "Who has the most right to complain, the Indian or the Negro?" and Abe would talk about it, up one way and down the other, while they were in the cornfield pulling fodder for the winter. When Abe got hold of a storybook and read about a boat that came near a magnetic rock, and how the magnets in the rock pulled all the nails out of the boat so it went to pieces and the people in the boat found themselves floundering in water, Abe thought it was funny and told it to other people. After Abe read poetry, especially Bobby Burns's poems, Abe began writing rhymes himself. When Abe sat with a girl, with their bare feet in the creek water, and she spoke of the moon rising, he explained to her it was the earth moving and not the moon—the moon only seemed to rise.

John Hanks, who worked in the fields barefooted with Abe, grubbing stumps, plowing, mowing, said: "When Abe and I came back to the house from work, he used to go to the cupboard, snatch a piece of corn bread, sit down, take a book, cock his legs up high as his head, and read. Whenever Abe had a chance in the field while at work, or at the house, he would stop and read." He liked to explain to other people what he was getting from books; explaining an idea to some one else made it clearer to him. The habit was growing on him of reading out loud; words came more real if picked from the silent page of the book and pronounced on the tongue; new balances and values of words stood out if spoken aloud. When writing letters for his father or the neighbors, he read the words out loud as they got written. Before writing a letter he asked questions such as: "What do you want to say in the letter? How do you want to say it? Are you sure that's the best way to say it? Or do you think we can fix up a better way to say it?"

As he studied his books his lower lip stuck out; Josiah Crawford noticed it was a habit and joked Abe about the "stuck-out lip." This habit too stayed with him.

He wrote in his Sum Book or arithmetic that Compound Division was "When several numbers of Divers Denominations are given to be divided by 1 common divisor," and worked on the exercise in multiplication; "If 1 foot contain 12 inches I demand how many there are in 126 feet." Thus the schoolboy.

What he got in the schools didn't satisfy him. He went to three different schools in Indiana, besides two in Kentucky—altogether about four months of school. He learned his A B C, how to spell, read, write. And he had been with the other barefoot boys in butternut jeans learning "manners" under the schoolteacher, Andrew Crawford, who had them open a door, walk in, and say, "Howdy do?" Yet what he tasted of books in school was only a beginning, only made him hungry and thirsty, shook him with a wanting and a wanting of more and more of what was hidden between the covers of books.

He kept on saying, "The things I want to know are in books; my best friend is the man who'll git me a book I ain't read." He said that to Pitcher, the lawyer over at Rockport, nearly twenty miles away, one fall afternoon, when he walked from Pigeon Creek to Rockport and borrowed a book from Pitcher. Then when fodder-pulling time came a few days later, he shucked corn from early daylight till sundown along with his father and Dennis Hanks and John Hanks, but after supper he read the book till midnight,

and at noon he hardly knew the taste of his corn bread because he had a book in front of him. It was a hundred little things like these which made Dennis Hanks say there was "suthin' peculiar-some" about Abe.

Besides reading the family Bible and figuring his way all through the old arithmetic they had at home, he got hold of "Aesop's Fables," "Pilgrim's Progress," "Robinson Crusoe," and Weems's "The Life of Francis Marion." The book of fables, written or collected thousands of years ago by the Greek slave, known as Aesop, sank deep in his mind. As he read through the book a second and third time, he had a feeling there were fables all around him, that everything he touched and handled, everything he saw and learned had a fable wrapped in it somewhere. One fable was about a bundle of sticks and a farmer whose sons were quarreling and fighting.

There was a fable in two sentences which read, "A coachman, hearing one of the wheels of his coach make a great noise, and perceiving that it was the worst one of the four, asked how it came to take such a liberty. The wheel answered that from the beginning of time, creaking had always been the privilege of the weak." And there were shrewd, brief incidents of foolery such as this: "A waggish, idle fellow in a country town, being desirous of playing a trick on the simplicity of his neighbors and at the same time putting a little money in his pocket at their cost, advertised that he would on a certain day show a wheel carriage that should be so contrived as to go without horses. By silly curiosity the rustics were taken in, and each succeeding group who came out from the show were ashamed to confess to their neighbors that they had seen nothing but a wheelbarrow."

The style of the Bible, of Aesop's fables, the hearts and minds back of those books, were much in his thoughts. His favorite pages in them he read over and over. Behind such proverbs as, "Muzzle not the ox that treadeth out the corn," and "He that ruleth his own spirit is greater than he that taketh a city," there was a music of simple wisdom and a mystery of common every-day life that touched deep spots in him, while out of the fables of the ancient Greek slave he came to see that cats, rats, dogs, horses, plows, hammers, fingers, toes, people, all had fables connected with their lives, characters, places. There was, perhaps, an outside for each thing as it stood alone, while inside of it was its fable.

One book came, titled, "The Life of George Washington, with Curious Anecdotes, Equally Honorable to Himself and Exemplary to His Young Countrymen. Embellished with Six Steel Engravings, by M. L. Weems, formerly Rector of Mt. Vernon Parish." It pictured men of passion and proud ignorance in the government of England driving their country into war on the American colonies. It quoted the far-visioned warning of Chatham to the British parliament, "For God's sake, then, my lords, let the way be instantly opened for reconciliation. I say instantly; or it will be too late forever."

The book told of war, as at Saratoga. "Hoarse as a mastiff of true British breed, Lord Balcarras was heard from rank to rank, loud-animating his troops; while on the other hand, fierce as a hungry Bengal tiger, the impetuous Arnold precipitated heroes on the stubborn foe. Shrill and terrible, from rank to rank, resounds the clash of bayonets—frequent and sad the groans of the dying. Pairs on Pairs, Britons and Americans, with each his bayonet at his brother's breast, fall forward together faint-shrieking in death, and mingle their smoking blood." Washington, the man, stood out, as when he wrote, "These things so harassed my heart with grief, that I solemnly declared to God, if I know myself, I would gladly offer myself a sacrifice to the butchering enemy, if I could thereby insure the safety of these my poor distressed countrymen."

The Weems book reached some deep spots in the boy. He asked himself what it meant that men should march, fight, bleed, go cold and hungry for the sake of what they called "freedom."

"Few great men are great in everything," said the book. And there was a cool sap in the passage: "His delight was in that of the manliest sort, which, by stringing the limbs and swelling the muscles, promotes the kindliest flow of blood and spirits. At jumping with a long pole, or heaving heavy weights, for his years he hardly had an equal."

Such book talk was a comfort against the same thing over

again, day after day, so many mornings the same kind of water from the same spring, the same fried pork and corn-meal to eat, the same drizzles of rain, spring plowing, summer weeds, fall fodder-pulling, each coming every year, with the same tired feeling at the end of the day, so many days alone in the woods or the fields or else the same people to talk with, people from whom he had learned all they could teach him. Yet there ran through his head the stories and sayings of other people, the stories and sayings of books, the learning his eyes had caught from books; they were a comfort; they were good to have because they were good by themselves; and they were still better because they broke the chill of the lonesome feeling.

He was thankful to the writer of Aesop's fables because that writer stood by him and walked with him, an invisible companion, when he pulled fodder or chopped wood. Books lighted lamps in the dark rooms of his gloomy hours. . . . Well—he would live on; maybe the time would come when he would be free from work for a few weeks, or a few months, with books, and then he would read. . . . God, then he would read. . . . Then he would go and get at the proud secrets of his books.

His father—would he be like his father when he grew up? He hoped not. Why should his father knock him off a fence rail when he was asking a neighbor, passing by, a question? Even if it was a smart question, too pert and too quick, it was no way to handle a boy in front of a neighbor. No, he was going to be a man different from his father. The books—his father hated the books. His father talked about "too much eddication"; after readin', writin', 'rithmetic, that was enough, his father said. He, Abe Lincoln, the boy, wanted to know more than the father, Tom Lincoln, wanted to know. Already Abe knew more than his father; he was writing letters for the neighbors; they hunted out the Lincoln farm to get young Abe to find his bottle of ink with blackberry brier root and copperas in it, and his pen made from a turkey buzzard feather, and write letters. Abe had a suspicion sometimes his father was a little proud to have a boy that could write letters, and tell about things in books, and outrun and outwrestle and rough-

and-tumble any boy or man in Spencer County. Yes, he would be different from his father; he was already so; it couldn't be helped.

In growing up from boyhood to young manhood, he had survived against lonesome, gnawing monotony and against floods, forest and prairie fires, snake-bites, horse-kicks, ague, chills, fever, malaria, "milk-sick."

A comic outline against the sky he was, hiking along the roads of Spencer and other counties in southern Indiana in those years when he read all the books within a fifty-mile circuit of his home. Stretching up on the long legs that ran from his moccasins to the body frame with its long, gangling arms, covered with linsey-woolsey, then the lean neck that carried the head with its surmounting coonskin cap or straw hat—it was, again, a comic outline—yet with a portent in its shadow. His laughing "Howdy," his yarns and drollery, opened the doors of men's hearts.

Starting along in his eleventh year came spells of abstraction. When he was spoken to, no answer came from him. "He might be a thousand miles away." The roaming, fathoming, searching, questioning operations of the minds and hearts of poets, inventors, beginners who take facts stark, these were at work in him. This was one sort of abstraction he knew; there was another: the blues took him; coils of multiplied melancholies wrapped their blue frustrations inside him, all that Hamlet, Koheleth, Schopenhauer have uttered, in a mesh of foiled hopes. "There was absolutely nothing to excite ambition for education," he wrote later of that Indiana region. Against these "blues," he found the best warfare was to find people and trade with them his yarns and drolleries. John Baldwin, the blacksmith, with many stories and odd talk and eye-slants, was a help and a light.

Days came when he sank deep in the stream of human life and felt himself kin of all that swam in it, whether the waters were crystal or mud.

He learned how suddenly life can spring a surprise. One day in the woods, as he was sharpening a wedge on a log, the ax glanced, nearly took his thumb off, and left a white scar after healing.

"You never cuss a good ax," was a saying in those timbers.

Penn

by ELIZABETH JANET GRAY

William Penn was the son of Sir William Penn, a notable British admiral, and he could have led the easy life of any 17th century wealthy aristocrat. But he early became interested in the search for religious truth, and was expelled from Oxford for expressing scruples against the established church. Sir Penn bitterly disapproved of his son's rebellious views and sent him to Europe in the hope that this would take his mind off serious things. Penn spent some time at the French court; but court life did not appeal to him at all, and he returned to England to become a convert to the Quaker religion. In the trial described here so dramatically, his noble and brilliant defense against the shameful conduct of the judges led to many reforms in trial by jury, both in England and the colonies. After he was released from prison, Penn went to America where he was able to found the city of Philadelphia according to his own liberal ideas of religious and political freedom for all.

On Thursday the first of September 1670, a sergeant and his yeomen came early in the morning to escort Penn and Mead out of Newgate and down the street called the Old Bailey to the Sessions House, where the court sat at seven. It was a "fair and stately building," with large galleries for spectators.

There were ten justices on the bench. Several of them young William Penn already knew. Sir Samuel Starling was Chief Jus-

tice. The Admiral's "buffle-headed" old friend, Sir John Robinson,
the Lord Lieutenant of the Tower, was another—and good reason
William had for remembering him! A third, Sir Richard Brown,
had been particularly brutal in his raids on the Friends' meeting-
houses a few years ago, and two more were well known as zealous
churchmen and persecutors of Non-Conformists. Altogether they
were about as arrogant, puffing, choleric, muddleheaded, prejudiced a lot of judges as one could find anywhere.

The jury was sworn in, twelve slow-witted, plain citizens, with
good plain English names, John and James and William and
Henry. There was an Edward Bushell, and Thomas Veer was
foreman.

The prisoners were brought before the bar, and the indictment
read. It was an astonishing piece of writing: a single sentence of
two hundred and fifty words looped and bunched together in alternately legal and hysterical phrases. The gist of it was that "William Penn, gent., and William Mead, linen-draper, the fifteenth
day of August, with force and arms unlawfully and tumultuously
did assemble, and the aforesaid William Penn by agreement between him and William Mead before made, then and there in the
open street did take upon himself to preach and speak, by reason
whereof a great concourse and tumult of people in the street, a
long time did remain and continue in contempt of the Lord the
King and of his law, to the great disturbance of his peace and to
the great terror of many of his liege subjects."

The Clerk then asked: "What say you, William Penn and William Mead? Are you guilty as you stand indicted, or not guilty?"

They pleaded "Not guilty," and the court was adjourned till
afternoon.

While they were waiting, they discussed the errors in the indictment. To begin with, the date was wrong; the day of the meeting was Sunday the fourteenth of August, not the fifteenth. In the
second place, they did not meet with force and arms. Nobody had
arms except the soldiers. Nobody used force except the soldiers.
Then, since they had never seen each other before, they obviously
could not have met by agreement before made. And finally, they

did not remain and continue in contempt of the King and his law, for the chief officer who came to take them had allowed the meeting to go on after Mead promised that Penn would go with them at the end of it.

In the afternoon they were brought back to the Sessions House, but instead of going on with their trial, the court, "both to affront and to tire them," kept them waiting there for five long hours while trials of felons and murderers were held, and at the end of the time adjourned.

September second they cooled their heels in Newgate.

September third was a Saturday. The sergeant and his yeomen came for them again before seven. Just as they went into the courtroom one of the officers, on a kindly impulse, took off their hats for them. Sir Samuel Starling was quick to see.

"Sirrah," he thundered, "who bid you put their hats off? Put them on again."

So, hats on, they stood before the bar. Ten judges in wigs and robes sat in a portentous row upon the bench and looked down with hostile eyes, while the chief among them proceeded solemnly to fine the prisoners forty marks apiece for wearing their hats in court.

It was childish; it was contemptible. William Penn, who was twenty-five, looked straight into all those hard and prejudiced old eyes, and said calmly: "I desire it may be observed that we came into the court with our hats off (that is, taken off), and if they have been put on since, it was by order from the Bench, and therefore not we, but the Bench, should be fined."

There being no answer to that, the jury was sworn again. Sir John Robinson objected to the way Edward Bushell took the oath. Bushell was known to be a man of tender conscience and tough will, and the judges were a little uneasy about him. They had no good excuse, however, for getting rid of him, and so the trial went forward.

The first witness was called and sworn to tell "the truth, the whole truth, and nothing but the truth, so help me God."

Lieutenant Cook, in command of the soldiers, testified that he saw Mr. Penn speaking to the people but could not hear what he said. Two others said that they saw Penn preaching to some four hundred people and Mead talking to Lieutenant Cook, but could not hear what either Penn or Mead said. There was no further evidence.

Then Penn spoke up and said: "I desire you would let me know by what law it is you prosecute me, and upon what law you ground my indictment."

The Recorder of London, who was the legal expert on the case, answered promptly: "The common law."

At once Penn asked: "What is that common law?" but the legal expert could not produce a definition or an example of it. The other justices on the bench began to shout at Penn, and the Recorder snapped:

"The question is whether you are guilty of this indictment."

Penn corrected him. "The question is not whether I am guilty of this indictment, but whether the indictment be legal." He pointed out that if the common law was so hard to understand it was very far from being common, and he quoted Coke and the Magna Carta.

The Recorder, losing his temper completely, shouted: "Sir, you are an arrogant fellow, and it is not for the honor of the court to suffer you to go on!" To which Penn answered mildly: "I have asked but one question, and you have not answered me; though the rights and privileges of every Englishman are concerned in it."

"If I should suffer you to ask questions till tomorrow morning," replied the Recorder huffily, "you would never be the wiser."

And young Penn could not resist the temptation to retort: "That is according as the answers are."

That was too much for the judges; they turned purple with rage.

"I desire no affront to the court but to be heard in my just plea. . . ."

The Mayor and the Recorder both broke out in indignant

shouts: "Take him away! Take him away! Turn him into the bale-dock."

The bale-dock was a sort of pen at the far end of the courtroom, open at the top but enclosed by high palings so that the prisoners could not see or hear what was going on. Before he was dragged off to this coop, William Penn delivered a ringing challenge:

"Is this justice or true judgment? Must I therefore be taken away because I plead for the fundamental laws of England? However, this I leave upon your consciences, who are of the jury and my sole judges, that if these ancient fundamental laws which relate to liberty and property (and are not limited to particular persuasions in the matter of religion) must not be indispensably maintained and observed, who can say he hath a right to the coat upon his back?"

"Be silent there."

"I am not to be silent in a case wherein I am so much concerned, and not only myself but many ten thousand families besides."

Roughly they pulled him off to the bale-dock. Mead had his turn, stood his ground well, quoted a Latin tag, defined a riot, and was also consigned for his pains to the bale-dock.

There, stuck away in the dimness, they could not hear what was going on in the court, but one of the officers whispered to them that the Recorder was charging the jury. It was absolutely against the law to charge the jury in the absence of the prisoners. Penn flung himself on the palings and pulled himself up so that he could shout over the top of them:

"I appeal to the jury who are my judges!" Loudly as he could, he quoted the law, and he called to the jury to take notice that he had not been heard in his own defense.

"Pull that fellow down, pull him down," bawled the Recorder.

The people in the galleries craned their necks and rustled and buzzed.

"I say these are barbarous and unjust proceedings!" shouted Penn, clinging to the side of the bale-dock.

"Take them away to the hole," commanded the Recorder.

To the hole they went, a sort of dungeon in the Sessions House,

a stinking hole, Penn said, and one that the Lord Mayor would not consider a fit sty for his swine. There they stayed while the jury deliberated.

They were a long time at it. After an hour and a half, eight of them returned to the court, and four who disagreed remained in the jury chamber above. The four, of whom Edward Bushell was recognized as the leader, were brought down and scolded and threatened by the court. All twelve of them were then sent back to reach a conclusion, and this time, after more deliberation, they brought the unanimous verdict that William Penn was guilty of speaking in Gracechurch Street.

This of course was equal to an acquittal. There was no law against speaking in Gracechurch Street. The Mayor tried to make them say "speaking to an unlawful assembly," but they refused. Determined to have a different verdict, he ordered them back to the jury chamber, and they asked for pen, ink, and paper to take with them.

In a little more than half an hour they returned, Penn and Mead were brought back to the bar, and the jury handed in its verdict again, this time written and signed. "We do find William Penn to be guilty of speaking or preaching to an assembly met together in Gracechurch Street, the fourteenth of August last, 1670, and that William Mead is not guilty of the said indictment."

Whereupon the Mayor called Bushell "an impudent, canting fellow," and the Recorder told them all:

"Gentlemen, you shall not be dismissed till we have a verdict the court will accept; and you shall be locked up without meat, drink, fire, and tobacco. You shall not think thus to abuse the court; we will have a verdict, or by the help of God you shall starve for it."

Before the jury departed again, Penn got his word in, and the voice of this young man of twenty-five, whom the Lord Mayor later called "that wild, rambling colt," was the only calm and authoritative voice in the whole amazing, hysterical courtroom.

"My jury, who are my judges, ought not to be thus menaced. Their verdict should be free and not compelled. The bench ought to wait upon them but not forestall them."

But the court was ready to break up for the day and "huddle the prisoners to the jail and the jury to their chamber." As the second day of the trial ended, Penn turned to the jury and said:

"You are Englishmen; mind your privileges, give not away your right."

To which Bushell stanchly made reply: "Nor will we ever do it."

And that night the jury was shut up without "meat, drink, fire, nor any other accommodation."

The next day was Sunday, and it was illegal to hold court. Nevertheless, at seven, the court sat.

The foreman of the jury read the verdict again: "William Penn is guilty of speaking in Gracechurch Street."

The Mayor prompted him: "To an unlawful assembly?" and Edward Bushell answered for him: "No, my lord, we give no other verdict than what we gave last night; we have no other verdict to give."

Another of the justices, Sir Thomas Bludworth, commented gloomily: "I knew Mr. Bushell would not yield," and the Recorder threatened again: "I will have a positive verdict, or you will starve for it." After the night they had just spent, the jury could not look on this as an empty threat.

Penn desired to ask one question: Did the court accept the verdict "Not guilty," given of William Mead?

"It cannot be a verdict," said the Recorder, "because you are indicted for a conspiracy; and one being found guilty and not the other, it could not be a verdict."

Penn's answer was quick. "If not guilty be not a verdict, then you make of the jury and Magna Carta a mere nose of wax. . . . And if William Mead be not guilty, it consequently follows that I am clear, since you have indicted us of a conspiracy, and I could not possibly conspire alone."

But for the third time the verdict was rejected and the jury sent back to find another. Again it returned with the one answer it had to give.

The court was well-nigh beside itself with rage. It threatened to set a mark on Edward Bushell, to have an eye on him, to cut his nose. And now Penn's voice rings out:

"It is intolerable that my jury should be thus menaced. Is this according to the fundamental law? Are they not my proper judges by the great charter of England? What hope is there of ever having justice done, when juries are threatened and their verdicts rejected? I am concerned to speak and grieved to see such arbitrary proceedings. Did not the Lieutenant of the Tower render one of them worse than a felon? And do you not plainly seem to condemn such for factious fellows who answer not your ends? Unhappy are those juries who are threatened to be fined and starved and ruined if they give not in their verdicts contrary to their consciences."

The Recorder had nothing to say in answer but: "My lord, you must take a course with that fellow."

"Jailer, bring fetters," commanded the Chief Justice, "and stake him to the ground."

"Do your pleasure," replied Penn superbly, "I matter not your fetters."

And now the Recorder's rage did what Penn was later to tell his children anger always does: it threw him into a desperate inconvenience. He made a speech that echoed around London and that he bitterly regretted afterwards.

"Till now," he said, "I never understood the reason of the policy and prudence of the Spaniards in suffering the Inquisition among them. And certainly it will never be well with us till something like the Spanish Inquisition be in England."

It was a dreadful thing to say. The torture and terror of the Spanish Inquisition were fresh in men's minds—Penn's grandfather, Giles Penn, had suffered from it—and in England Popery was more feared and detested than non-conformity.

For the fourth time the jury was ordered to go find another verdict; this time they refused to go, saying there was no other verdict. The Recorder in a passion left the bench, sputtering: "I protest I will sit here no longer to hear these things," but the Mayor called to him to stay while he uttered a few more threats, had the sheriff take the jury up to their room, and adjourned the court.

The prisoners were sent back to Newgate, where at least they had more freedom and comfort than the jury.

At seven o'clock on the morning of Monday, September fifth, the court sat again. The jury staggered in, wan, white, hungry, thirsty, and disheveled.

"Look upon the prisoners," said the Clerk. "What say you, is William Penn guilty or not guilty?"

"Not guilty."

"What say you? Is William Mead guilty, or not guilty?"

"Not guilty."

It was plain and definite this time. There was nothing the Bench could do except to call the roll and make each juror give his verdict separately. Everyone answered firmly: "Not guilty."

The people in the galleries were pleased, so pleased that they "made a kind of hymn about it." All over the courtroom there were little murmurs of satisfaction.

But the affair was not over. The Recorder had his last word. "I am sorry, gentlemen, you have followed your own judgments and opinions rather than the good and wholesome advice which was given you. God keep my life out of your hands: but for this the court fines you forty marks a man, and imprisonment till paid."

They had been threatened with fines and imprisonment, they had faced the ugly temper of the Bench, they must have known this was coming. But forty marks was a lot of money, about twenty-six pounds sterling, in a day when a lieutenant in the Plymouth colony, for instance, got an annual salary of twenty marks, and women worked in the hayfields for a penny a day.

Penn then stepped up toward the Bench and demanded his liberty. He was told that he too was in for fines—the forty mark fine imposed at the beginning of the session for wearing his hat. He began to quote the Magna Carta again, but the Recorder had had all he could stand. "Take him away," he implored, "take him away, take him out of the court."

But before he went young William Penn had one thing more to say. He said it. "I can never urge the fundamental laws of England but you cry: 'Take him away, take him away.' But it is no wonder, since the Spanish Inquisition hath so great a place in the Recorder's heart. God Almighty, who is just, will judge you for these things."

So the prisoners who had been acquitted, and the jury who had acquitted them, went together to Newgate prison.

That night Penn wrote to his father. "Because I cannot come, I write." He told him the story of the trial, ending: "I am more concerned at thy distemper and the pains that attend it, than at my own mere imprisonment, which works for the best."

The next day he wrote: "I entreat thee not to purchase my liberty. They will repent them of their proceedings. I am now a prisoner notoriously against law."

And the next: "I am persuaded some clearer way will suddenly be found to obtain my liberty, which is no way so desirable to me as on the account of being with thee. . . . My present restraint is so far from being humor that I would rather perish than release myself by so indirect a course as to satiate their revengeful, avaricious appetites. The advantage of such freedom would fall very far short of the trouble of accepting it."

To pay the fine would be to admit its justice. What he wanted was either to be released by the court, or to bring suit against the judges for illegal imprisonment. In this way a principle could be established. This was the course the jury was taking. Every six hours they demanded their freedom, and when at length they were released on bail, they brought suit against the judges—and won their case. The whole body of judges in the King's Bench Court decided that no jury could be fined for its verdict. So it was that as a result of the trial of William Penn the sacredness of trial by jury was established for all time.

But that was nearly a year later.

The Admiral could not wait. He was dying, and he wanted to see his beloved son William again. He secretly paid his fine, and Mead's too, and they were set free.

The Admiral's Ghost

by ALFRED NOYES

I tell you a tale to-night
   Which a seaman told to me,
With eyes that gleamed in the lanthorn light
   And a voice as low as the sea.

You could almost hear the stars
   Twinkling up in the sky,
And the old wind woke and moaned in the spars
   And the same old waves went by,

Singing the same old song
   As ages and ages ago,
While he froze my blood in that deep-sea night
   With the things that he seemed to know.

A bare foot pattered on deck;
   Ropes creaked; then—all grew still,
And he pointed his finger straight in my face
   And growled, as a sea-dog will.

"Do 'ee know who Nelson was?
   That pore little shrivelled form
With the patch on his eye and the pinned-up sleeve
   And a soul like a North Sea storm?

"Ask of the Devonshire men!
  They know, and they'll tell you true;
He wasn't the pore little chawed-up chap
  That Hardy thought he knew.

"He wasn't the man you think!
  His patch was a dern disguise!
For he knew that they'd find him out, d'you see,
  If they looked him in both his eyes.

"He was twice as big as he seemed;
  But his clothes were cunningly made.
He'd both of his hairy arms all right!
  The sleeve was a trick of the trade.

"You've heard of sperrits, no doubt;
  Well, there's more in the matter than that!
But he wasn't the patch and he wasn't the sleeve,
  And he wasn't the laced cocked-hat.

"*Nelson was just—a Ghost!*
  You may laugh! But the Devonshire men
They knew that he'd come when England called,
  And they know that he'll come again.

"I'll tell you the way it was
  (For none of the landsmen know),
And to tell it you right, you must go a-starn
  Two hundred years or so.

             *   *   *

"The waves were lapping and slapping
  The same as they are to-day;
And Drake lay dying aboard his ship
  In Nombre Dios Bay.

"The scent of the foreign flowers
  Came floating all around;

'But I'd give my soul for the smell o' the pitch,'
  Says he, 'in Plymouth Sound.

" 'What shall I do,' he says,
  'When the guns begin to roar,
An' England wants me, and me not there
  To shatter 'er fores once more?'

"(You've heard what he said, maybe,
  But I'll mark you the p'ints again;
For I want you to box your compass right
  And get my story plain.)

" 'You must take my drum,' he says,
  'To the old sea-wall at home;
And if ever you strike that drum,' he says,
  'Why, strike me blind, I'll come!

" 'If England needs me, dead
  Or living, I'll rise that day!
I'll rise from the darkness under the sea
  Ten thousand miles away.'

"That's what he said; and he died;
  An' his pirates, listenin' roun'
With their crimson doublets and jewelled swords
  That flashed as the sun went down.

"They sewed him up in his shroud
  With a round-shot top and toe,
To sink him under the salt sharp sea
  Where all good seamen go.

"They lowered him down in the deep,
  And there in the sunset light
They boomed a broadside over his grave,
  As meanin' to say 'Good-night.'

"They sailed away in the dark
  To the dear little isle they knew;

And they hung his drum by the old sea-wall
   The same as he told them to.

*   *   *

"Two hundred years went by,
   And the guns began to roar,
And England was fighting hard for her life,
   As ever she fought of yore.

" 'It's only my dead that count,'
   She said, as she says to-day;
'It isn't the ships and it isn't the guns
   'Ull sweep Trafalgar's Bay.'

"D'you guess who Nelson was?
   You may laugh, but it's true as true!
There was more in that pore little chawed-up chap
   Than ever his best friend knew.

"The foe was creepin' close,
   In the dark, to our white-cliffed isle;
They were ready to leap at England's throat,
   When—O, you may smile, you may smile;

"But—ask of the Devonshire men;
   For they heard in the dead of night
The roll of a drum, and they saw him pass
   On a ship all shining white.

"He stretched out his dead cold face
   And he sailed in the grand old way!
The fishes had taken an eye and his arm,
   But he swept Trafalgar's Bay.

"Nelson—was Francis Drake!
   O, what matters the uniform,
Or the patch on your eye or your pinned-up sleeve,
   If your soul's like a North Sea storm?"

Madame Curie

FOUR YEARS IN A SHED

by EVE CURIE

When Marya Sklodovska is living in a tiny cold garret as a
desperately poor Polish governess in Paris struggling to pay for
her university education, her life is hard enough; but nothing com-
pared to what she and her distinguished physicist husband, Pierre
Curie, will have to endure when they try to prove the existence
of radium to an unbelieving world. The four years described here,
in which they freeze and suffer in the primitive shed that serves
them as laboratory, point up the superhuman determination and
energy that Marie summons up in order to extract one tenth of a
gram of radium from eight tons of pitchblende. Having succeeded, the Curies refuse to patent their process or to profit in
any way from the commercial use of radium. Many honors come
to them now—in 1904 she and Pierre receive the Nobel prize in
physics; and in 1911 Marie receives the Nobel prize in chemistry.
She is the first person to be awarded the prize twice.

But this shy genius has no taste for fame or honors; all she asks
is a laboratory in which to do her work. Pierre Curie had been
tragically killed in a street accident before the French government
ever got around to supplying him with a proper laboratory. Madame Curie, broken-hearted, continues her selfless, terribly devoted
research almost to the day of her death, a death by anaemia
brought on by her long years of close work with those same radioactive bodies that she has so generously given to the world. More
than any others, hers was the inspired life of a pure scientist. In

*this biography of her mother, Eve Curie has produced a beauti-
fully written study of a beautiful life.*

A man chosen at random from a crowd to read an account of the
discovery of radium would not have doubted for one moment that
radium existed: beings whose critical sense has not been sharpened and simultaneously deformed by specialized culture keep
their imaginations fresh. They are ready to accept an unexpected
fact, however extraordinary it may appear, and to wonder at it.

The physicist colleagues of the Curies received the news in
slightly different fashion. The special properties of polonium and
radium upset fundamental theories in which scientists had believed for centuries. How was one to explain the spontaneous
radiation of the radioactive bodies? The discovery upset a world
of acquired knowledge and contradicted the most firmly established ideas on the composition of matter. Thus the physicist kept
on the reserve. He was violently interested in Pierre and Marie's
work, he could perceive its infinite developments, but before being
convinced he awaited the acquisition of decisive results.

The attitude of the chemist was even more downright. By definition, a chemist only believes in the existence of a new substance
when he has seen the substance, touched it, weighed and examined it, confronted it with acids, bottled it, and when he has
determined its "atomic weight."

Now, up to the present, nobody had "seen" radium. Nobody
knew the atomic weight of radium. And the chemists, faithful
to their principles, concluded: "No atomic weight, no radium.
Show us some radium and we will believe you."

To show polonium and radium to the incredulous, to prove to
the world the existence of their "children," and to complete their
own conviction, M. and Mme. Curie were now to labor for four
years.

The aim was to obtain pure radium and polonium. In the most
strongly radioactive products the scientists had prepared, these
substances figured only in imperceptible traces. Pierre and Marie

already knew the method by which they could hope to isolate the new metals, but the separation could not be made except by treating very large quantities of crude material.

Here arose three agonizing questions:

How were they to get a sufficient quantity of ore? What premises could they use to effect their treatment? What money was there to pay the inevitable cost of the work?

Pitchblende, in which polonium and radium were hidden, was a costly ore, treated at the St. Joachimsthal mines in Bohemia for the extraction of uranium salts used in the manufacture of glass. Tons of pitchblende would cost a great deal: a great deal too much for the Curie household.

Ingenuity was to make up for wealth. According to the expectation of the two scientists, the extraction of uranium should leave, intact in the ore, such traces of polonium and radium as the ore contains. There was no reason why these traces should not be found in the residue. And, whereas crude pitchblende was costly, its residue after treatment had very slight value. By asking an Austrian colleague for a recommendation to the directors of the mine of St. Joachimsthal would it not be possible to obtain a considerable quantity of such residue for a reasonable price?

It was simple enough: but somebody had to think of it.

It was necessary, of course, to buy this crude material and pay for its transportation to Paris. Pierre and Marie appropriated the required sum from their very slight savings. They were not so foolish as to ask for official credits. . . . If two physicists on the scent of an immense discovery had asked the University of Paris or the French government for a grant to buy pitchblende residue they would have been laughed at. In any case their letter would have been lost in the files of some office, and they would have had to wait months for a reply, probably unfavorable in the end. Out of the traditions and principles of the French Revolution, which had created the metric system, founded the Normal School, and encouraged science in many circumstances, the State seemed to have retained, after more than a century, only the deplorable words pronounced by Fouquier-Tinville at the trial in which Lavoisier was condemned to the guillotine: "The Republic has no need for scientists."

But at least could there not be found, in the numerous buildings attached to the Sorbonne, some kind of suitable workroom to lend to the Curie couple? Apparently not. After vain attempts, Pierre and Marie staggered back to their point of departure, which is to say to the School of Physics where Pierre taught, to the little room where Marie had done her first experiments. The room gave on a courtyard, and on the other side of the yard there was a wooden shack, an abandoned shed, with a skylight roof in such bad condition that it admitted the rain. The Faculty of Medicine had formerly used the place as a dissecting room, but for a long time now it had not even been considered fit to house the cadavers. No floor: an uncertain layer of bitumen covered the earth. It was furnished with some worn kitchen tables, a blackboard which had landed there for no known reason, and an old cast-iron stove with a rusty pipe.

A workman would not willingly have worked in such a place: Marie and Pierre, nevertheless, resigned themselves to it. The shed had one advantage: it was so untempting, so miserable, that nobody thought of refusing them the use of it. Schutzenberger, the director of the school, had always been very kind to Pierre Curie and no doubt regretted that he had nothing better to offer. However that may be, he offered nothing else; and the couple, very pleased at not being put out into the street with their material, thanked him, saying that "this would do" and that they would "make the best of it."

As they were taking possession of the shed, a reply arrived from Austria. Good news! By extraordinary luck, the residue of recent extractions of uranium had not been scattered. The useless material had been piled up in a no-man's-land planted with pine trees, near the mine of St. Joachimsthal. Thanks to the intercession of Professor Suess and the Academy of Science of Vienna, the Austrian government, which was the proprietor of the State factory there, decided to present a ton of residue to the two French lunatics who thought they needed it. If, later on, they wished to be

sent a greater quantity of the material, they could obtain it at the mine on the best terms. For the moment the Curies had to pay only the transportation charges on a ton of ore.

One morning a heavy wagon, like those which deliver coal, drew up in the Rue Lhomond before the School of Physics. Pierre and Marie were notified. They hurried bareheaded into the street in their laboratory gowns. Pierre, who was never agitated, kept his calm; but the more exuberant Marie could not contain her joy at the sight of the sacks that were being unloaded. It was pitchblende, *her* pitchblende, for which she had received a notice some days before from the freight station. Full of curiosity and impatience, she wanted to open one of the sacks and contemplate her treasure without further waiting. She cut the strings, undid the coarse sackcloth and plunged her two hands into the dull brown ore, still mixed with pine needles from Bohemia.

There was where radium was hidden. It was from there that Marie must extract it, even if she had to treat a mountain of this inert stuff like dust on the road.

Marya Sklodovska had lived through the most intoxicating moments of her student life in a garret; Marie Curie was to know wonderful joys again in a dilapidated shed. It was a strange sort of beginning over again, in which a sharp subtle happiness (which probably no woman before Marie had ever experienced) twice elected the most miserable setting.

The shed in the Rue Lhomond surpassed the most pessimistic expectations of discomfort. In summer, because of its skylights, it was as stifling as a hothouse. In winter one did not know whether to wish for rain or frost; if it rained, the water fell drop by drop, with a soft, nerve-racking noise, on the ground or on the worktables, in places which the physicists had to mark in order to avoid putting apparatus there. If it froze, one froze. There was no recourse. The stove, even when it was stoked white, was a complete disappointment. If one went near enough to touch it one received a little heat, but two steps away and one was back in the zone of ice.

It was almost better for Marie and Pierre to get used to the cruelty of the outside temperature, since their technical installation—hardly existent—possessed no chimneys to carry off noxious gases, and the greater part of their treatment had to be made in the open air, in the courtyard. When a shower came the physicists hastily moved their apparatus inside: to keep on working without being suffocated they set up draughts between the opened door and windows.

Marie probably did not boast to Dr. Vauthier of this very peculiar cure for attacks of tuberculosis.

> We had no money, no laboratory and no help in the conduct of this important and difficult task [she was to write later]. It was like creating something out of nothing, and if Casimir Dluski once called my student years "the heroic years of my sister-in-law's life," I may say without exaggeration that this period was, for my husband and myself, the heroic period of our common existence.
>
> . . . And yet it was in this miserable old shed that the best and happiest years of our life were spent, entirely consecrated to work. I sometimes passed the whole day stirring a mass in ebullition, with an iron rod nearly as big as myself. In the evening I was broken with fatigue.

In such conditions M. and Mme. Curie worked for four years from 1898 to 1902.

During the first year they busied themselves with the chemical separation of radium and polonium and they studied the radiation of the products (more and more active) thus obtained. Before long they considered it more practical to separate their efforts. Pierre Curie tried to determine the properties of radium, and to know the new metal better. Marie continued those chemical treatments which would permit her to obtain salts of pure radium.

In this division of labor Marie had chosen the "man's job." She accomplished the toil of a day laborer. Inside the shed her husband was absorbed by delicate experiments. In the courtyard, dressed in her old dust-covered and acid-stained smock, her hair blown by the wind, surrounded by smoke which stung her eyes and throat, Marie was a sort of factory all by herself.

> I came to treat as many as twenty kilograms of matter at a time [she writes], which had the effect of filling the shed with great jars full of precipitates and liquids. It was killing work to carry the receivers, to pour off the liquids and to stir, for hours at a stretch, the boiling matter in a smelting basin.

Radium showed no intention of allowing itself to be known by human creatures. Where were the days when Marie naïvely expected the radium content of pitchblende to be *one per cent?* The radiation of the new substance was so powerful that a tiny quantity of radium, disseminated through the ore, was the source of striking phenomena which could be easily observed and measured. The difficult, the impossible thing, was to isolate this minute quantity, to separate it from the gangue in which it was so intimately mixed.

The days of work became months and years: Pierre and Marie were not discouraged. This material which resisted them, which defended its secrets, fascinated them. United by their tenderness, united by their intellectual passions, they had, in a wooden shack, the "anti-natural" existence for which they had both been made, she as well as he.

> At this period we were entirely absorbed by the new realm that was, thanks to an unhoped-for discovery, opening before us [Marie was to write]. In spite of the difficulties of our working conditions, we felt very happy. Our days were spent at the laboratory. In our poor shed there reigned a great tranquillity: sometimes, as we watched over some operation, we would walk up and down, talking about work in the present and in the future; when we were cold a cup of hot tea taken near the stove comforted us. We lived in our single preoccupation as if in a dream.
> . . . We saw only very few persons at the laboratory; among the physicists and chemists there were a few who came from time to time, either to see our experiments or to ask for advice from Pierre Curie, whose competence in several branches of physics was well-known. Then took place some conversations be-

fore the blackboard—the sort of conversation one remembers well because it acts as a stimulant for scientific interest and the ardor for work without interrupting the course of reflection and without troubling that atmosphere of peace and meditation which is the true atmosphere of a laboratory.

Whenever Pierre and Marie, alone in this poor place, left their apparatus for a moment and quietly let their tongues run on, their talk about their beloved radium passed from the transcendent to the childish.

"I wonder what *It* will be like, what *It* will look like," Marie said one day with the feverish curiosity of a child who has been promised a toy. "Pierre, what form do you imagine *It* will take?"

"I don't know," the physicist answered gently. "I should like it to have a very beautiful color. . . ."

It is odd to observe that in Marie Curie's correspondence we find, upon this prodigious effort, none of the sensitive comments, decked out with imagery, which used to flash suddenly amid the familiarity of her letters. Was it because the years of exile had somewhat relaxed the young woman's intimacy with her people? Was she too pressed by work to find time?

The essential reason for this reserve is perhaps to be sought elsewhere. It was not by chance that Mme. Curie's letters ceased to be original at the exact moment when the story of her life became exceptional. As student, teacher or young wife, Marie could tell her story. . . . But now she was isolated by all that was secret and inexpressible in her scientific vocation. Among those she loved there was no longer anybody able to understand, to realize her worries and her difficult design. She could share her obsessions with only one person, Pierre Curie, companion. To him alone could she confide rare thoughts and dreams. Marie, from now on, was to present to all others, however near they might be to her heart, an almost commonplace picture of herself. She was to paint for them only the bourgeois side of her life. She was to find sometimes accents full of contained emotion to express her happiness as a woman. But of her work she was to speak only in laconic, inexpressive little phrases: news in three lines, without even attempting to suggest the wonders that work meant to her.

Here we feel an absolute determination not to illustrate the singular profession she had chosen by literature. Through subtle modesty, and also through horror of vain talk and everything superfluous, Marie concealed herself, dug herself in; or rather, she offered only one of her profiles. Shyness, boredom, or reason, whatever it may have been, the scientist of genius effaced and dissimulated herself behind "a woman like all others."

Marie to Bronya, 1899:

> Our life is always the same. We work a lot but we sleep well, so our health does not suffer. The evenings are taken up by caring for the child. In the morning I dress her and give her her food, then I can generally go out at about nine. During the whole of this year we have not been either to the theater or a concert, and we have not paid one visit. For that matter, we feel very well. . . . I miss my family enormously, above all you, my dears, and Father. I often think of my isolation with grief. I cannot complain of anything else, for our health is not bad, the child is growing well, and I have the best husband one could dream of; I could never have imagined finding one like him. He is a true gift of heaven, and the more we live together the more we love each other.
>
> Our work is progressing. I shall soon have a lecture to deliver on the subject. It should have been last Saturday but I was prevented from giving it, so it will no doubt be this Saturday, or else in a fortnight.

This work, which is so dryly mentioned in passing, was in fact progressing magnificently. In the course of the years 1899 and 1900 Pierre and Marie Curie published a report on the discovery of "induced radioactivity" due to radium, another on the effects of radioactivity, and another on the electric charge carried by the rays. And at last they drew up, for the Congress of Physics of 1900, a general report on the radioactive substances, which aroused immense interest among the scientists of Europe.

The development of the new science of radioactivity was rapid, overwhelming—the Curies needed fellow workers. Up to now they had had only the intermittent help of a laboratory assistant named Petit, an honest man who came to work for them outside his hours of service—working out of personal enthusiasm, almost in secret. But they now required technicians of the first order. Their discovery had important extensions in the domain of chemistry, which demanded attentive study. They wished to associate competent research workers with them.

> Our work on radioactivity began in solitude [Marie was to write]. But before the breadth of the task it became more and more evident that collaboration would be useful. Already in 1898 one of the laboratory chiefs of the school, G. Bémont, had given us some passing help. Toward 1900 Pierre Curie entered into relations with a young chemist, André Debierne, assistant in the laboratory of Professor Friedel, who esteemed him highly. André Debierne willingly accepted work on radioactivity. He undertook especially the research of a new radio element, the existence of which was suspected in the group of iron and rare clays. He discovered this element, named "actinium." Even though he worked in the physico-chemical laboratory at the Sorbonne directed by Jean Perrin, he frequently came to see us in our shed and soon became a very close friend to us, to Dr. Curie and later on to our children.

Thus, even before radium and polonium were isolated, a French scientist, André Debierne, had discovered a "brother," *actinium*.

> At about the same period [Marie tells us], a young physicist, Georges Sagnac, engaged in studying X rays, came frequently to talk to Pierre Curie about the analogies that might exist between these rays, their secondary rays, and the radiation of radioactive bodies. Together they performed a work on the electric charge carried by these secondary rays.

Marie continued to treat, kilogram by kilogram, the tons of pitchblende residue which were sent her on several occasions from St. Joachimsthal. With her terrible patience, she was able to be, every day for four years, a physicist, a chemist, a specialized worker, an engineer and a laboring man all at once. Thanks to her brain and muscle, the old tables in the shed held more and more concentrated products—products more and more rich in radium. Mme. Curie was approaching the end: she no longer stood in the courtyard, enveloped in bitter smoke, to watch the heavy basins of material in fusion. She was now at the stage of purification and of the "fractional crystallization" of strongly radioactive solutions. But the poverty of her haphazard equipment hindered her work more than ever. It was now that she needed a spotlessly clean workroom and apparatus perfectly protected against cold, heat and dirt. In this shed, open to every wind, iron and coal dust was afloat which, to Marie's despair, mixed itself into the products purified with so much care. Her heart sometimes constricted before these little daily accidents, which took so much of her time and her strength.

Pierre was so tired of the interminable struggle that he would have been quite ready to abandon it. Of course, he did not dream of dropping the study of radium and of radioactivity. But he would willingly have renounced, for the time being, the special operation of preparing pure radium. The obstacles seemed insurmountable. Could they not resume this work later on, under better conditions? More attached to the meaning of natural phenomena than to their material reality, Pierre Curie was exasperated to see the paltry results to which Marie's exhausting effort had led. He advised an armistice.

He counted without his wife's character. Marie wanted to isolate radium and she would isolate it. She scorned fatigue and difficulties, and even the gaps in her own knowledge which complicated her task. After all, she was only a very young scientist: she still had not the certainty and great culture Pierre had acquired by twenty years' work, and sometimes she stumbled across phenomena or methods of calculation which she knew very little, and for which she had to make hasty studies.

So much the worse! With stubborn eyes under her great brow, she clung to her apparatus and her test tubes.

In 1902, forty-five months after the day on which the Curies announced the probable existence of radium, Marie finally carried off the victory in this war of attrition: she succeeded in preparing a decigram of pure radium, and made a first determination of the atomic weight of the new substance, which was 225.

The incredulous chemists—of whom there were still a few—could only bow before the facts, before the superhuman obstinacy of a woman.

Radium officially existed.

It was nine o'clock at night. Pierre and Marie Curie were in their little house at 108 Boulevard Kellermann, where they had been living since 1900. The house suited them well. From the boulevard, where three rows of trees half hid the fortifications, could be seen only a dull wall and a tiny door. But behind the one-story house, hidden from all eyes, there was a narrow provincial garden, rather pretty and very quiet. And from the "barrier" of Gentilly they could escape on their bicycles toward the suburbs and the woods. . . .

Old Dr. Curie, who lived with the couple, had retired to his room. Marie had bathed her child and put it to bed, and had stayed for a long time beside the cot. This was a rite. When Irène did not feel her mother near her at night she would call out for her incessantly, with that "Mé!" which was to be our substitute for "Mamma" always. And Marie, yielding to the implacability of the four-year-old baby, climbed the stairs, seated herself beside the child and stayed there in the darkness until the young voice gave way to light, regular breathing. Only then would she go down again to Pierre, who was growing impatient. In spite of his kindness, he was the most possessive and jealous of husbands. He was so used to the constant presence of his wife that her least eclipse kept him from thinking freely. If Marie delayed too long near her daughter, he received her on her return with a reproach so unjust as to be comic:

"You never think of anything but that child!"

Pierre walked slowly about the room. Marie sat down and made some stitches on the hem of Irène's new apron. One of her principles was never to buy ready-made clothes for the child: she thought them too fancy and impractical. In the days when Bronya was in Paris the two sisters cut out their children's dresses together, according to patterns of their own invention. These patterns still served for Marie.

But this evening she could not fix her attention. Nervous, she got up; then, suddenly:

"Suppose we go down there for a moment?"

There was a note of supplication in her voice—altogether superfluous, for Pierre, like herself, longed to go back to the shed they had left two hours before. Radium, fanciful as a living creature, endearing as a love, called them back to its dwelling, to the wretched laboratory.

The day's work had been hard, and it would have been more reasonable for the couple to rest. But Pierre and Marie were not always reasonable. As soon as they had put on their coats and told Dr. Curie of their flight, they were in the street. They went on foot, arm in arm, exchanging few words. After the crowded streets of this queer district, with its factory buildings, wastelands and poor tenements, they arrived in the Rue Lhomond and crossed the little courtyard. Pierre put the key in the lock. The door squeaked, as it had squeaked thousands of times, and admitted them to their realm, to their dream.

"Don't light the lamps!" Marie said in the darkness. Then she added with a little laugh:

"Do you remember the day when you said to me 'I should like radium to have a beautiful color'?"

The reality was more entrancing than the simple wish of long ago. Radium had something better than "a beautiful color": it was spontaneously luminous. And in the somber shed where, in the absence of cupboards, the precious particles in their tiny glass receivers were placed on tables or on shelves nailed to the wall, their phosphorescent bluish outlines gleamed, suspended in the night.

"Look . . . Look!" the young woman murmured.

She went forward cautiously, looked for and found a straw-bottomed chair. She sat down in the darkness and silence. Their two faces turned toward the pale glimmering, the mysterious sources of radiation, toward radium—their radium. Her body leaning forward, her head eager, Marie took up again the attitude which had been hers an hour earlier at the bedside of her sleeping child.

Her companion's hand lightly touched her hair.

She was to remember forever this evening of glowworms, this magic.

A Glimpse into . . .

The Wide
Wonderful
World

Exploring with Beebe

by WILLIAM BEEBE

As Director of Tropical Research for the New York Zoological Society, William Beebe headed many ocean exploring expeditions to obtain marine specimens and information. And he then wrote scientifically accurate yet popular and vivid descriptions of what he discovered on these trips. He became particularly famous for his work at the bottom of the sea with the bathysphere, a diving apparatus which permitted him to study exotic deep-sea fish at close range in their natural surroundings. This selection about albatrosses first appeared in The Arcturus Adventure, *an account of a trip to the Galápagos Islands in the South Pacific; it was later included in* Exploring with Beebe, *a collection for younger readers selected by the author from his various books. Finding an albatross rookery was not part of Beebe's original goal on the island, but it turned out to be an unexpected and delightful highlight of the expedition.*

The first time I ever saw an albatross was at dawn far out in the Indian Ocean. It was that hour at sea when perspective does not exist, and, like the houses of a tropical coastal city, everything appears flat and on one plane. I was observing a small flock of petrels from the rail of my vessel when a lighter colored bird appeared above them, apparently of the same size. As I watched, it grew larger and larger, until, to my amazement, it joined the petrels, and in the same instant they were dwarfed to insect size while

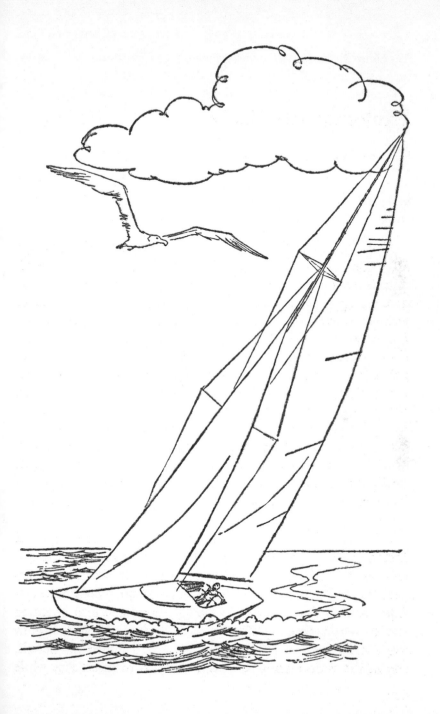

this white bird assumed relatively gigantic proportions, and I knew that I was seeing the effortless flight of an albatross.

For years thereafter my eyes were always on the lookout for these birds. In southern seas and in the north Pacific one may hope to find them, but not on our own boreal Atlantic. A great many years ago, however, long before man began to have sufficient perspective of his ancestry to worry about it, albatrosses were calmly winging their way over our northern seas, and we find their fossil bones both in England and America. A vast amount has been written about their flight but today we watch them with quite as much ignorance of how they contrive it as when the first mariner saw and marvelled. So close to the water they skim, so automatically they rise and fall, outlining the unpredictable movements of waves, that they seem to possess all the secrets of white shadows. When we watch closely and less emotionally we begin to see the part which wind plays in the support of this relatively heavy mass of flesh and feathers, throughout the tens of thousands of its miles of progress. The albatross is never so supreme and relaxed and effortless as when it is coasting upwind, but a breeze on the quarter is less sustaining, and when flying with the wind, frequent circles and intersecting spirals are necessary to attain and sustain sufficient impetus and altitude. This is the fame of the bird, and throughout history and literature almost every mention of it has been synonymous with supremacy in flight.

Once seen and recognized, an albatross can never again be mistaken for any other bird; its great size, the unusual length and ribbon-like narrowness of its wings, the large, yellow, hooked beak —all these mark it even at a distance. The ease and lack of effort of its flight are deceiving, and only when it circles and encircles a fast-moving steamer do we realize the terrific speed of which it is capable.

Albatrosses are usually classified as a family in the order of birds known as Procellariiformes, or oceanic swimming birds with the nostrils arranged in two long tubes lying along the beak. Their nearest relatives are the hosts of little black and white petrels or Mother Cary's chickens which abound on every ocean and are familiar in storm and calm. In fact it would not be far from the truth were we to call petrels dwarf albatrosses, or the latter giant petrels. Diversity in size is probably as great in this group of birds as in any corresponding assemblage of animals on the earth. Within sight of one another I have collected an albatross and a petrel, the former weighing one hundred and fifty times as much as the latter, while the albatross had a spread of wing seven times as great as that of its tiny relative. There has been much written of truth and of exaggeration in regard to the wing spread of albatrosses. I am inclined to agree with the words of Dr. Lucas, who writes of the wandering albatross "it is also the largest species, having a stretch of wings of about twelve feet—an assigned dimension of seventeen and a half feet being either a great exaggeration or highly exceptional." In the Eocene, however, there lived an albatross-like bird, which, judged by the size of its fossil bones, must have had a spread of wing of at least twenty-two feet.

In birds so evidently related as petrels and albatrosses but differing so greatly in actual size we have most interesting evidence of possibilities of flight character. It would seem impossible for any small bird to soar for any length of time or to go for any distance without actually flapping. I can recall no bird of small size which has this ability, while such past masters of non-flapping flight as vultures, pelicans, screamers and albatrosses are all large and heavy of body. I have made over three hundred flights in airplanes myself, in peace and war, close to the ground and once up to an altitude of twenty-two thousand feet, yet the way of an eagle in the air is still, to me, inimitable, and always will be unless we can duplicate its great air chambers, the lightness and strength of its hollow bones, and the friction-evading plumage.

The part which albatrosses have played in relation to man is interesting. First, admiration for its flight by early mariners, and a sense of companionship and camaraderie in its society in the desolateness of mid-ocean.

> "And a good south wind sprung up behind;
> The Albatross did follow,
> And every day, for food or play,
> Came to the mariners' hollo!"

This feeling, in the course of years, very naturally developed into an affection, and this, vitalized by the superstitious substratum of the seaman's mind, increased to a resentment of any attempted injury.

> "God save thee, ancient Mariner,
> From the fiends that plague thee thus!—
> Why look'st thou so?" "With my crossbow
> I shot the Albatross."

> And I had done a hellish thing,
> And it would work 'em woe:
> For all averred I had killed the bird
> That made the breeze to blow.
> "Ah wretch!" said they, "the bird to slay,
> That made the breeze to blow!"

The extreme of ridiculous theory is to be found in a very old book by Wiquefort, who says "these birds are often seen sleeping in the air, entirely remote from land, with their head under one wing, and the other employed in beating the air!"

There came a day when the homes of these birds were discovered, usually a tiny coral focus of the scattered individuals which roam so far and wide over the oceans. One island became known to some Japanese who had neither pity nor superstitions, and before President Roosevelt could enforce his sanctuary legislation they had starved or carved alive nearly a million albatrosses for their wing feathers which were sold to milliners as eagle plumes. Then sentiment and kindness again became dominant— the feather markets in our cities were closed and wardens appointed on the tiny islets, and if the desire which museums have for endless series of skins can be controlled, it may be that for many years these magnificent birds will continue to share this good earth with us.

There is an authentic record of an invaluable, although it must be admitted involuntary, benefit rendered to man by an albatross. Some years ago there fell exhausted and dying from starvation upon the beach at Freemantle, West Australia, a great albatross. When found, it had a tin plate fastened around its neck on which was scratched the news of the wrecking of the French ship *Tamaris* three weeks before, and the survival of thirteen of her crew on Crozet Island. During this period the albatross had flown over four thousand miles of ocean, too terrified by its burden to stop to feed. It was a remarkable incident, quite reversing the experience of the ancient mariner;

> "Instead of the cross, the Albatross
> About my neck was hung."

Intellectually, man's relation with albatrosses has been less spectacular but of equal interest. Linnæus, one hundred and sixty-eight years ago, first played taxonomic Adam to the albatross, calling it *Diomedea exulans*. Its godfather was probably therefore the famous hero of the siege of Troy, but Grecian etymology provides a much more poetic and appropriate derivation, and it is pleasant to think of the albatross, whether winging over foam crests or at home on its little isle as being every *Dio-medea* or God-counseled. In its specific appelation Linnæus was also happy for to the ordinary observer, the wandering albatross is truly *exulans* —homeless, banished apparently from all connection with solid land.

It must be confessed, however, that Linnæus made a *faux pas* when he was led to associate in the genus of the great-winged albatross, the little fin-winged penguin—birds as unlike in habits as they are in physical makeup—suffering comparison only in their astonishing divorce from land, and their extreme adaptations for continued existence in the air and the water respectively. One can readily tell that Linnæus was a closet, or at least a terrestrial, rather than a sea-going scientist, for his contribution to the habits of the wandering albatross are, "*æthera altissime scandens; victitans e Triglis volitantibus a Coryphæna exagitatis.*" But this bird neither attains great altitudes in the air, nor does it, to my knowledge, capture living flying fish.

When I first saw albatrosses at their breeding ground I experienced a slight feeling of embarrassment, as if I were peeking through the blinds, or looking behind the scenes. I feel much the same when, in the rotagravure section of the Sunday paper, I see a photograph of some famous prima donna making an apple pie in her kitchenette. The voice of a *chanteuse* and the flight of an albatross are among the more wonderful things in the world, so much so that at first we hesitate even to think of the authors in relation to the trivial things of life. Whatever may be the case with the home life of a great singer, that of these famous birds shows the inevitable law of compensation. I have already courted displeasure in revealing an unromantic side of the Sargasso Sea, so I might as well continue and describe the gait of the Galápagos albatross. Its progress on land makes that of Charlie Chaplin appear grace itself, but for sheer amazing interest, the courtship and dances of these birds vie with its flight.

I had read accounts of this at other rookeries of albatrosses, but no description prepares one for the actual performance. My bird walked up to its mate which, in its turn, rose and faced the new arrival. They stood with their breasts about a foot apart. My albatross suddenly shot its head and neck straight up, the bill pointing skyward, uttering at the same time a deep, grunting moan. Its partner followed suit, then, alternately, each bird bowed deeply and quickly three times. Without an instant's delay they next crossed bills and with quick, vibrating movements of the head, they fenced—there is absolutely no other word for it—with closed mandibles. Without warning my bird ceased and again shot his head high up into the air. Its mate instantly turned her head and neck far sideways and held them motionless and concealed from my point of view, close to the left wing and side. Then another double bow and a second bout. Next, both birds rested, looking quietly around as though nothing unusual were in progress, when the mate gave the stretching cue in her turn, and there followed a long bout of the fencing, this time my bird with widely opened mandibles, the other's beak even entering its mouth once or twice. For five minutes this performance kept up, when a third bird approached, bowed and engaged my albatross. This was only half-hearted however, and the third individual soon waddled painfully away, and the first two resumed the astonishing ritual.

I walked over to the third bird and bowed deeply and to my delight it bowed in return. Seeing no rapier bill, however, it solemnly walked away, until I again faced it and bowed when it returned my salutation twice and took a step toward me. That, alas, was as near as we could come to an engagement, but I shall never forget my amenities with this feathered D'Artagnan of Hood Island.

Silver

by WALTER DE LA MARE

Slowly, silently, now the moon
Walks the night in her silver shoon;
This way, and that, she peers, and sees
Silver fruit upon silver trees;
One by one the casements catch
Her beams beneath the silvery thatch;
Couched in his kennel, like a log,
With paws of silver sleeps the dog;
From their shadowy cote the white breasts peep
Of doves in a silver-feathered sleep;
A harvest mouse goes scampering by,
With silver claws, and silver eye;
And moveless fish in the water gleam,
By silver reeds in a silver stream.

Stopping by Woods on a Snowy Evening

by ROBERT FROST

Whose woods these are I think I know.
His house is in the village though;
He will not see me stopping here
To watch his woods fill up with snow.

My little horse must think it queer
To stop without a farmhouse near
Between the woods and frozen lake
The darkest evening of the year.

He gives his harness bells a shake
To ask if there is some mistake.
The only other sound's the sweep
Of easy wind and downy flake.

The woods are lovely, dark and deep.
But I have promises to keep,
And miles to go before I sleep,
And miles to go before I sleep.

The Rainbow

by WILLIAM WORDSWORTH

My heart leaps up when I behold
  A rainbow in the sky:
So was it when my life began;
So is it now I am a man;
So be it when I shall grow old,
  Or let me die!

Walden

THE LOON

by HENRY DAVID THOREAU

Thoreau was a naturalist, and rather an eccentric and extremely individualistic man who rebelled against the demands of materialistic civilization. For two years he retired to a hut on the shores of Walden Pond, near Concord, Massachusetts, where he cultivated his garden, kept his eyes and ears open, and lived a life of Spartan-like simplicity, spending exactly eight dollars a year. He went to the woods, he said, because "I wished to live deliberately, to front only the essential facts of life, and see if I could learn what it had to teach, and not, when I came to die, discover that I had not lived." His best known work, Walden or Life in the Woods *is an account of his observations at Walden Pond that has become a classic. This description of the little game between Thoreau and the wierd laughing loon bears the unique stamp of all his writings: seeing things about him with a fresh eye, he wrote as if everything in nature was a discovery of his own.*

In the fall the loon (*Colymbus glacialis*) came, as usual, to molt and bathe in the pond, making the woods ring with his wild laughter before I had risen.

As I was paddling along the north shore one very calm October afternoon, for such days especially they settle on to the lakes, like the milkweed down, having looked in vain over the pond for a loon, suddenly one, sailing out from the shore toward the middle a few rods in front of me, set up his wild laugh and betrayed himself. I pursued with a paddle and he dived, but when he came up I was nearer than before. He dived again, but I miscalculated the direction he would take, and we were fifty rods apart when he came to the surface this time, for I had helped to widen the interval; and again he laughed long and loud, and with more reason than before. He manœuvred so cunningly that I could not get within half a dozen rods of him. Each time, when he came to the surface, turning his head this way and that, he coolly surveyed the water and the land, and apparently chose his course so that he might come up where there was the widest expanse of water and at the greatest distance from the boat. It was surprising how quickly he made up his mind and put his resolve into execution. He led me at once to the widest part of the pond, and could not be driven from it. While he was thinking one thing in his brain, I was endeavoring to divine his thought in mine.

It was a pretty game, played on the smooth surface of the pond, a man against a loon. Suddenly your adversary's checker disappears beneath the board, and the problem is to place yours nearest to where his will appear again. Sometimes he would come up unexpectedly on the opposite side of me, having apparently passed directly under the boat. So long-winded was he and so unweariable, that when he had swum farthest he would immediately plunge again, nevertheless; and then no wit could divine where in the deep pond, beneath the smooth surface, he might be speeding his way like a fish, for he had time and ability to visit the bottom of the pond in its deepest part. It is said that loons have been caught in the New York lakes eighty feet beneath the surface, with hooks set for trout—though Walden is deeper than that. How surprised must the fishes be to see this ungainly visitor from another sphere speeding his way amid their schools! Yet he appeared to know his course as surely under water as on the surface, and swam much faster there. Once or twice I saw a ripple where he approached the surface, just put his head out to reconnoitre, and instantly dived again. I found that it was as well for me to rest on my oars and wait his reappearing as to endeavor to calculate where he would rise; for again and again, when I was straining

my eyes over the surface one way, I would suddenly be startled by his unearthly laugh behind me.

But why, after displaying so much cunning, did he invariably betray himself the moment he came up by that loud laugh? Did not his white breast enough betray him? He was indeed a silly loon, I thought. I could commonly hear the plash of the water when he came up, and so also detected him. But after an hour he seemed as fresh as ever, dived as willingly and swam yet farther than at first. It was surprising to see how serenely he sailed off with unruffled breast when he came to the surface, doing all the work with his webbed feet beneath. His usual note was this demoniac laughter, yet somewhat like that of a water-fowl; but occasionally, when he had balked me most successfully and come up a long way off, he uttered a long-drawn unearthly howl, probably more like that of a wolf than any bird; as when a beast puts his muzzle to the ground and deliberately howls. This was his looning—perhaps the wildest sound that is ever heard here, making the woods ring far and wide. I concluded that he laughed in derision of my efforts, confident of his own resources.

Though the sky was by this time overcast, the pond was so smooth that I could see where he broke the surface when I did not hear him. His white breast, the stillness of the air, and the smoothness of the water were all against him. At length, having come up fifty rods off, he uttered one of those prolonged howls, as if calling on the god of loons to aid him, and immediately there came a wind from the east and rippled the surface, and filled the whole air with misty rain, and I was impressed as if it were the prayer of the loon answered, and his god was angry with me; and so I left him disappearing far away on the tumultuous surface.

Loveliest of Trees

by A. E. HOUSMAN

Loveliest of trees, the cherry now
Is hung with bloom along the bough
And stands about the woodland ride
Wearing white for Eastertide.

Now, of my threescore years and ten,
Twenty will not come again,
And take from seventy springs a score,
It only leaves me fifty more.

And since to look at things in bloom
Fifty springs are little room,
About the woodlands I will go
To see the cherry hung with snow.

Under the Greenwood Tree

by WILLIAM SHAKESPEARE

Under the greenwood tree
Who loves to lie with me,
And turn his merry note
Unto the sweet bird's throat,
Come hither, come hither, come hither:
Here shall he see
No enemy
But winter and rough weather.

From *As You Like It*

Far Away and Long Ago

A SERPENT MYSTERY

by W. H. HUDSON

No one has written more beautifully about the wild life of South America than W. H. Hudson, the English naturalist who was born on a large ranch on the plains outside of Buenos Aires. He looked at the world around him with keen intensity and was able to express his delight in it with both force and charm. Though not a professional naturalist, his observations are remarkable for their accuracy as well as their excellent style. Hudson had to spend most of his life in England, but his books are mainly about what he loved and remembered in South America. Far Away and Long Ago, the story of his boyhood days, gives a fascinating picture of strange birds, animals, and life on the great pampas of Argentina.

One hot day in December I had been standing perfectly still for a few minutes among the dry weeds when a slight rustling sound came from near my feet, and glancing down I saw the head and neck of a large black serpent moving slowly past me. In a moment or two the flat head was lost to sight among the close-growing weeds, but the long body continued moving slowly by—so slowly that it hardly appeared to move, and as the creature must have been not less than six feet long, and probably more, it took a very long time, while I stood thrilled with terror, not daring to make the slightest movement, gazing down upon it. Although so long it was not a thick snake, and as it moved on over the white ground it had the appearance of a coal-black current flowing past me—a

current not of water or other liquid but of some such element as quicksilver moving on in a rope-like stream. At last it vanished, and turning I fled from the ground, thinking that never again would I venture into or near that frightfully dangerous spot in spite of its fascination.

Nevertheless I did venture. The image of that black mysterious serpent was always in my mind from the moment of waking in the morning until I fell asleep at night. Yet I never said a word about the snake to any one: it was my secret, and I knew it was a dangerous secret, but I did not want to be told not to visit that spot again. And I simply could not keep away from it; the desire to look again at that strange being was too strong. I began to visit the place again, day after day, and would hang about the borders of the barren weedy ground watching and listening, and still no black serpent appeared.

Then one day I ventured, though in fear and trembling, to go right in among the weeds, and still finding nothing began to advance step by step until I was right in the middle of the weedy ground and stood there a long time, waiting and watching. All I wanted was just to see it once more, and I had made up my mind that immediately on its appearance, if it did appear, I would take to my heels. It was when standing in this central spot that once again that slight rustling sound, like that of a few days before, reached my straining sense and sent an icy chill down my back. And there, within six inches of my toes, appeared the black head and neck, followed by the long, seemingly endless body. I dared not move, since to have attempted flight might have been fatal. The weeds were thinnest here, and the black head and slow-moving black coil could be followed by the eye for a little distance. About a yard from me there was a hole in the ground about the circumference of a breakfast cup at the top, and into this hole the serpent put his head and slowly, slowly drew himself in, while I stood waiting until the whole body to the tip of the tail had vanished and all danger was over.

I had seen my wonderful creature, my black serpent unlike any serpent in the land, and the excitement following the first thrill of terror was still on me, but I was conscious of an element of delight in it, and I would not now resolve not to visit the spot again. Still, I was in fear, and kept away three or four days. Thinking about the snake I formed the conclusion that the hole he had taken refuge in was his den, where he lived, that he was often out roaming about in search of prey, and could hear footsteps at a considerable distance, and that when I walked about at that spot my footsteps disturbed him and caused him to go straight to his hole to hide himself from a possible danger. It struck me that if I went to the middle of the ground and stationed myself near the hole, I would be sure to see him. It would indeed be difficult to see him any other way, since one could never know in which direction he had gone out to seek for food. But no, it was too dangerous: the serpent might come upon me unawares and would probably resent always finding a boy hanging about his den. Still, I could not endure to think I had seen the last of him, and day after day I continued to haunt the spot, and going a few yards into the little weedy wilderness would stand and peer, and at the slightest rustling sound of an insect or falling leaf would experience a thrill of fearful joy, and still the black majestical creature failed to appear.

One day in my eagerness and impatience I pushed my way through the crowded weeds right to the middle of the ground and gazed with a mixed delight and fear at the hole: would he find me there, as on a former occasion? Would he come? I held my breath, I strained my sight and hearing in vain, the hope and fear of his appearance gradually died out, and I left the place bitterly disappointed and walked to a spot about fifty yards away, where mulberry trees grew on the slope of the mound inside the moat.

Looking up into the masses of big clustering leaves over my head I spied a bat hanging suspended from a twig. The bats, I must explain, in that part of the world, that illimitable plain where there were no caverns and old buildings and other dark places to hide in by day, are not so intolerant of the bright light as in other lands. They do not come forth until evening, but by day they are content to hitch themselves to the twig of a tree under a thick cluster of leaves and rest there until it is dark.

Gazing up at this bat suspended under a big green leaf, wrapped in his black and buff-coloured wings as in a mantle, I forgot my disappointment, forgot the serpent, and was so entirely taken up with the bat that I paid no attention to a sensation like a pressure or a dull pain on the instep of my right foot. Then the feeling of pressure increased and was very curious and was as if I had a heavy object like a crowbar lying across my foot, and at length I looked down at my feet, and to my amazement and horror spied the great black snake slowly drawing his long coil across my instep! I dared not move, but gazed down fascinated with the sight of that glistening black cylindrical body drawn so slowly over my foot. He had come out of the moat, which was riddled at the sides with rat-holes, and had most probably been there hunting for rats when my wandering footsteps disturbed him and sent him home to his den; and making straight for it, as his way was, he came to my foot, and instead of going round drew himself over it.

After the first spasm of terror I knew I was perfectly safe, and that he would not turn upon me so long as I remained quiescent, and would presently be gone from sight. And that was my last sight of him; in vain I watched and waited for him to appear on many subsequent days. But that last encounter had left in me a sense of a mysterious being, dangerous on occasion as when attacked or insulted, and able in some cases to inflict death with a sudden blow, but harmless and even friendly or beneficent towards those who regarded it with kindly and reverent feelings in place of hatred. It is in part the feeling of the Hindoo with regard to the cobra which inhabits his house and may one day accidently cause his death, but is not to be persecuted.

Possibly something of that feeling about serpents has survived in me; but in time, as my curiosity about all wild creatures grew, as I looked more on them with the naturalist's eyes, the mystery of the large black snake pressed for an answer. It seemed impossible to believe that any species of snake of large size and black as jet or anthracite coal in colour could exist in any inhabited country without being known, yet no person I interrogated on the subject had ever seen or heard of such an ophidian. The only conclusion appeared to be that this snake was the sole one of its kind in the land. Eventually I heard of the phenomenon of melanism in animals, less rare in snakes perhaps than in animals of other classes, and I was satisfied that the problem was partly solved. My serpent was a black individual of a species of some other colour. But it was not one of our common species—not one of those I knew. It was not a thick blunt-bodied serpent like our venomous pit-viper, our largest snake, and though in shape it conformed to our two common harmless species it was twice as big as the biggest specimens I had ever seen of them. Then I recalled that two years before my discovery of the black snake, our house had been visited by a large unknown snake which measured two or three inches over six feet and was similar in form to my black serpent. The colour of this strange and unwelcome visitor was a pale greenish grey, with numerous dull black mottlings and small spots. The story of its appearance is perhaps worth giving.

It happened that I had a baby sister who could just toddle about on two legs, having previously gone on all-fours. One midsummer day she was taken up and put on a rug in the shade of a tree, twenty-five yards from the sitting-room door, and left alone there to amuse herself with her dolls and toys. After half an hour or so she appeared at the door of the sitting-room where her mother was at work, and standing there with wide-open astonished eyes and moving her hand and arm as if to point to the place she came from, she uttered the mysterious word *kú-ku*. It is a wonderful word which the southern South American mother teaches her child from the moment it begins to toddle, and is useful in a desert and sparsely inhabited country where biting, stinging, and other injurious creatures are common. For babies when they learn to crawl and to walk are eager to investigate and have no natural sense of danger. Take as an illustration the case of the gigantic hairy brown spider, which is excessively abundant in summer and has the habit of wandering about as if always seeking something— "something it cannot find, it knows not what"; and in these wanderings it comes in at the open door and rambles about the room. At the sight of such a creature the baby is snatched up with the cry of *kú-ku* and the intruder slain with a broom or other weapon and thrown out. *Kú-ku* means dangerous, and the terrified gestures and the expression of the nurse or mother when using the word sink into the infant mind, and when that sound or word is heard there is an instant response, as in the case of a warning note or cry uttered by a parent bird which causes the young to fly away or crouch down and hide.

The child's gestures and the word it used caused her mother to run to the spot where it had been left in the shade, and to her horror she saw there a huge serpent coiled up in the middle of the rug. Her cries brought my father on the scene, and seizing a big stick he promptly dispatched the snake.

The child, said everybody, had had a marvellous escape, and as she had never previously seen a snake and could not intuitively know it as dangerous, or *kú-ku*, it was conjectured that she had made some gesture or attempted to push the snake away when it came on to the rug, and that it had reared its head and struck viciously at her.

Recalling this incident I concluded that this unknown serpent, which had been killed because it wanted to share my baby sister's rug, and my black serpent were one and the same species—possibly they had been mates—and that they had strayed a distance away from their native place or else were the last survivors of a colony of their kind in our plantation. It was not until twelve or fourteen years later that I discovered that it was even as I had conjectured. At a distance of about forty miles from my home, or rather from the home of my boyhood where I no longer lived, I found a snake that was new to me, the *Philodryas scotti* of naturalists, a not uncommon Argentine snake, and recognized it as the same species as the one found coiled up on my little sister's rug and presumably as my mysterious black serpent. Some of the specimens which I measured exceeded six feet in length.

Fog

by CARL SANDBURG

The fog comes
on little cat feet.

It sits looking
over harbor and city
on silent haunches
and then moves on.

The Falling Star

by SARA TEASDALE

I saw a star slide down the sky,
Blinding the north as it went by,
Too burning and too quick to hold,
Too lovely to be bought or sold,
Good only to make wishes on
And then forever to be gone.

The Insect World

THE GREAT PEACOCK MOTH

by J. HENRI FABRE

Though he was the greatest French naturalist, Fabre spent almost all of his long life working in obscurity and terrible poverty. For many years this "Homer of the insects" lacked even a microscope; he had only a pocket lens with which to make his astonishingly accurate observations of insect life. No other scientist has done so much with so little. It was not until the end of his life, when he was over 80 and too old to use it, that the state finally presented him with a modern laboratory. But Fabre's instruments were his keen observations, extraordinary intuitive powers, unending patience, and undeniable genius. His laboratory was the sun-scorched little plot of earth around his home in the south of France. Though he was one of the greatest entomologists of all time, he did not obtain public recognition until the age of 84 when the last of the ten volumes of his writings appeared. The most famous of his experiments—and this account of the assembling of the male moths is one of the most interesting—have been collected into a single volume called The Insect World of J. Henri Fabre, *by Edwin Way Teale. Even to the age of 92, Fabre never lost his zest for exploring the insect mysteries, and he was able to convey his enthusiasm in his beautifully clear writings about their fascinating world.*

It was a memorable evening. I shall call it the Great Peacock evening. Who does not know the magnificent Moth, the largest

in Europe, clad in maroon velvet with a necktie of white fur?
The wings, with their sprinkling of grey and brown, crossed by a
faint zig-zag and edged with smoky white, have in the centre a
round patch, a great eye with a black pupil and a variegated iris
containing successive black, white, chestnut and purple arcs.

Well, on the morning of the 6th of May, a female emerges from
her cocoon in my presence, on the table of my insect-laboratory.
I forthwith cloister her, still damp with the humours of the hatch-
ing, under a wire-gauze bell-jar. For the rest, I cherish no particular
plans. I incarcerate her from mere habit, the habit of the observer
always on the look-out for what may happen.

It was a lucky thought. At nine o'clock in the evening, just as
the household is going to bed, there is a great stir in the room next
to mine. Little Paul, half-undressed, is rushing about, jumping
and stamping, knocking the chairs over like a mad thing. I hear
him call me:

"Come quick!" he screams. "Come and see these Moths, big
as birds! The room is full of them!"

I hurry in. There is enough to justify the child's enthusiastic and
hyperbolical exclamations, an invasion as yet unprecedented in
our house, a raid of giant Moths. Four are already caught and
lodged in a bird-cage. Others, more numerous, are fluttering on
the ceiling.

At this sight, the prisoner of the morning is recalled to my mind.

"Put on your things, laddie," I say to my son. "Leave your cage
and come with me. We shall see something interesting."

We run downstairs to go to my study, which occupies the right
wing of the house. In the kitchen I find the servant, who is also
bewildered by what is happening and stands flicking her apron at
great Moths whom she took at first for Bats.

The Great Peacock, it would seem, has taken possession of
pretty well every part of the house. What will it be around my
prisoner, the cause of this incursion? Luckily, one of the two windows of the study had been left open. The approach is not blocked.

We enter the room, candle in hand. What we see is unforgettable. With a soft flick-flack the great Moths fly around the bell-jar,

alight, set off again, come back, fly up to the ceiling and down. They rush at the candle, putting it out with a stroke of their wings; they descend on our shoulders, clinging to our clothes, grazing our faces. The scene suggests a wizard's cave, with its whirl of Bats. Little Paul holds my hand tighter than usual, to keep up his courage.

How many of them are there? About a score. Add to these the number that have strayed into the kitchen, the nursery and the other rooms of the house; and the total of those who have arrived from the outside cannot fall far short of forty. As I said, it was a memorable evening, this Great Peacock evening. Coming from every direction and apprised I know not how, here are forty lovers eager to pay their respects to the marriageable bride born that morning amid the mysteries of my study.

For the moment let us disturb the swarm of wooers no further. The flame of the candle is a danger to the visitors, who fling themselves into it madly and singe their wings. We will resume the observation tomorrow with an experimental interrogatory thought out beforehand.

But first let us clear the ground and speak of what happens every night during the week that my observation lasts. Each time it is pitch dark, between eight and ten o'clock, when the Moths arrive one by one. It is stormy weather, the sky is very much over-cast and the darkness is so profound that even in the open air, in the garden, far from the shadow of the trees, it is hardly possible to see one's hand before one's face.

In addition to this darkness there is the difficulty of access. The house is hidden by tall plane-trees; it is approached by a walk thickly bordered with lilac- and rose-trees, forming a sort of outer vestibule; it is protected against the *mistral* by clumps of pines and screens of cypresses. Clusters of bushy shrubs make a rampart a few steps away from the door. It is through this tangle of branches, in complete darkness, that the Great Peacock has to tack about to reach the object of his pilgrimage.

Under such conditions, the Brown Owl would not dare leave the hole in his olive-tree. The Moth, better-endowed with his

faceted optical organs than the night-bird with its great eyes, goes forward without hesitating and passes through without knocking against things. He directs his tortuous flight so skilfully that, despite the obstacles overcome, he arrives in a state of perfect freshness, with his big wings intact, with not a scratch upon him. The darkness is light enough for him.

Even if we grant that it perceives certain rays unknown to common retinæ, this extraordinary power of sight cannot be what warns the Moth from afar and brings him hurrying to the spot. The distance and the screens interposed make this quite impossible.

Besides, apart from deceptive refractions, of which there is no question in this case, the indications provided by light are so precise that we go straight to the thing seen. Now the Moth sometimes blunders, not as to the general direction which he is to take, but as to the exact spot where the interesting events are happening. I have said that the children's nursery, which is at the side of the house opposite my study, the real goal of my visitors at the present moment, was occupied by the Moths before I went there with a light in my hand. These certainly were ill-informed. There was the same throng of hesitating visitors in the kitchen; but here the light of a lamp, that irresistible lure to nocturnal insects, may have beguiled the eager ones.

Let us consider only the places that were in the dark. In these there are several stray Moths. I find them more or less everywhere around the actual spot aimed at. For instance, when the captive is in my study, the visitors do not all enter by the open window, the safe and direct road, only two or three yards away from the caged prisoner. Several of them come in downstairs, wander about the hall and at most reach the staircase, a blind alley barred at the top by a closed door.

These data tell us that the guests at this nuptial feast do not make straight for their object, as they would if they derived their information from some kind of luminous radiation, whether known or unknown to our physical science. It is something else that apprises them from afar, leads them to the proximity of the exact spot and then leaves the final discovery to the airy uncertainty of random searching. It is very much like the way in which we ourselves are informed by hearing and smell, guides which are far from accurate when we want to decide the precise point of origin of the sound or the smell.

What are the organs of information that direct the rutting Moth on his nightly pilgrimage? One suspects the antennæ, which, in the males, do in fact seem to be questioning space with their spreading tufts of feathers. Are those glorious plumes mere ornaments, or do they at the same time play a part in the perception of the effluvia that guide the enamoured swain? A conclusive experiment seems to present no difficulty. Let us try it.

On the day after the invasion, I find in the study eight of my visitors of the day before. They are perched motionless on the transoms of the second window, which is kept closed. The others, when their dance was over, about ten o'clock in the evening, went out as they came in, that is to say, through the first window, which is left open day and night. Those eight persevering ones are just what I want for my schemes.

With a sharp pair of scissors, without otherwise touching the Moths, I cut off their antennæ, near the base. The patients take hardly any notice of the operation. Not one moves; there is scarcely a flutter of the wings. These are excellent conditions: the wound does not seem at all serious. Undistraught by pain, the Moths bereft of their horns will adapt themselves all the better to my plans. The rest of the day is spent in placid immobility on the cross-bars of the window.

There are still a few arrangements to be made. It is important in particular to shift the scene of operations and not to leave the female before the eyes of the maimed ones at the moment when they resume their nocturnal flight, else the merit of their quest would disappear. I therefore move the bell-jar with its captive and place it under a porch at the other end of the house, some fifty yards from my study.

When night comes, I go to make a last inspection of my eight victims. Six have flown out through the open window; two remain behind, but these have dropped to the floor and no longer have the strength to turn over if I lay them on their backs. They are exhausted, dying. Pray do not blame my surgical work. This quick decrepitude occurs invariably, even without the intervention of my scissors.

Six, in better condition, have gone off. Will they return to the bait that attracted them yesterday? Though deprived of their antennæ, will they be able to find the cage, now put in another place, at a considerable distance from its original position?

The cage is standing in the dark, almost in the open air. From time to time, I go out with a lantern and a Butterfly net. Each visitor is captured, examined, catalogued and forthwith let loose in an adjoining room, of which I close the door. This gradual elimination will enable me to tell the exact number, with no risk of counting the same Moth more than once. Moreover, the temporary jail, which is spacious and bare, will in no way endanger the prisoners, who will find a quiet retreat there and plenty of room. I shall take similar precautions during my subsequent investigations.

At half past ten no more arrive. The sitting is over. In all, twenty-five males have been caught, of whom only one was without antennæ. Therefore, of the six on whom I operated yesterday and who were hale enough to leave my study and go back to the fields, one alone has returned to the bell-jar. It is a poor result, on which I dare not rely when it comes to asserting or denying that the antennæ play a guiding part. We must begin all over again, on a larger scale.

Next morning I pay a visit to the prisoners of the day before. What I see is not encouraging. Many are spread out on the floor, almost lifeless. Several of them give hardly a sign of life when I take them in my fingers. What can I hope from these cripples? Still, let us try. Perhaps they will recover their vigour when the time comes to dance the lovers' round.

The twenty-four new ones undergo amputation of the antennæ. The old, hornless one is left out of count, as dying or close to it. Lastly, the prison-door is left open for the remainder of the day.

He who will may leave the room, he who can shall join in the evening festival. In order to put such as go out to the test of searching for the bride, the cage, which they would be sure to notice on the threshold, is once more removed. I shift it to a room in the opposite wing, on the ground-floor. The access to this room is of course left free.

Of the twenty-four deprived of their antennæ, only sixteen go outside. Eight remain, powerless to move. They will soon die where they are. Out of the sixteen who have left, how many are there that return to the cage in the evening? Not one! I sit up to capture just seven, all newcomers, all sporting feathers. This result would seem to show that the amputation of the antennæ is a rather serious matter. Let us not draw conclusions yet: a doubt remains and an important one.

"A nice state I'm in!" said Mouflard, the Bull-pup, when his pitiless breeder has docked his ears. "How dare I show my face before the other Dogs?"

Can it be that my Moths entertain Master Mouflard's apprehensions? Once deprived of their fine plumes, dare they no longer appear amidst their rivals and a-wooing go? Is it bashfulness on their part or lack of guidance? Or might it not rather be exhaustion after a wait that exceeds the duration of an ephemeral flame? Experiment shall tell us.

On the fourth evening, I take fourteen Moths, all new ones, and imprison them, as they arrive, in a room where I intend them to pass the night. Next morning, taking advantage of their day-time immobility, I remove a little of the fur from the center of their corselet. The silky fleece comes off so easily that this slight tonsure does not inconvenience the insects at all; it deprives them of no organ which may be necessary to them later, when the time comes to find the cage. It means nothing to the shorn ones; to me it means the unmistakable sign that the callers have repeated their visit.

This time there are no weaklings incapable of flight. At night, the fourteen shaven Moths escape into the open. Of course the place of the cage is once more changed. In two hours, I capture twenty Moths, including two tonsured ones, no more. Of those who lost their antennæ two days ago, not one puts in an appearance. Their nuptial time is over for good and all.

Only two return out of the fourteen marked with a bald patch. Why do the twelve others hang back, although supplied with what we have assumed to be their guides, their antennary plumes? Why again that formidable list of defaulters, which we find nearly always after a night of sequestration? I perceive but one reply: the Great Peacock is quickly worn out by the ardours of pairing-time.

With a view to his wedding, the one and only object of his life, the Moth is gifted with a wonderful prerogative. He is able to discover the object of his desire in spite of distance, obstacles and darkness. For two or three evenings, he is allowed a few hours wherein to indulge his search and his amorous exploits. If he cannot avail himself of them, all is over: the most exact of compasses fails, the brightest of lamps expires. What is the use of living after that? Stoically we withdraw into a corner and sleep our last sleep, which is the end of our illusions and of our woes alike.

The Great Peacock becomes a Moth only in order to perpetuate his species. He knows nothing of eating. While so many others, jolly companions one and all, flit from flower to flower, unrolling the spiral of their proboscis and dipping it into the honeyed cups, he, the incomparable faster, wholly freed from the bondage of the belly, has no thought of refreshment. His mouth-parts are mere rudiments, vain simulacra, not real organs capable of performing their functions. Not a sup enters his stomach: a glorious privilege, save that it involves a brief existence. The lamp needs its drop of oil, if it is not to be extinguished. The Great Peacock renounces that drop, but at the same time he renounces long life. Two or three evenings, just time enough to allow the couple to meet, and that is all: the big Moth has lived.

Sea-Fever

by JOHN MASEFIELD

I must go down to the seas again, to the lonely sea and the sky,
And all I ask is a tall ship and a star to steer her by,
And the wheel's kick and the wind's song and the white sail's
 shaking
And a gray mist on the sea's face and a gray dawn breaking.

I must go down to the seas again, for the call of the running tide
Is a wild call and a clear call that may not be denied;
And all I ask is a windy day with the white clouds flying,
And the flung spray and the blown spume, and the sea-gulls crying.

I must go down to the seas again to the vagrant gypsy life,
To the gull's way and the whale's way where the wind's like a
 whetted knife;
And all I ask is a merry yarn from a laughing fellow-rover,
And quiet sleep and a sweet dream when the long trick's over.

The Sea Around Us

THE PATTERN OF THE SURFACE

by RACHEL L. CARSON

Since the beginning of time man has been fascinated by the sea and has written innumerable stories, both true and imaginary, with the sea as background. But it remained for a marine biologist, Rachel Carson, to write the story of the sea itself in such an eloquent way that it was at once acclaimed by authorities as one of the finest scientific studies ever written in non-technical language, and by the public as a best seller. The Sea Around Us *is a highly authentic, informative, and absorbing history of the sea from its earliest beginnings to the very latest discoveries, of the exciting riches to be found on the surface and in the depths, and of the many paradoxes and mysteries of the ocean waters. All this becomes doubly interesting because the author writes about her material with rare charm and imagination.*

Nowhere in all the sea does life exist in such bewildering abundance as in the surface waters. From the deck of a vessel you may look down, hour after hour, on the shimmering discs of jellyfish, their gently pulsating bells dotting the surface as far as you can see. Or one day you may notice early in the morning that you are passing through a sea that has taken on a brick-red color from billions upon billions of microscopic creatures, each of which contains an orange pigment granule. At noon you are still moving through red seas, and when darkness falls the waters shine with an eerie glow from the phosphorescent fires of yet more billions and trillions of these same creatures.

And again you may glimpse not only the abundance but something of the fierce uncompromisingness of sea life when, as you look over the rail and down, down into water of a clear, deep green, suddenly there passes a silver shower of finger-long fishlets. The sun strikes a metallic gleam from their flanks as they streak by, driving deeper into the green depths with the desperate speed of the hunted. Perhaps you never see the hunters, but you sense their presence as you see the gulls hovering, with eager, mewing cries, waiting for the little fish to be driven to the surface.

Or again, perhaps, you may sail for days on end without seeing anything you could recognize as life or the indications of life, day after day of empty water and empty sky, and so you may reasonably conclude that there is no spot on earth so barren of life as the open ocean. But if you had the opportunity to tow a fine-meshed net through the seemingly lifeless water and then to examine the washings of the net, you would find that life is scattered almost everywhere through the surface waters like a fine dust. A cupful of water may contain millions upon millions of diatoms, tiny plant cells, each of them far too small to be seen by the human eye; or it may swarm with an infinitude of animal creatures, none larger than a dust mote, which live on plant cells still smaller than themselves.

If you could be close to the surface waters of the ocean at night, you would realize that then they are alive with myriads of strange creatures never seen by day. They are alive with the moving lamps of small shrimplike beings that spend the daylight hours in the gloom of deep water, and with the shadowy forms of hungry fish and the dark shapes of squid. These things were seen, as few men have seen them, by the Norwegian ethnologist Thor Heyerdahl in the course of one of the most unusual journeys of modern time. In the summer of 1947 Heyerdahl and five companions drifted 4300 miles across the Pacific on a raft of balsa logs, to test a theory that the original inhabitants of Polynesia might have come from South America by raft. For 101 days and nights these men lived practically on the surface of the sea, driven by the trade wind, carried on the strong drift of the Equatorial Current, as much a part of the inexorable westward movement of wind and water as the creatures of the sea. Because of his enviable opportunity to observe the life of the surface while living as an actual part of it for so many weeks, I asked Mr. Heyerdahl about some of his impressions, especially of the sea at night, and he has written me as follows:

'Chiefly at night, but occasionally in broad daylight, a shoal of small squids shot out of the water precisely like flying fish, gliding through the air as much as up to six feet above the surface, until they lost the speed accumulated below water, and fell down helplessly. In their gliding flight with flaps out they were so much like small flying fish at a distance, that we had no idea we saw anything unusual until a live squid flew right into one of the crew and fell down on deck. Almost every night we found one or two on the deck or on the roof of the bamboo hut.

'It was my own definite impression that the marine life in general went deeper down in the daytime than during the nights, and that the darker the night was, the more life we had around us. At two different occasions, a snake-mackerel, Gempylus, never before seen by man except as skeletal remains washed ashore on South America and the Galápagos, came jumping clear out of the water and right up on the raft (once right into the hut). To judge from the huge eyes and the fact that the fish has never before been observed, I am inclined to suspect that it is a deep-sea fish that comes to the surface only at night.

'On dark nights we could see much marine life which we were unable to identify. They seemed to be deep-sea fishes approaching the surface at night. Generally we saw it as vaguely phosphorescent bodies, often the size and shape of a dinner plate, but at least one night in the shape of three immense bodies of irregular and changing shape and dimensions which appeared to exceed those of the raft (KON-TIKI measured about 45 by 18 feet). Apart from these greater bodies, we observed occasionally great quanti-

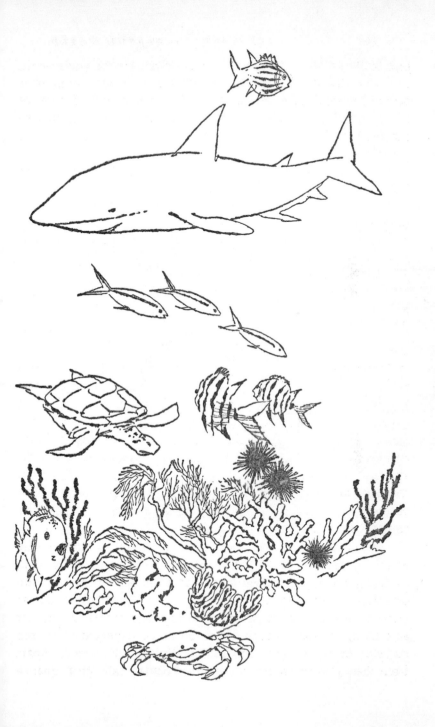

ties of phosphorescent plankton, often containing illuminating copepods up to the size of a millimeter or more.'

With these surface waters, through a series of delicately adjusted, interlocking relationships, the life of all parts of the sea is linked. What happens to a diatom in the upper, sunlit strata of the sea may well determine what happens to a cod lying on a ledge of some rocky canyon a hundred fathoms below, or to a bed of multicolored, gorgeously plumed sea worms carpeting an underlying shoal, or to a prawn creeping over the soft oozes of the sea floor in the blackness of mile-deep water.

The activities of the microscopic vegetables of the sea, of which the diatoms are most important, make the mineral wealth of the water available to the animals. Feeding directly on the diatoms and other groups of minute unicellular algae are the marine protozoa, many crustaceans, the young of crabs, barnacles, sea worms, and fishes. Hordes of the small carnivores, the first link in the chain of flesh eaters, move among these peaceful grazers. There are fierce little dragons half an inch long, the sharp-jawed arrowworms. There are gooseberry-like comb jellies, armed with grasping tentacles, and there are the shrimp-like euphausiids that strain food from the water with their bristly appendages. Since they drift where the currents carry them, with no power or will to oppose that of the sea, this strange community of creatures and the marine plants that sustain them are called 'plankton,' a word derived from the Greek, meaning 'wandering.'

From the plankton the food chains lead on, to the schools of plankton-feeding fishes like the herring, menhaden, and mackerel; to the fish-eating fishes like the bluefish and tuna and sharks; to the pelagic squids that prey on fishes; to the great whales who, according to their species but not according to their size, may live on fishes, on shrimps, or on some of the smallest of the plankton creatures.

Unmarked and trackless though it may seem to us, the surface of the ocean is divided into definite zones, and the pattern of the surface water controls the distribution of its life. Fishes and plankton, whales and squids, birds and sea turtles, all are linked by unbreakable ties to certain kinds of water—to warm water or cold water, to clear or turbid water, to water rich in phosphates or in silicates. For the animals higher in the food chains the ties are less direct; they are bound to water where their food is plentiful, and the food animals are there because the water conditions are right.

The change from zone to zone may be abrupt. It may come upon us unseen, as our ship at night crosses an invisible boundary line. So Charles Darwin on H.M.S. *Beagle* one dark night off the coast of South America crossed from tropical water into that of the cool south. Instantly the vessel was surrounded by numerous seals and penguins, which made such a bedlam of strange noises that the officer on watch was deceived into thinking the ship had, by some miscalculation, run close inshore, and that the sounds he heard were the bellowing of cattle.

To the human senses, the most obvious patterning of the surface waters is indicated by color. The deep blue water of the open sea far from land is the color of emptiness and barrenness; the green water of the coastal areas, with all its varying hues, is the color of life. The sea is blue because the sunlight is reflected back to our eyes from the water molecules or from very minute particles suspended in the sea. In the journey of the light rays into deep water all the red rays and most of the yellow rays of the spectrum have been absorbed, so when the light returns to our eyes it is chiefly the cool blue rays that we see. Where the water is rich in plankton, it loses the glassy transparency that permits this deep penetration of the light rays. The yellow and brown and green hues of the coastal waters are derived from the minute algae and other micro-organisms so abundant there. Seasonal abundance of certain forms containing reddish or brown pigments may cause the 'red water' known from ancient times in many parts of the world, and so common is this condition in some enclosed seas that they owe their names to it—the Red Sea and the Vermillion Sea are examples.

The colors of the sea are only the indirect signs of the presence or absence of conditions needed to support the surface life; other zones, invisible to the eye, are the ones that largely determine where marine creatures may live. For the sea is by no means a uniform solution of water; parts of it are more salty than others, and parts are warmer or colder.

The saltiest ocean water in the world is that of the Red Sea, where the burning sun and the fierce heat of the atmosphere produce such rapid evaporation that the salt content is 40 parts per thousand. The Sargasso Sea, an area of high air temperatures, receiving no inflow of river water or melting ice because of its remoteness from land, is the saltiest part of the Atlantic, which in turn is the saltiest of the oceans. The polar seas, as one would expect, are the least salty, because they are constantly being diluted by rain, snow, and melting ice. Along the Atlantic coast of the United States, the salinity range from about 33 parts per thousand off Cape Cod to about 36 off Florida is a difference easily perceptible to the senses of human bathers.

Ocean temperatures vary from about 28° F. in polar seas to 96° in the Persian Gulf, which contains the hottest ocean water in the world. To creatures of the sea, which with few exceptions must match in their own bodies the temperature of the surrounding water, this range is tremendous, and change of temperature is probably the most important single condition that controls the distribution of marine animals.

The beautiful reef corals are a perfect example of the way the inhabitable areas for any particular class of creatures may be established by temperatures. If you took a map of the world and drew a line 30° north of the Equator and another 30° south of it, you would have outlined in general the waters where reef corals are found at the present time. It is true that the remains of ancient coral reefs have been discovered in arctic waters, but this means that in some past ages the climate of these northern seas was tropical. The calcareous structure of the coral reef can be fashioned only in water at least as warm as 70° Fahrenheit. We would have to make one northward extension of our map, where the Gulf Stream carries water warm enough for corals to Bermuda, at 32° north latitude. On the other hand, within our tropical belt, we would have to erase large areas on the west coasts of South

America and Africa, where upwelling of cold water from lower ocean levels prevents the growth of corals. Most of the east coast of Florida has no coral reefs because of a cool inshore current, running southward between the coast and the Gulf Stream.

As between tropical and polar regions, the differences in the kinds and abundance of life are tremendous. The warm temperatures of the tropics speed up the processes of reproduction and growth, so that many generations are produced in the time required to bring one to maturity in cold seas. There is more opportunity for genetic mutations to be produced within a given time; hence the bewildering variety of tropical life. Yet in any species there are far fewer individuals than in the colder zones, where the mineral content of the water is richer, and there are no dense swarms of surface plankton, like the copepods of the Arctic. The pelagic, or free-swimming forms of the tropics live deeper than those of the colder regions, and so there is less food for large surface-feeders. In the tropics, therefore, the sea birds do not compare in abundance with the clouds of shearwaters, fulmars, auks, whalebirds, albatrosses, and other birds seen over far northern or far southern fishing grounds.

In the cold-water communities of the polar seas, fewer of the animals have swimming larvae. Generation after generation settle down near the parents, so that large areas of bottom may be covered with the descendants of a very few animals. In the Barents Sea a research vessel once brought up more than a ton of one of the siliceous sponges at a single haul, and enormous patches of a single species of annelid worm carpet the east coast of Spitsbergen. Copepods and swimming snails fill the surface waters of the cold seas, and lure the herring and the mackerel, the flocks of sea birds, the whales, and the seals.

In the tropics, then, sea life is intense, vivid, and infinitely varied. In cold seas life proceeds at a pace slowed by the icy water in which it exists, but the mineral richness of these waters (largely a result of seasonal overturn and consequent mixing) makes possible the enormous abundance of the forms that inhabit them. For a good many years it has been said categorically that the total productivity of the colder temperate and polar seas is far greater than the tropical. Now it is becoming plain that there are important exceptions to this statement. In certain tropical and subtropical waters, there are areas where the sheer abundance of life rivals the Grand Banks or the Barents Sea or any antarctic whaling ground. Perhaps the best examples are the Humboldt Current, off the west coast of South America, and the Benguela Current, off the west coast of Africa. In both currents, upwelling of cold, mineral-laden water from deeper layers of the sea provides the fertilizing elements to sustain the great food chains.

And wherever two currents meet, especially if they differ sharply in temperature or salinity, there are zones of great turbulence and unrest, with water sinking or rising up from the depths and with shifting eddies and foam lines at the surface. At such places the richness and abundance of marine life reveals itself most strikingly. This changing life, seen as his ship cut across the pathways of the great currents of the Pacific and the Atlantic, was described with vivid detail by S. C. Brooks:

'Within a few degrees of the equator, the scattered cumulus clouds become thicker and grayer, a confused swell makes up, rain squalls come and go, and birds appear. At first there is only a greater abundance of storm petrels, with here and there petrels of other kinds hunting along utterly indifferent to the ship, or small groups of tropic birds flying along with the ship, off to one side or high overhead. Then scattered groups of various petrels appear, and finally for an hour or two there are birds on every hand. If one is not too far from land, a few hundred miles perhaps, as in the case of the south equatorial drift north of the Marquesas, one may also see multitudes of sooty or crested terns. Occasionally one sees the grayish blue form of a shark gliding along, or a big purplish-brown hammerhead lazily twisting around as though trying to get a better view of the ship. Flying fish, while not so closely localized as the birds, are breaking the water every few seconds, and bewitch the beholder by their myriad sizes, shapes, and antics, and their bewildering patterns and shades of deep brown, opal blue, yellow and purple. Then the sun comes out again, the sea takes on its deep tropical blue, the birds become more and more scarce, and gradually, as the ship moves on, the ocean resumes its desert aspect.

'If it were daylight all the time, this same sequence might be seen in a more or less striking fashion twice or perhaps even three or four times. Inquiry soon reveals that this sequence marks the time of passing the edge of one of the great currents . . .

'In the North Atlantic ship lanes the same play is staged with different actors. Instead of the equatorial currents there are the Gulf Stream and its continuation, the North Atlantic Drift, and the Arctic Current; instead of confused swell and squalls of rain there are slicks and fogs. Tropic-birds are replaced by jaegers and skuas; and different species of the petrel group, usually here spoken of as shearwaters and fulmars, are flying or swimming about, often in great flocks . . . Here, too, perhaps, one sees less of sharks and more of porpoise racing with the cut-water or doggedly hurrying, school after school, toward some unguessable objective. The flashing black and white of the young orcas, or the distant sudden spurt and lazy drift of a whale's spouting, lend life to the water, as do the antics of flying fish, distant though they be from their traditional home in the tropics . . . One may pass from the blue water of the Stream, with floating gulf weed (Sargassum), and perhaps here and there the iridescent float of a Portuguese man-of-war, into the gray-green water of the Arctic Current with its thousands of jelly fish, and in a few hours back again into the Stream. Each time, at the margin, one is likely to see the surface display of that abundance of life which has made the Grand Banks one of the great fisheries of the world.'

The mid-ocean regions, bounded by the currents that sweep around the ocean basins, are in general the deserts of the sea. There are few birds and few surface-feeding fishes, and indeed there is little surface plankton to attract them. The life of these regions is largely confined to deep water. The Sargasso Sea is an exception, not matched in the anticyclonic centers of other ocean basins. It is so different from any other place on earth that it may well be considered a definite geographic region. A line drawn from the mouth of Chesapeake Bay to Gibraltar would skirt its northern border; another from Haiti to Dakar would mark its southern boundary. It lies all about Bermuda and extends more than half-way across the Atlantic, its entire area being roughly as large as the United States. The Sargasso, with all its legendary terrors for sailing ships, is a creation of the great currents of the North Atlantic that encircle it and bring into it the millions of tons of floating sargassum weed from which the place derives its name, and all the weird assemblage of animals that live in the weed.

The Sargasso is a place forgotten by the winds, undisturbed by the strong flow of waters that girdle it as with a river. Under the seldom-clouded skies, its waters are warm and heavy with salt. Separated widely from coastal rivers and from polar ice, there is no inflow of fresh water to dilute its saltiness; the only influx is of saline water from the adjacent currents, especially from the Gulf Stream or North Atlantic Current as it crosses from America to Europe. And with the little, inflowing streams of surface water come the plants and animals that for months or years have drifted in the Gulf Stream.

The sargassum weeds are brown algae belonging to several species. Quantities of the weeds live attached to reefs or rocky outcroppings off the coasts of the West Indies and Florida. Many of the plants are torn away by storms, especially during the hurricane season. They are picked up by the Gulf Stream and are drifted northward. With the weeds go, as involuntary passengers, many small fishes, crabs, shrimps, and innumerable larvae of assorted species of marine creatures, whose home had been the coastal banks of sargassum weed.

Curious things happen to the animals that have ridden on the sargassum weed into a new home. Once they lived near the sea's edge, a few feet or a few fathoms below the surface, but never far above a firm bottom. They knew the rhythmic movements of waves and tides. They could leave the shelter of the weeds at will and creep or swim about over the bottom in search of food.

Now, in the middle of the ocean, they are in a new world. The bottom lies two or three miles below them. Those who are poor swimmers must cling to the weed, which now represents a life raft, supporting them above the abyss. Over the ages since their ancestors came here, some species have developed special organs of attachment, either for themselves or for their eggs, so that they may not sink into the cold, dark water far below. The flying fish make nests of the weed to contain their eggs, which bear an amazing resemblance to the sargassum floats or 'berries.'

Indeed, many of the little marine beasts of the weedy jungle seem to be playing an elaborate game of disguise in which each is camouflaged to hide it from the others. The Sargasso sea slug— a snail without a shell—has a soft, shapeless brown body spotted with dark-edged circles and fringed with flaps and folds of skin, so that as it creeps over the weed in search of prey it can scarcely be distinguished from the vegetation. One of the fiercest carnivores of the place, the sargassum fish Pterophryne, has copied with utmost fidelity the branching fronds of the weed, its golden berries, its rich brown color, and even the white dots of encrusting worm tubes. All these elaborate bits of mimicry are indications of the fierce internecine wars of the Sargasso jungles, which go on without quarter and without mercy for the weak or the unwary.

In the science of the sea there has been a long-standing controversy about the origin of the drifting weeds of the Sargasso Sea. Some have held that the supply is maintained by weeds recently torn away from coastal beds; others say that the rather limited sargassum fields of the West Indies and Florida cannot possibly supply the immense area of the Sargasso. They believe that we find here a self-perpetuating community of plants that have become adapted to life in the open sea, needing no roots or hold-fasts for attachment, and able to propagate vegetatively. Probably there is truth in both ideas. New plants do come in each year in small numbers, and now cover an immense area because of their very long life once they have reached this quiet central region of the Atlantic.

It takes about half a year for the plants torn from West Indian shores to reach the northern border of the Sargasso, perhaps several years for them to be carried into the inner parts of this area.

Meanwhile, some have been swept onto the shores of North America by storms, others have been killed by cold during the passage from offshore New England across the Atlantic, where the Gulf Stream comes into contact with waters from the Arctic. For the plants that reach the calm of the Sargasso, there is virtual immortality. A. E. Parr of the American Museum has recently suggested that the individual plants may live, some for decades, others for centuries, according to their species. It might well be that some of the very weeds you would see if you visited the place today were seen by Columbus and his men. Here, in the heart of the Atlantic, the weed drifts endlessly, growing, reproducing vegetatively by a process of fragmentation. Apparently almost the only plants that die are the ones that drift into unfavorable conditions around the edges of the Sargasso or are picked up by outward-moving currents.

Such losses are balanced, or possibly a little more than balanced, by the annual addition of weeds from distant coasts. It must have taken eons of time to accumulate the present enormous quantities of weed, which Parr estimates as about 10 million tons. But this, of course, is distributed over so large an area that most of the Sargasso is open water. The dense fields of weeds waiting to entrap a vessel never existed except in the imaginations of sailors, and the gloomy hulks of vessels doomed to endless drifting in the clinging weed are only the ghosts of things that never were.

Night

by SARA TEASDALE

Stars over snow,
   And in the west a planet
Swinging below a star—
   Look for a lovely thing and you will find it,
It is not far—
   It never will be far.

A Taste of . . .

The Pleasures

of

Great Books

Robinson Crusoe

EXPLORING THE ISLAND

by DANIEL DEFOE

When you meet Robinson Crusoe in this chapter, his ship
has just been wrecked during a violent hurricane, and he is now
the sole survivor on an uninhabited island in the Pacific off the
coast of South America. Defoe is supposed to have got the idea
for his story from the actual experience of a man who was shipwrecked off the coast of Chile and lived on an island by himself
for four years. The book was written for adults and was immediately popular with them, but children quickly took it over as
their own. The theme of a person thrown completely on his own
resources on a desert island is in itself immensely appealing to
youngsters. And the way that Crusoe manages the daily details of his struggle for existence allows any young reader to
picture himself as Robinson Crusoe—working out the problems
of building his hut, figuring out how to make bread out of corn,
or clumsily trying to bake a simple clay pot in the fire. Crusoe has
many adventures, but the special fascination of the story lies in
learning exactly how Crusoe did everything. Because Robinson
Crusoe was so enormously successful it has been followed by many
stories of castaways in the more than 200 years since it was written. But this masterpiece of human invention has never been surpassed as the best desert island story.

When I waked it was broad day, the weather clear, and the storm
abated, so that the sea did not rage and swell as before; but that

which surprised me most was, that the ship was lifted off in the night from the sand where she lay by the swelling of the tide, and was driven up almost as far as the rock which I first mentioned, where I had been so bruised by the dashing me against it. This being within about a mile from the shore where I was, and the ship seeming to stand upright still, I wished myself on board, that, at least, I might save some necessary things for my use.

When I came down from my apartment in the tree, I looked about me again, and the first thing I found was the boat, which lay as the wind and the sea had tossed her, up upon the land, about two miles on my right hand. I walked as far as I could upon the shore to have got to her, but found a neck or inlet of water between me and the boat, which was about half a mile broad; so I came back for the present, being more intent upon getting at the ship, where I hoped to find something for my present subsistence.

A little after noon I found the sea very calm, and the tide ebbed so far out that I could come within a quarter of a mile of the ship, and here I found a fresh renewing of my grief; for I saw evidently, that if we had kept on board, we had been all safe, that is to say, we had all got safe on shore, and I had not been so miserable as to be left entirely destitute of all comfort and company, as I now was. This forced tears from my eyes again, but as there was little relief in that, I resolved, if possible, to get to the ship, so I pulled off my clothes, for the weather was hot to extremity, and took the water; but when I came to the ship, my difficulty was still greater to know how to get on board, for as she lay a-ground, and high out of the water, there was nothing within my reach to lay hold of. I swam round her twice, and the second time I spied a small piece of rope, which I wondered I did not see at first, hang down by the fore-chains so low as that with great difficulty I got hold of it, and by the help of that rope got up into the forecastle of the ship.

Here I found that the ship was bulged, and had a great deal of water in her hold, but that she lay so on the side of a bank of hard sand, or rather earth, that her stern lay lifted up upon the bank, and her head low almost to the water. By this means all her quarter was free, and all that was in that part was dry; for you may be sure my first work was to search and to see what was spoiled and what was free; and first I found that all the ship's provisions were dry and untouched by the water; and being very well disposed to eat, I went to the bread-room and filled my pockets with biscuit, and eat it as I went about other things, for I had no time to lose. I also found some rum in the great cabin, of which I took a large dram, and which I had indeed need enough of to spirit me for what was before me. Now I wanted nothing but a boat to furnish myself with many things which I foresaw would be very necessary to me.

It was in vain to sit still and wish for what was not to be had, and this extremity roused my application. We had several spare yards, and two or three large spars of wood, and a spare top-mast or two in the ship. I resolved to fall to work with these, and flung as many of them overboard as I could manage for their weight, tying every one with a rope that they might not drive away. When this was done I went down the ship's side, and pulling them to me, I tied four of them fast together at both ends, as well as I could, in the form of a raft, and laying two or three short pieces of plank upon them cross-ways, I found I could walk upon it very well, but that it was not able to bear any great weight, the pieces being too light. So I went to work, and with the carpenter's saw I cut a spare top-mast into three lengths, and added them to my raft, with a great deal of labour and pains: but hope of furnishing myself with necessaries encouraged me to go beyond what I should have been able to have done upon another occasion.

My raft was now strong enough to bear any reasonable weight; my next care was what to load it with, and how to preserve what I laid upon it from the surf of the sea; but I was not long considering this. I first laid all the planks or boards upon it that I could get, and having considered well what I most wanted, I first got three of the seamen's chests, which I had broken open and emptied, and lowered them down upon my raft. The first of these I filled with provisions, namely, bread, rice, three Dutch cheeses, five pieces of dried goat's flesh, which we lived much upon, and a little remainder of European corn which had been laid by for some fowls which we brought to sea with us, but the fowls were killed. There had been some barley and wheat together; but, to my great disappointment, I found afterwards that the rats had eaten or spoiled it all. As for liquors, I found several cases of bottles belonging to our skipper, in which were some cordial waters, and in all about five or six gallons of arrack; these I stowed by themselves, there being no need to put them into the chest, nor no room for them.

While I was doing this, I found the tide began to flow, though very calm; and I had the mortification to see my coat, shirt, and waistcoat, which I had left on shore upon the sand, swim away; as for my breeches, which were only linen and open-kneed, I swam on board in them and my stockings. However, this put me upon rummaging for clothes, of which I found enough, but took no more than I wanted for present use; for I had other things which my eye was more upon——as, first, tools to work with on shore; and it was after long searching that I found out the carpenter's chest, which was indeed a very useful prize to me, and much more valuable than a ship-loading of gold would have been at that time. I got it down to my raft, even whole as it was, without losing time to look into it, for I knew in general what it contained.

My next care was for some ammunition and arms. There were two very good fowling-pieces in the great cabin, and two pistols; these I secured first, with some powder-horns, and a small bag of shot, and two old rusty swords. I knew there were three barrels of powder in the ship, but knew not where our gunner had stowed them; but with much search I found them, two of them dry and good, the third had taken water. Those two I got to my raft, with the arms; and now I thought myself pretty well freighted, and began to think how I should get to shore with them, having neither sail, oar, nor rudder, and the least cap-full of wind would have overset all my navigation.

I had three encouragements: a smooth, calm sea, the tide rising and setting into the shore, and what little wind there was blew me towards the land. And thus, having found two or three broken oars belonging to the boat, and besides the tools which were in the chest, I found two saws, an axe and a hammer, and with this cargo I put to sea. For a mile, or thereabouts, my raft went very well, only that I found it drive a little distant from the place where I had landed before, by which I perceived that there was some in-draft of the water, and consequently I hoped to find some creek or river there, which I might make use of as a port to get to land with my cargo.

As I imagined, so it was. There appeared before me a little open-ing of the land, and I found a strong current of the tide set into it, so I guided my raft as well as I could to keep in the middle of the stream. But here I had like to have suffered a second shipwreck, which, if I had, I think verily would have broke my heart; for knowing nothing of the coast, my raft run a-ground at one end of it upon a shoal, and not being a-ground at the other end, it wanted but a little that all my cargo had slipped off towards that end that was afloat, and so fallen into the water. I did my utmost, by set-ting my back against the chests, to keep them in their places, but could not thrust off the raft with all my strength, neither durst I stir from the posture I was in; but holding up the chests with all my might, stood in that manner near half an hour, in which time the rising of the water brought me a little more upon a level. And a little after, the water still rising, my raft floated again, and I thrust her off with the oar I had into the channel; and then driving up higher, I at length found myself in the mouth of a little river, with land on both sides, and a strong current or tide running up. I looked on both sides for a proper place to get to shore, for I was not willing to be driven too high up the river, hoping in time to see some ship at sea, and therefore resolved to place myself as near the coast as I could.

At length I spied a little cove on the right shore of the creek, to which, with great pain and difficulty, I guided my raft, and at last got so near, as that, reaching ground with my oar, I could thrust her directly in. But here I had liked to have dipped all my cargo in the sea again; for that shore lying pretty steep, that is to say slop-ing, there was no place to land, but where one end of the float, if it run on shore, would lie so high, and the other sink lower as be-

fore, that it would endanger my cargo again. All that I could do, was to wait till the tide was at the highest, keeping the raft with my oar like an anchor to hold the side of it fast to the shore, near a flat piece of ground, which I expected the water would flow over; and so it did. As soon as I found water enough (for my raft drew about a foot of water), I thrust her on upon that flat piece of ground, and there fastened or moored her by sticking my two broken oars into the ground; one on one side near one end, and one on the other side near the other end. And thus I lay till the water ebbed away, and left my raft and all my cargo safe on shore.

My next work was to view the country, and seek a proper place for my habitation, and where to stow my goods to secure them from whatever might happen. Where I was I yet knew not; whether on the continent or on an island, whether inhabited or not inhabited, whether in danger of wild beasts or not. There was a hill not above a mile from me, which rose up very steep and high, and which seemed to over-top some other hills which lay as in a ridge from it northward. I took out one of the fowling-pieces, and one of the pistols, and an horn of powder, and thus armed, I travelled for discovery up to the top of that hill; where, after I had with great labour and difficulty got to the top, I saw my fate to my great affliction, namely, that I was in an island environed every way with the sea, no land to be seen, except some rocks which lay a great way off, and two small islands less than this, which lay about three leagues to the west.

I found also that the island I was in was barren, and, as I saw good reason to believe, uninhabited, except by wild beasts, of whom however I saw none; yet I saw abundance of fowls, but knew not their kinds, neither when I killed them could I tell what was fit for food, and what not. At my coming back, I shot at a great bird, which I saw sitting upon a tree on the side of a great wood—I believe it was the first gun that had been fired there since the creation of the world. I had no sooner fired, but from all parts of the wood there arose an innumerable number of fowls of many sorts, making a confused screaming, and crying every one according to his usual note; but not one of them of any kind that I knew.

As for the creature I killed, I took it to be a kind of hawk, its colour and beak resembling it, but had no talons or claws more than common; its flesh was carrion and fit for nothing.

Contented with this discovery, I came back to my raft, and fell to work to bring my cargo on shore, which took me up the rest of that day. And what to do with myself at night I knew not, nor indeed where to rest; for I was afraid to lie down on the ground, not knowing but some wild beast might devour me, though, as I afterwards found, there was really no need for those fears.

However, as well as I could, I barricaded myself round with the chests and boards that I had brought on shore, and made a kind of a hut for that night's lodging. As for food, I yet saw not which way to supply myself, except that I had seen two or three creatures, like hares, run out of the wood where I shot the bird.

I now began to consider that I might yet get a great many things out of the ship which would be useful to me, and particularly some of the rigging and sails, and such other things as might come to land, and I resolved to make another voyage to board the vessel, if possible. And as I knew that the first storm that blew must necessarily break her all in pieces, I resolved to set all other things apart till I got everything out of the ship that I could get. Then I called a council, that is to say, in my thoughts, whether I should take back the raft. But this appeared impracticable, so I resolved to go as before, when the tide was down, and I did so, only that I stripped before I went from my hut, having nothing on but a chequered shirt, and a pair of linen trousers, and a pair of pumps on my feet.

I got on board the ship, as before, and prepared a second raft, and having had experience of the first, I neither made this so unwieldy, nor loaded it so hard. Yet I brought away several things very useful to me; as first, in the carpenter's stores, I found two or three bags full of nails and spikes, a great screw jack, a dozen or two of hatchets, and above all, that most useful thing called a grindstone. All these I secured, together with several things belonging to the gunner, particularly two or three iron crows, and two barrels of musket-bullets, seven muskets, and another fowling-piece, with some small quantity of powder more, a large bag full of small shot, and a great roll of sheet lead. But this last was so heavy I could not hoist it up to get it over the ship's side.

Besides these things, I took all the men's clothes that I could find, and a spare fore-top-sail, hammock, and some bedding; and with this I loaded my second raft, and brought them all safe on shore, to my very great comfort.

I was under some apprehensions during my absence from the land, that at least my provisions might be devoured on shore; but when I came back, I found no sign of any visitor, only there sat a creature like a wild cat upon one of the chests, which, when I came towards it, ran away a little distance, and then stood still. She sat very composed and unconcerned, and looked full in my face, as if she had a mind to be acquainted with me. I presented my gun at her, but as she did not understand it, she was perfectly unconcerned at it, nor did she offer to stir away. Upon which I tossed her a bit of biscuit, though by the way I was not very free of it, for my store was not great. However, I spared her a bit, I say, and she went to it, smelled it, ate it, and looked, as pleased, for more; but I thanked her, and could spare no more, so she marched off.

Having got my second cargo on shore, though I was fain to open the barrels of powder, and bring them by parcels (for they were too heavy, being large casks), I went to work to make me a little tent with the sail and some poles which I cut for that purpose; and into this tent I brought everything that I knew would spoil, either with rain or sun, and I piled all the empty chests and casks up in a circle round the tent, to fortify it from any sudden attempt, either from man or beast.

When I had done this, I blocked up the door of the tent with some boards within, and an empty chest set up on-end without; and spreading one of the beds on the ground, laying my two pistols just at my head, and my gun at length by me, I went to bed for the first time, and slept very quietly all night, for I was very weary and heavy. For the night before I had slept little, and had laboured very hard all day, as well to fetch all those things from the ship as to get them on shore.

I had the biggest magazine of all kinds now that ever were laid up, I believe, for one man, but I was not satisfied still; for while the ship sat upright in that posture, I thought I ought to get everything out of her that I could. So every day at low water I went on board, and brought away something or other; but particularly the third time I went, I brought away as much of the rigging as I could, as also all the small ropes and rope-twine I could get, with a piece of spare canvas, which was to mend the sails upon occasion, and the barrel of wet gunpowder. In a word, I brought away all the sails first and last, only that I was fain to cut them in pieces, and bring as much at a time as I could; for they were no more useful to be sails, but as mere canvas only.

But that which comforted me more still, was that, last of all, after I had made five or six such voyages as these, and thought I had nothing more to expect from the ship that was worth my meddling with; I say, after all this, I found a great hogshead of bread, and three large runlets of rum or spirits, and a box of sugar, and a barrel of fine flour. This was surprising to me, because I had given over expecting any more provisions, except what was spoiled by the water. I soon emptied the hogshead of that bread, and wrapped it up, parcel by parcel, in pieces of the sails, which I cut out; and, in a word, I got all this safe on shore also.

The next day I made another voyage; and now, having plundered the ship of what was portable and fit to hand out, I began with the cables; and cutting the great cable into pieces, such as I could move, I got two cables and a hawser on shore, with all the iron-work I could get; and having cut down the spritsail-yard, and the mizen-yard, and everything I could to make a large raft, I loaded it with all those heavy goods and came away. But my good luck began now to leave me. For this raft was so unwieldy and so overladen, that after I had entered the little cove, where I had landed the rest of my goods, not being able to guide it so handily as I did the other, it overset, and threw me and all my cargo into the water. As for myself it was no great harm, for I was near the shore; but as to my cargo, it was great part of it lost, especially the iron, which I expected would have been of great use to me. However, when the tide was out, I got most of the pieces of cable ashore, and some of the iron, though with infinite labour; for I was fain to dip for it into the water—a work which fatigued me very much. After this, I went every day on board and brought away what I could get.

I had been now thirteen days on shore, and had been eleven times on board the ship, in which time I had brought away all that one pair of hands could be well supposed capable to bring; though I believe verily, had the calm weather held, I should have brought away the whole ship, piece by piece. But preparing the twelfth time to go on board, I found the wind begin to rise; however, at low water I went on board, and though I thought I had rummaged the cabin so effectually, as that nothing more could be found, yet I discovered a locker with drawers in it, in one of which I found two or three razors, and one pair of large scissors, with some ten or a dozen of good knives and forks. In another I found about thirty-six pounds value in money, some European coin, some Brasil, some pieces of eight, some gold, some silver.

I smiled to myself at the sight of this money. "O Drug!" said I, aloud, "what art thou good for? thou art not worth to me, no, not the taking off the ground. One of these knives is worth all this heap. I have no manner of use for thee, even remain where thou art and go to the bottom, as a creature whose life is not worth saving." However, upon second thoughts, I took it away, and wrapping all this in a piece of canvas, I began to think of making another raft. But while I was preparing this, I found the sky overcast, and the wind began to rise, and in a quarter of an hour it blew a fresh gale from the shore. It presently occurred to me, that it was in vain to pretend to make a raft with the wind off shore, and that it was my business to be gone before the tide of flood began, otherwise I might not be able to reach the shore at all. Accordingly I let myself down into the water, and swam across the channel, which lay between the ship and the sands, and even that with difficulty enough, partly with the weight of things I had about me, and partly the roughness of the water; for the wind rose very hastily, and before it was quite high water it blew a storm.

But I was gotten home to my little tent, where I lay with all my wealth about me very secure. It blew very hard all that night; and in the morning when I looked out, behold no more ship was to be seen. I was a little surprised, but recovered myself with this satisfactory reflection; namely, that I had lost no time, nor abated any diligence, to get everything out of her that could be useful to me; and that indeed there was little left in her that I was able to bring away, if I had had more time.

I now gave over any more thoughts of the ship, or of any thing out of her, except what might drive on shore from her wreck, as indeed divers pieces of her afterwards did; but those things were of small use to me.

My thoughts were now wholly employed about securing myself against either savages (if any should appear) or wild beasts, if any were in the island; and I had many thoughts of the method how to do this, and what kind of dwelling to make; whether I should make me a cave in the earth, or a tent upon the earth; and, in short, I resolved upon both, of the manner, and description of which it may not be improper to give an account.

I soon found the place I was in was not for my settlement, particularly because it was upon a low moorish ground near the sea, and I believed would not be wholesome, and more particularly because there was no fresh water near it, so I resolved to find a more healthy and more convenient spot of ground.

I consulted several things in my situation which I found would be proper for me. Health, and fresh water, I just now mentioned; shelter from the heat of the sun; security from ravenous creatures, whether man or beast; a view to the sea, that if God sent any ship in sight, I might not lose any advantage for my deliverance, of which I was not willing to banish all my expectation yet.

In search of a place proper for this, I found a little plain on the side of a rising hill, whose front towards this little plain was steep as a house-side, so that nothing could come down upon me from the top. On the side of this rock there was a hollow place, worn a little way in, like the entrance or door of a cave: but there was not really any cave or way into the rock at all.

On the flat of the green, just before this hollow place, I resolved to pitch my tent. This plain was not above an hundred yards broad, and about twice as long, and lay like a green before my door, and at the end it descended irregularly every way down into the low grounds by the sea-side. It was on the N.N.W. side of the hill, so that I was sheltered from the heat every day, till it came to a W. and by S. sun, or thereabouts, which in those countries is near the setting.

Before I set up my tent, I drew a half circle before the hollow place, which took in about ten yards in its semi-diameter, from the rock, and twenty yards in its diameter, from its beginning and ending. In this half circle I pitched two rows of strong stakes, driving them into the ground till they stood very firm, like piles, the biggest end being out of the ground about five foot and a half, and sharpened on the top; the two rows did not stand above six inches from one another.

Then I took the pieces of cable which I had cut in the ship, and laid them in rows one upon another, within the circle between these two rows of stakes, up to the top, placing other stakes in the inside, leaning against them, about two foot and a half high, like a spur to a post. And this fence was so strong, that neither man nor beast could get into it or over it. This cost me a great deal of time and labour, especially to cut the piles in the woods, bring them to the place, and drive them into the earth.

The entrance into this place I made to be not by a door, but by a short ladder to go over the top; which ladder, when I was in, I lifted over after me. And so I was completely fenced in and fortified, as I thought, from all the world, and consequently slept secure in the night, which otherwise I could not have done; though, as it appeared afterward, there was no need of all this caution from the enemies that I apprehended danger from.

David Copperfield

MY AUNT MAKES UP HER MIND ABOUT ME

by CHARLES DICKENS

Of all the children in Dickens' novels, David Copperfield was closest to Dickens as he remembered himself as a small boy. Before this chapter opens, we have learned why David is so anxious for his aunt to let him stay with her: after his mother's death, he had been sent by his harsh stepfather, Mr. Murdstone, to work in a warehouse in London. The young boy finally runs away from his miserable life there to his great-aunt, Betsy Trotwood, whose eccentric exterior hides the kindest of hearts. Dickens is renowned for his striking character types, and David Copperfield contains some of the most famous of them. The amiable but balmy Mr. Dick, the fawning Uriah Heep, the ever-hopeful Micawber, and Barkis who is always "willing", all these have become symbols of the character quirks they represent. In David Copperfield Dickens has created a rich novel which once read can never be forgotten.

On going down in the morning, I found my aunt musing so profoundly over the breakfast table, with her elbow on the tray, that the contents of the urn had overflowed the teapot, and were laying the whole table cloth under water, when my entrance put her meditations to flight. I felt sure that I had been the subject of her reflections, and was more than ever anxious to know her intentions towards me. Yet I dared not express my anxiety, lest it should give her offence.

My eyes, however, not being so much under control as my

tongue, were attracted towards my aunt very often during break-fast. I never could look at her for a few moments together but I found her looking at me—in an odd thoughtful manner, as if I were an immense way off, instead of being on the other side of the small round table. When she had finished her breakfast, my aunt very deliberately leaned back in her chair, knitted her brows, folded her arms, and contemplated me at her leisure, with such a fixedness of attention that I was quite overpowered by embar-rassment. Not having as yet finished my own breakfast, I at-tempted to hide my confusion by proceeding with it; but my knife tumbled over my fork, my fork tripped up my knife, I chipped bits of bacon a surprising height into the air instead of cutting them for my own eating, and choked myself with my tea, which per-sisted in going the wrong way instead of the right one, until I gave in altogether, and sat blushing under my aunt's close scru-tiny.

"Hallo!" said my aunt, after a long time.

I looked up, and met her sharp bright glance respectfully.

"I have written to him," said my aunt.

"To——?"

"To your father-in-law," [stepfather] said my aunt. "I have sent him a letter that I'll trouble him to attend to, or he and I will fall out, I can tell him!"

"Does he know where I am, aunt?" I inquired, alarmed.

"I have told him," said my aunt, with a nod.

"Shall I—be—given up to him?" I faltered.

"I don't know," said my aunt. "We shall see."

"Oh! I can't think what I shall do," I exclaimed, "if I have to go back to Mr. Murdstone!"

"I don't know anything about it," said my aunt, shaking her head. "I can't say, I am sure. We shall see."

The anxiety I underwent in the interval which necessarily elapsed before a reply could be received to her letter to Mr. Murdstone was extreme; but I made an endeavour to suppress it, and to be as agreeable as I could in a quiet way both to my aunt and Mr. Dick. The latter and I would have gone out to fly the great kite; but that I had still no other clothes than the anything but ornamental garments with which I had been decorated on the first day, and which confined me to the house except for an hour after dark, when my aunt, for my health's sake, paraded me up and down on the cliff outside before going to bed. At length the reply from Mr. Murdstone came, and my aunt informed me, to my infinite terror, that he was coming to speak to her himself on the next day. On the next day, still bundled up in my curious habiliments, I sat counting the time, flushed and heated by the conflict of sinking hopes and rising fears within me, and waiting to be startled by the sight of the gloomy face, whose non-arrival startled me every minute.

My aunt was a little more imperious and stern than usual, but I observed no other token of her preparing herself to receive the visitor so much dreaded by me. She sat at work in the window, and I sat by, with my thoughts running astray on all possible and impossible results of Mr. Murdstone's visit, until pretty late in the afternoon. Our dinner had been indefinitely postponed; but it was growing so late, that my aunt had ordered it to be got ready, when she gave a sudden alarm of "donkeys!" and to my consternation and amazement, I beheld Miss Murdstone, on a side-saddle, ride deliberately over the sacred piece of green, and stop in front of the house, looking about her.

"Go along with you!" cried my aunt, shaking her head and her fist at the window. "You have no business there. How dare you trespass? Go along! Oh, you bold-faced thing!"

My aunt was so exasperated by the coolness with which Miss Murdstone looked about her, that I really believe she was motionless, and unable for the moment to dart out according to custom. I seized the opportunity to inform her who it was, and that the gentleman now coming near the offender (for the way up was very steep, and he had dropped behind) was Mr. Murdstone himself.

"I don't care who it is!" cried my aunt, still shaking her head, and gesticulating anything but welcome from the bow-window. "I won't be trespassed upon. I won't allow it. Go away! Janet, turn him round. Lead him off!" and I saw, from behind my aunt, a sort of hurried battle-piece, in which the donkey stood resisting everybody, with all his four legs planted different ways, while Janet tried to pull him round by the bridle, Mr. Murdstone tried to lead him on, Miss Murdstone struck at Janet with a parasol, and several boys, who had come to see the engagement, shouted vigorously. But my aunt, suddenly descrying among them the young malefactor who was the donkey's guardian, and who was one of the most inveterate offenders against her, though hardly in his teens, rushed out to the scene of action, pounced upon him, captured him, dragged him, with his jacket over his head and his heels grinding the ground, into the garden, and, calling upon Janet to fetch the constables and justices, that he might be taken, tried, and executed on the spot, held him at bay there. This part of the business, however, did not last long; for the young rascal, being expert at a variety of feints and dodges, of which my aunt had no conception, soon went whooping away, leaving some deep impressions of his nailed boots in the flower-beds, and taking his donkey in triumph with him.

Miss Murdstone, during the latter portion of the contest, had dismounted, and was now waiting with her brother at the bottom of the steps until my aunt should be at leisure to receive them. My aunt, a little ruffled by the combat, marched past them into the house with great dignity, and took no notice of their presence, until they were announced by Janet.

"Shall I go away, aunt?" I asked, trembling.

"No, sir," said my aunt; "certainly not!" With which she pushed me into a corner near her, and fenced me in with a chair, as if it were a prison or a bar of justice. This position I continued to occupy during the whole interview, and from it I now saw Mr. and Miss Murdstone enter the room.

"Oh!" said my aunt, "I was not aware at first to whom I had the pleasure of objecting. But I don't allow anybody to ride over that turf. I make no exceptions. I don't allow anybody to do it."

"Your regulation is rather awkward to strangers," said Miss Murdstone.

"Is it?" said my aunt.

Mr. Murdstone seemed afraid of a renewal of hostilities, and interposing began,—

"Miss Trotwood!"

"I beg your pardon," observed my aunt, with a keen look. "You are the Mr. Murdstone who married the widow of my late nephew, David Copperfield, of Blunderstone Rookery?—Though why Rookery, *I* don't know!"

"I am," said Mr. Murdstone.

"You'll excuse my saying, sir," returned my aunt, "that I think it would have been a much better and happier thing if you had left that poor child alone."

"I so far agree with what Miss Trotwood has remarked," observed Miss Murdstone, bridling, "that I consider our lamented Clara to have been, in all essential respects, a mere child."

"It is a comfort to you and me, ma'am," said my aunt, "who are getting on in life, and are not likely to be made unhappy by our personal attractions, that nobody can say the same of us."

"No doubt!" returned Miss Murdstone, though, I thought, not with a very ready or gracious assent. "And it certainly might have been, as you say, a better and happier thing for my brother if he had never entered into such a marriage. I have always been of that opinion."

"I have no doubt you have," said my aunt—"Janet," ringing the bell, "my compliments to Mr. Dick, and beg him to come down."

Until he came, my aunt sat perfectly upright and stiff, frowning at the wall. When he came, my aunt performed the ceremony of introduction.

"Mr. Dick—an old and intimate friend, on whose judgment," said my aunt, with emphasis, as an admonition to Mr. Dick, who was biting his forefinger and looking rather foolish, "I rely."

Mr. Dick took his finger out of his mouth on this hint, and stood among the group with a grave and attentive expression of face. My aunt inclined her head to Mr. Murdstone, who went on,—

"Miss Trotwood, on the receipt of your letter, I considered it an act of greater justice to myself, and perhaps of more respect to you——"

"Thank you," said my aunt, still eyeing him keenly; "you needn't mind me."

"To answer it in person, however inconvenient the journey," pursued Mr. Murdstone, "rather than by letter. This unhappy boy, who has run away from his friends and his occupation——"

"And whose appearance," interposed his sister, directing general attention to me in my indefinable costume, "is perfectly scandalous and disgraceful."

"Jane Murdstone," said her brother, "have the goodness not to interrupt me. This unhappy boy, Miss Trotwood, has been the occasion of much domestic trouble and uneasiness, both during the lifetime of my late dear wife, and since. He has a sullen, rebellious spirit, a violent temper, and an untoward, intractable disposition. Both my sister and myself have endeavoured to correct his vices, but ineffectually. And I have felt—we both have felt, I may say; my sister being fully in my confidence—that it is right you should receive this grave and dispassionate assurance from our lips."

"It can hardly be necessary for me to confirm anything stated by my brother," said Miss Murdstone, "but I beg to observe that, of all the boys in the world, I believe this is the worst boy."

"Strong!" said my aunt shortly.

"But not at all too strong for the facts," returned Miss Murdstone.

"Ha!" said my aunt. "Well, sir?"

"I have my own opinions," resumed Mr. Murdstone, whose face darkened more and more, the more he and my aunt observed each other, which they did very narrowly, "as to the best mode of bringing him up; they are founded, in part, on my knowledge of him, and in part on my knowledge of my own means and resources. I am responsible for them to myself, I act upon them, and I say no more about them. It is enough that I place this boy under the eye of a friend of my own, in a respectable business;

that it does not please him; that he runs away from it, makes himself a common vagabond about the country, and comes here, in rags, to appeal to you, Miss Trotwood. I wish to set before you, honourably, the exact consequences—so far as they are within my knowledge—of your abetting him in this appeal."

"But about the respectable business first," said my aunt. "If he had been your own boy, you would have put him to it, just the same, I suppose?"

"If he had been my brother's own boy," returned Miss Murdstone, striking in, "his character, I trust, would have been altogether different."

"Or if the poor child, his mother, had been alive, he would still have gone into the respectable business, would he?" said my aunt.

"I believe," said Mr. Murdstone, with an inclination of his head, "that Clara would have disputed nothing which myself and my sister, Jane Murdstone, were agreed was for the best."

Miss Murdstone confirmed this with an audible murmur.

"Humph!" said my aunt. "Unfortunate Baby!"

Mr. Dick, who had been rattling his money all this time, was rattling it so loudly now that my aunt felt it necessary to check him with a look, before saying,—

"The poor child's annuity died with her?"

"Died with her," replied Mr. Murdstone.

"And there was no settlement of the little property—the house and garden—the what's-its-name Rookery without any rooks in it —upon her boy?"

"It had been left to her, unconditionally, by her first husband," Mr. Murdstone began, when my aunt caught him up with the greatest irascibility and impatience.

"Good Lord, man, there's no occasion to say that. Left to her unconditionally! I think I see David Copperfield looking forward to any condition of any sort or kind, though it stared him point-blank in the face! Of course it was left to her unconditionally. But when she married again—when she took that most disastrous step of marrying you, in short," said my aunt, "to be plain—did no one put in a word for the boy at that time?"

"My late wife loved her second husband, madam," said Mr. Murdstone, "and trusted implicitly in him."

"Your late wife, sir, was a most unworldly, most unhappy, most unfortunate Baby," returned my aunt, shaking her head at him. "That's what *she* was. And now, what have you got to say next?"

"Merely this, Miss Trotwood," he returned. "I am here to take David back; to take him back unconditionally, to dispose of him as I think proper, and to deal with him as I think right. I am not here to make any promise, or give any pledge to anybody. You may possibly have some idea, Miss Trotwood, of abetting him in his running away, and in his complaints to you. Your manner, which I must say does not seem intended to propitiate, induces me think it possible. Now I must caution you that if you abet him once, you abet him for good and all; if you step in between him and me now, you must step in, Miss Trotwood, for ever. I cannot trifle or be trifled with. I am here, for the first and last time, to take him away. Is he ready to go? If he is not—and you tell me he is not, on any pretence; it is indifferent to me what—my doors are shut against him henceforth, and yours, I take it for granted, are open to him."

To this address my aunt had listened with the closest attention, sitting perfectly upright, with her hands folded on one knee, and looking grimly on the speaker. When he had finished, she turned her eyes so as to command Miss Murdstone, without otherwise disturbing her attitude, and said,—

"Well, ma'am, have *you* got anything to remark?"

"Indeed, Miss Trotwood," said Miss Murdstone, "all that I could say has been so well said by my brother, and all that I know to be the fact has been so plainly stated by him, that I have nothing to add except my thanks for your politeness—for your very great politeness, I am sure," said Miss Murdstone, with an irony which no more affected my aunt than it discomposed the cannon I had slept by at Chatham.

"And what does the boy say?" said my aunt. "Are you ready to go, David?"

I answered no, and entreated her not to let me go. I said that neither Mr. nor Miss Murdstone had ever liked me, or had ever been kind to me; that they had made my mamma, who always loved me dearly, unhappy about me, and that I knew it well, and that Peggotty knew it. I said that I had been more miserable than I thought anybody could believe who only knew how young I was. And I begged and prayed my aunt—I forget in what terms now, but I remember that they affected me very much then—to befriend and protect me, for my father's sake.

"Mr. Dick," said my aunt, "what shall I do with this child?"

Mr. Dick considered, hesitated, brightened, and rejoined, "Have him measured for a suit of clothes directly."

"Mr. Dick," said my aunt triumphantly, "give me your hand, for your common sense is invaluable." Having shaken it with great cordiality, she pulled me towards her, and said to Mr. Murdstone,—

"You can go when you like; I'll take my chance with the boy. If he's all you say he is, at least I can do as much for him then as you have done. But I don't believe a word of it."

The Adventures of Tom Sawyer

THE CAT AND THE PAIN-KILLER

by MARK TWAIN

The Adventures of Tom Sawyer *and its sequel,* Huckleberry Finn, *both based on Mark Twain's memories of his early days in a small town in Missouri on the banks of the Mississippi, turned out to be such a true and essentially American picture of boyhood that they quickly became famous not only in this country but all over the world. This escapade with the Pain-killer, in which Tom manages for once to outwit his Aunt Polly, and numerous others like the whitewashing of the fence, Tom and Becky lost in the cave, the club members solemnly signing their names in blood, have become so well known that they are almost part of American folklore. Never has the basic nature of boys been revealed with such high-spirited humor and understanding. Tom Sawyer has been called the best boy's story ever written, and even the greatest American novel. And young people find it especially refreshing to discover a great book written in the colloquial language of everyday Midwestern talk.*

One of the reasons why Tom's mind had drifted away from its secret troubles was that it had found a new and weighty matter to interest itself about. Becky Thatcher had stopped coming to school. Tom had struggled with his pride a few days, and tried to "whistle her down the wind," but failed. He began to find himself hanging around her father's house, nights, and feeling very miserable. She was ill. What if she should die! There was distraction in the thought. He no longer took an interest in war, nor even in piracy. The charm of life was gone; there was nothing but dreariness left. He put his hoop away, and his bat; there was no joy in them any more.

His aunt was concerned. She began to try all manner of remedies on him. She was one of those people who are infatuated with patent medicines and all new-fangled methods of producing health or mending it. She was an inveterate experimenter in these things. When something fresh in this line came out she was in a fever, right away, to try it; not on herself, for she was never ailing, but on anybody else that came handy. She was a subscriber for all the "Health" periodicals and phrenological frauds; and the solemn ignorance they were inflated with was breath to her nostrils. All the "rot" they contained about ventilation, and how to go to bed, and how to get up, and what to eat, and what to drink, and how much exercise to take, and what frame of mind to keep oneself in, and what sort of clothing to wear, was all gospel to her, and she never observed that her health-journals of the current month customarily upset everything they had recommended the month before. She was as simple-hearted and honest as the day was long, and so she was an easy victim. She gathered together her quack periodicals and quack medicines, and thus armed with death, went about on her pale horse, metaphorically speaking, with "hell following after." But she never suspected that she was not an angel of healing and the balm of Gilead in disguise, to the suffering neighbors.

The water treatment was new, now, and Tom's low condition was a windfall to her. She had him out at daylight every morning, stood him up in the woodshed and drowned him with a deluge of cold water; then she scrubbed him down with a towel like a file, and so brought him to; then she rolled him up in a wet sheet and put him away under blankets till she sweated his soul clean and "the yellowish stains of it came through his pores"—as Tom said.

Yet notwithstanding all this, the boy grew more and more melancholy and pale and dejected. She added hot baths, sitz baths, shower baths, and plunges. The boy remained as dismal as a hearse. She began to assist the water with a slim oatmeal diet and blister-plasters. She calculated his capacity as she would a jug's, and filled him up every day with quack cure-alls. Tom had become indifferent to persecution by this time. This phase filled the old lady's heart with consternation. This indifference must be broken up at any cost. Now she heard of Pain-killer for the first time. She ordered a lot at once. She tasted it and was filled with gratitude. It was simply fire in a liquid form. She dropped the water treatment and everything else, and pinned her faith to Pain-killer. She gave Tom a teaspoonful and watched with the deepest anxiety for the result. Her troubles were instantly at rest, her soul at peace again; for the "indifference" was broken up. The boy could not have shown a wilder heartier interest if she had built a fire under him.

Tom felt that it was time to wake up; this sort of life might be romantic enough, in his blighted condition, but it was getting to have too little sentiment and too much distracting variety about it. So he thought over various plans for relief, and finally hit upon that of professing to be fond of Pain-killer. He asked for it so often that he became a nuisance, and his aunt ended by telling him to help himself and quit bothering her. If it had been Sid, she would have had no misgivings to alloy her delight; but since it was Tom, she watched the bottle clandestinely. She found that the medicine did really diminish, but it did not occur to her that the boy was mending the health of a crack in the sitting-room floor with it.

One day Tom was in the act of dosing the crack when his aunt's yellow cat came along, purring, eyeing the teaspoon avariciously, and begging for a taste. Tom said: "Don't ask for it unless you want it, Peter." But Peter signified that he did want it.

"You better make sure."

Peter was sure.

"Now you've asked for it, and I'll give it to you, because there ain't anything mean about *me*; but if you find you don't like it, you mustn't blame anybody but your own self."

Peter was agreeable. So Tom pried his mouth open and poured down the Pain-killer. Peter sprang a couple of yards in the air, and then delivered a war whoop and set off round and round the room, banging against furniture, upsetting flowerpots, and making general havoc. Next he rose on his hind feet and pranced around, in a frenzy of enjoyment, with his head over his shoulder and his voice proclaiming his unappeasable happiness. Then he went tearing around the house again spreading chaos and destruction in his path. Aunt Polly entered in time to see him throw a few double somersets, deliver a final mighty hurrah, and sail through the open window, carrying the rest of the flowerpots with him. The old lady stood petrified with astonishment, peering over her glasses; Tom lay on the floor expiring with laughter.

"Tom, what on earth ails that cat?"

"I don't know, aunt," gasped the boy.

"Why, I never see anything like it. What *did* make him act so?"

" 'Deed I don't know, Aunt Polly; cats always act so when they're having a good time."

"They do, do they?" There was something in the tone that made Tom apprehensive.

"Yes'm. That is, I believe they do."

"You do?"

"Yes'm."

The old lady was bending down, Tom watching, with interest emphasized by anxiety. Too late he divined her "drift." The handle of the telltale teaspoon was visible under the bed-valance. Aunt Polly took it, held it up. Tom winced, and dropped his eyes. Aunt Polly raised him by the usual handle—his ear—and cracked his head soundly with her thimble.

"Now, sir, what did you want to treat that poor dumb beast so for?"

"I done it out of pity for him—because he hadn't any aunt."

"Hadn't any aunt!—you numskull. What has that got to do with it?"

"Heaps. Because if he'd 'a' had one she'd 'a' burnt him out herself! She'd 'a' roasted his bowels out of him 'thout any more feeling than if he was a human!"

Aunt Polly felt a sudden pang of remorse. This was putting the thing in a new light; what was cruelty to a cat *might* be cruelty to a boy, too. She began to soften; she felt sorry. Her eyes watered a little, and she put her hand on Tom's head and said gently:

"I was meaning for the best, Tom. And, Tom, it *did* do you good."

Tom looked up in her face with just a perceptible twinkle peeping through his gravity:

"I know you was meaning for the best, auntie, and so was I with Peter. It done *him* good, too. I never see him get around so since—"

"Oh, go 'long with you, Tom, before you aggravate me again. And you try and see if you can't be a good boy, for once, and you needn't take any more medicine."

Gulliver's Travels

A VOYAGE TO LILLIPUT

by JONATHAN SWIFT

Like many other famous juvenile books, Gulliver's Travels *began as a book for adults; it was intended, in fact, as a blistering social and political satire. But young people have continued to enjoy it as a superb story of strange adventures. It opens with Lemuel Gulliver being shipwrecked on the coast of Lilliput, a country of miniature people where he has his pleasantest encounters. His thirst for seeing the world leads him on a voyage to the land of Brobdingnag, inhabited by giants of tremendous size; then he goes to Laputa, a nation of fantastic quack scientists; and his fourth and last voyage brings him to the country of the Houynhms which is ruled by horses. The favorite has always been the land of Lilliput, constructed with such ingenuity that the reader delights in the perfection and consistency in scale of every tiny detail. Whether read for its satire and philosophy, or simply for its story,* Gulliver's Travels *stands out as unique in the world's literature for its highly imaginative qualities.*

I lay down on the grass, which was very short and soft, where I slept sounder than ever I remember to have done in my life, and, as I reckoned, above nine hours; for when I awakened, it was just daylight.

I attempted to rise, but was not able to stir: for, as I happened to lie on my back, I found my arms and legs were strongly fastened on each side to the ground; and my hair, which was long and thick,

tied down in the same manner. I likewise felt several slender liga-
tures across my body, from my armpits to my thighs. I could only
look upwards; the sun began to grow hot, and the light offended
my eyes. I heard a confused noise about me, but in the posture
I lay, could see nothing except the sky. In a little time I felt something alive moving on my left leg, which advancing gently forward over my breast, came almost up to my chin. When bending
my eyes downwards as much as I could, I perceived it to be a
human creature not six inches high, with a bow and arrow in his
hands, and a quiver at his back. In the meantime, I felt at least
forty more of the same kind (as I conjectured) following the first.

I was in the utmost astonishment, and roared so loud, that they
all ran back in a fright; and some of them, as I was afterwards
told, were hurt with the falls they got by leaping from my sides
upon the ground. However, they soon returned, and one of them,
who ventured so far as to get a full sight of my face, lifting up
his hands and eyes by way of admiration, cried out in a shrill but
distinct voice, *Hekinah degul*: the others repeated the same words
several times, but I then knew not what they meant.

I lay all this while, as the reader may believe, in great uneasiness: at length, struggling to get loose, I had the fortune to break
the strings, and wrench out the pegs that fastened my left arm to
the ground; for, by lifting it up to my face, I discovered the
methods they had taken to bind me, and at the same time, with
a violent pull, which gave me excessive pain, I a little loosened
the strings that tied down my hair on the left side, so that I was
just able to turn my head about two inches. But the creatures ran
off a second time, before I could seize them; whereupon there was
a great shout in a very shrill accent, and after it ceased, I heard one
of them cry aloud, *Tolgo phonac*; when in an instant I felt above
a hundred arrows discharged on my left hand, which pricked me
like so many needles; and besides they shot another flight into the
air, as we do bombs in Europe, whereof many, I suppose, fell on
my body (though I felt them not) and some on my face, which I
immediately covered with my left hand.

When this shower of arrows was over, I fell a groaning with

grief and pain, and then striving again to get loose, they discharged another volley larger than the first, and some of them attempted with spears to stick me in the sides; but, by good luck, I had on me a buff jerkin, which they could not pierce. I thought it the most prudent method to lie still, and my design was to continue so till night, when, my left hand being already loose, I could easily free myself: and as for the inhabitants, I had reason to believe I might be a match for the greatest armies they could bring against me, if they were all of the same size with him that I saw.

But fortune disposed otherwise of me. When the people observed I was quiet, they discharged no more arrows; but, by the noise I heard, I knew their numbers increased; and about four yards from me, over against my right ear, I heard a knocking for above an hour, like that of people at work; when turning my head that way, as well as the pegs and strings would permit me, I saw a stage erected, about a foot and a half from the ground, capable of holding four of the inhabitants, with two or three ladders to mount it: from whence one of them, who seemed to be a person of quality, made me a long speech, whereof I understood not one syllable. But I should have mentioned, that before the principal person began his oration, he cried out three times, *Langro dehul san* (these words and the former were afterwards repeated and explained to me). Whereupon immediately about fifty of the inhabitants came, and cut the strings that fastened the left side of my head, which gave me the liberty of turning it to the right, and of observing the person and gesture of him that was to speak. He appeared to be of a middle age, and taller than any of the other three who attended him, whereof one was a page that held up his train, and seemed to be somewhat longer than my middle finger; the other two stood one on each side to support him. He acted every part of an orator, and I could observe many periods of threatenings, and others of promises, pity, and kindness.

I answered in a few words, but in the most submissive manner, lifting up my left hand and both my eyes to the sun, as calling him for a witness; and being almost famished with hunger, having not eaten a morsel for some hours before I left the ship, I found

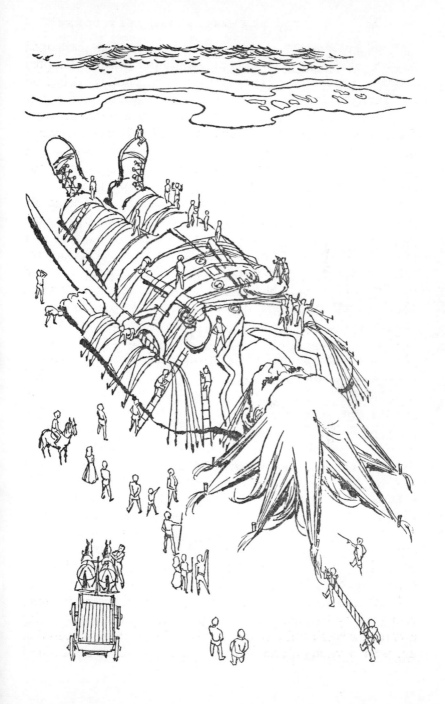

the demands of nature so strong upon me, that I could not forbear showing my impatience (perhaps against the strict rules of decency) by putting my finger frequently on my mouth, to signify that I wanted food. The *Hurgo* (for so they call a great lord, as I afterwards learned) understood me very well. He descended from the stage, and commanded that several ladders should be applied to my sides, on which above a hundred of the inhabitants mounted, and walked towards my mouth, laden with baskets full of meat, which had been provided, and sent thither by the King's orders, upon the first intelligence he received of me. I observed there was the flesh of several animals, but could not distinguish them by the taste. There were shoulders, legs, and loins, shaped like those of mutton, and very well dressed, but smaller than the wings of a lark. I ate them by two or three at a mouthful, and took three loaves at a time, about the bigness of musket bullets. They supplied me as they could, showing a thousand marks of wonder and astonishment at my bulk and appetite. I then made another sign that I wanted drink. They found by my eating that a small quantity would not suffice me, and being a most ingenious people, they slung up with great dexterity one of their largest hogsheads, then rolled it toward my hand, and beat out the top; I drank it off at a draught, which I might well do, for it did not hold half a pint, and tasted like a small wine of Burgundy, but much more delicious. They brought me a second hogshead, which I drank in the same manner, and made signs for more, but they had none to give me.

When I had performed these wonders, they shouted for joy, and danced upon my breast, repeating several times as they did at first, *Hekinah degul*. They made me a sign that I should throw down the two hogsheads, but first warning the people below to stand out of the way, crying aloud, *Borach mivola*, and when they saw the vessels in the air, there was a universal shout of *Hekinah degul*. I confess I was often tempted, while they were passing backwards and forwards on my body, to seize forty or fifty of the first that came in my reach, and dash them against the ground. But the remembrance of what I had felt, which probably might not be the worst they could do, and the promise of honor I made them, for so I interpreted my submissive behavior, soon drove out these imaginations. Besides, I now considered myself as bound by the laws of hospitality to a people who had treated me with so much expense and magnificence. However, in my thoughts I could not sufficiently wonder at the intrepidity of these diminutive mortals, who dare venture to mount and walk upon my body, while one of my hands was at liberty, without trembling at the very sight of so prodigious a creature as I must appear to them.

After some time, when they observed that I made no more demands for meat, there appeared before me a person of high rank from his Imperial Majesty. His Excellency, having mounted on the small of my right leg, advanced forwards up to my face, with about a dozen of his retinue. And producing his credentials under the Signet Royal, which he applied close to my eyes, spoke about ten minutes, without any signs of anger, but with a kind of determinate resolution; often pointing forwards, which, as I afterwards found, was towards the capital city, about half a mile distant, whither it was agreed by his Majesty in council that I must be conveyed. I answered in few words, but to no purpose, and made a sign with my hand that was loose, putting it to the other (but over his Excellency's head, for fear of hurting him or his train) and then to my own head and body, to signify that I desired my liberty.

It appeared that he understood me well enough, for he shook his head by way of disapprobation, and held his hand in a posture to show that I must be carried as a prisoner. However, he made other signs to let me understand that I should have meat and drink enough, and very good treatment. Whereupon I once more thought of attempting to break my bonds, but again, when I felt the smart of their arrows upon my face and hands, which were all in blisters, and many of the darts still sticking in them, and observing likewise that the number of my enemies increased, I gave tokens to let them know that they might do with me what they pleased. Upon this the *Hurgo* and his train withdrew with much civility and cheerful countenances. But before this, they daubed my face and both my hands with a sort of ointment very pleasant to the smell, which in a few minutes removed all the smart of their arrows. These circumstances, added to the refreshment I had received by their victuals and drink, which were very nourishing, disposed me to sleep. I slept about eight hours, as I was afterwards assured; and it was no wonder, for the physicians, by the Emperor's order, had mingled a sleepy potion in the hogsheads of wine.

It seems that upon the first moment I was discovered sleeping on the ground after my landing, the Emperor had early notice of it by an express; and determined in council that I should be tied in the manner I have related (which was done in the night while I slept), that plenty of meat and drink should be sent me, and a machine prepared to carry me to the capital city.

This resolution perhaps may appear very bold and dangerous, and I am confident would not be imitated by any prince in Europe on the like occasion; however, in my opinion, it was extremely prudent, as well as generous. For supposing these people had endeavored to kill me with their spears and arrows while I was asleep, I should certainly have awakened with the first sense of smart, which might so far have roused my rage and strength, as to have enabled me to break the strings wherewith I was tied; after which, as they were not able to make resistance, so they could expect no mercy.

These people are most excellent mathematicians, and arrived to a great perfection in mechanics by the countenance and encouragement of the Emperor, who is a renowned patron of learning. This prince has several machines fixed on wheels for the carriage of trees and other great weights. He often builds his largest men of war, whereof some are nine feet long, in the woods where the timber grows, and has them carried on these engines three or four hundred yards to the sea. Five hundred carpenters and engineers were immediately set at work to prepare the greatest engine they had. It was a frame of wood raised three inches from the ground, about seven feet long and four wide, moving upon twenty-two wheels. The shout I heard was upon the arrival of this engine, which it seems set out in four hours after my landing. It was brought parallel to me as I lay. But the principal difficulty was to raise and place me in this vehicle. Eighty poles, each of one foot high, were erected for this purpose, and very strong cords of the bigness of packthread were fastened by hooks to many bandages, which the workmen had girt round my neck, my hands, my body, and my legs. Nine hundred of the strongest men were employed to draw up these cords by many pulleys fastened on the poles, and thus, in less than three hours, I was raised and slung into the engine, and there tied fast. All this I was told, for while the whole operation was performing, I lay in a profound sleep, by the force of that soporiferous medicine infused into my liquor. Fifteen hundred of the Emperor's largest horses, each about four inches and a half high, were employed to draw me towards the metropolis, which, as I said, was half a mile distant.

About four hours after we began our journey, I awaked by a very ridiculous accident; for the carriage being stopped a while to adjust something that was out of order, two or three of the young natives had the curiosity to see how I looked when I was asleep; they climbed up into the engine, and advancing very softly to my face, one of them, an officer in the Guards, put the sharp end of his half-pike a good way up into my left nostril, which tickled my nose like a straw, and made me sneeze violently: whereupon they stole off unperceived, and it was three weeks before I knew the cause of my awaking so suddenly. We made a long march the remaining part of that day, and rested at night with five hundred guards on each side of me, half with torches, and half with bows and arrows, ready to shoot me if I should offer to stir. The next morning at sunrise we continued our march, and arrived within two hundred yards of the city gates about noon. The Emperor, and all his court, came out to meet us; but his great officers would by no means suffer his Majesty to endanger his person by mounting on my body.

At the place where the carriage stopped, there stood an ancient temple, esteemed to be the largest in the whole kingdom, which having been polluted some years before by an unnatural murder, was, according to the zeal of those people, looked on as profane, and therefore had been applied to common uses, and all the ornaments and furniture carried away. In this edifice it was determined I should lodge. The great gate fronting to the north was about four feet high, and almost two feet wide, through which I could easily creep. On each side of the gate was a small window not above six inches from the ground: into that on the left side, the King's smiths conveyed fourscore and eleven chains, like those that hang to a lady's watch in Europe, and almost as large, which were locked to my left leg with six and thirty padlocks.

Over against this temple, on the other side of the great highway, at twenty feet distance, there was a turret at least five feet high. Here the Emperor ascended with many principal lords of his court, to have an opportunity of viewing me, as I was told, for I could not see them. It was reckoned that above a hundred thousand inhabitants came out of the town upon the same errand; and in spite of my guards, I believe there could not be fewer than ten thousand, at several times, who mounted upon my body by the help of ladders. But a proclamation was soon issued to forbid it upon pain of death. When the workmen found it was impossible for me to break loose, they cut all the strings that bound me; whereupon I rose up with as melancholy a disposition as ever I had in my life. But the noise and astonishment of the people at seeing me rise and walk, are not to be expressed. The chains that held my left leg were about two yards long, and gave me not only the liberty of walking backwards and forwards in a semi-circle; but, being fixed within four inches of the gate, allowed me to creep in, and lie at my full length in the temple.

THE COURT OF LILLIPUT

My gentleness and good behavior had gained so far on the Emperor and his court, and indeed upon the army and people in general, that I began to conceive hopes of getting my liberty in a short time. I took all possible methods to cultivate this favorable disposition. The natives came by degrees to be less apprehensive of any danger from me. I would sometimes lie down, and let five or six of them dance on my hand. And at last the boys and girls would venture to come and play at hide and seek in my hair. I had now made good progress in understanding and speaking their language. The Emperor had a mind one day to entertain me with several of the country shows, wherein they exceeded all nations I have known, both for dexterity and magnificence. I was diverted with none so much as that of the rope-dancers, performed upon a slender white thread, extended about two feet, and twelve inches from the ground. Upon which I shall desire liberty, with the reader's patience, to enlarge a little.

This diversion is only practiced by those persons who are candidates for great employments and high favors at court. They are trained in this art from their youth, and are not always of noble birth, or liberal education. When a great office is vacant either by death or disgrace (which often happens) five or six of those candidates petition the Emperor to entertain his Majesty and the court with a dance on the rope, and whoever jumps the highest without falling, succeeds in the office. Very often the chief ministers themselves are commanded to show their skill, and to convince the Emperor that they have not lost their faculty. Flimnap, the Treasurer, is allowed to cut a caper on the straight rope, at least an inch higher than any other lord in the whole empire. I have seen him do the summerset several times together upon a trencher fixed on the rope, which is no thicker than a common packthread in England. My friend Reldresal, principal Secretary for Private Affairs, is, in my opinion, if I am not partial, the second after the Treasurer; the rest of the great officers are much upon a par.

These diversions are often attended with fatal accidents, whereof great numbers are on record. I myself have seen two or three candidates break a limb. But the danger is much greater when the ministers themselves are commanded to show their dexterity; for by contending to excel themselves and their fellows, they strain so far, that there is hardly one of them who has not received a fall, and some of them two or three. I was assured that a year or two before my arrival, Flimnap would have infallibly broken his neck, if one of the King's cushions, that accidentally lay on the ground, had not weakened the force of his fall.

There is likewise another diversion, which is only shown before the Emperor and Empress, and first minister, upon particular occasions. The Emperor lays on the table three fine silken threads of six inches long. One is blue, the other red, and the third green. These threads are proposed as prizes for those persons whom the Emperor has a mind to distinguish by a peculiar mark of his favor. The ceremony is performed in his Majesty's great chamber of state, where the candidates are to undergo a trial of dexterity very different from the former, and such as I have not observed the least resemblance of in any other country of the old or the new world. The Emperor holds a stick in his hands, both ends parallel to the horizon, while the candidates, advancing one by one, sometimes leap over the stick, sometimes creep under it backwards and forwards several times, according as the stick is advanced or depressed. Sometimes the Emperor holds one end of the stick, and his first minister the other; sometimes the minister has it entirely to himself. Whoever performs his part with most agility, and holds out the longest in leaping and creeping, is rewarded with the blue-colored silk; the red is given to the next, and the green to the third, which they all wear girt twice round about the middle; and you see few great persons about this court who are not adorned with one of these girdles.

The horses of the army, and those of the royal stables, having been daily led before me, were no longer shy, but would come up to my very feet without starting. The riders would leap them over my hand as I held it on the ground, and one of the Emperor's huntsmen, upon a large courser, took my foot, shoe and all; which was indeed a prodigious leap. I had the good fortune to divert the Emperor one day after a very extraordinary manner. I desired he would order several sticks two feet high, and the thickness of an ordinary cane, to be brought me; whereupon his Majesty commanded the master of his woods to give directions accordingly, and the next morning six woodmen arrived with as many carriages, drawn by eight horses to each. I took nine of these sticks, and fixing them firmly in the ground in a quadrangular figure, two feet and a half square, I took four other sticks, and tied them parallel at each corner, about two feet from the ground. Then I fastened my handkerchief to the nine sticks that stood erect, and extended it on all sides till it was as tight as the top of a drum; and the four parallel sticks rising about five inches higher than the handkerchief served as ledges on each side. When I had finished my work, I desired the Emperor to let a troop of his best horse, twenty-four in number, come and exercise upon this plain.

His Majesty approved of the proposal, and I took them up one by one in my hands, ready mounted and armed, with the proper officers to exercise them. As soon as they got into order, they divided into two parties, performed mock skirmishes, discharged blunt arrows, drew their swords, fled and pursued, attacked and retired, and in short discovered the best military discipline I ever beheld. The parallel sticks secured them and their horses from falling over the stage; and the Emperor was so much delighted, that he ordered this entertainment to be repeated several days, and once was pleased to be lifted up and give the word of command; and, with great difficulty, persuaded even the Empress herself to let me hold her in her close chair within two yards of the stage, from whence she was able to take a full view of the whole performance. It was my good fortune that no ill accident happened in these entertainments, only once a fiery horse that belonged to one of the captains pawing with his hoof struck a hole in my handkerchief, and his foot slipping, he overthrew his rider and himself; but I immediately relieved them both, and covering the hole with one hand, I set down the troop with the other, in the same manner as I took them up. The horse that fell was strained in the left shoulder, but the rider got no hurt, and I repaired my handkerchief as well as I could. However I would not trust to the strength of it any more in such dangerous enterprises.

About two or three days before I was set at liberty, as I was entertaining the court with this kind of feats, there arrived an express to inform his Majesty that some of his subjects riding near the place where I was first taken up, had seen a great black substance lying on the ground, very oddly shaped, extending its edges round as wide as his Majesty's bedchamber, and rising up in the middle as high as a man; that it was no living creature, as they at first apprehended, for it lay on the grass without motion, and some of them had walked round it several times: that by mounting upon each other's shoulders, they had got to the top, which was flat and even, and stamping upon it they found it was hollow within; that they humbly conceived it might be something belonging to the Man-Mountain, and if his Majesty pleased, they would undertake to bring it with only five horses. I presently knew what they meant, and was glad at heart to receive this intelligence.

It seems upon my first reaching the shore after our shipwreck, I was in such confusion, that before I came to the place where I went to sleep, my hat, which I had fastened with a string to my head while I was rowing, and had stuck on all the time I was swimming, fell off after I came to land. The string, as I conjecture, breaking by some accident which I never observed, but thought my hat had been lost at sea. I entreated his Imperial Majesty to give orders it might be brought to me as soon as possible, describing to him the use and the nature of it: and the next day the wagoners arrived with it, but not in a very good condition; they had bored two holes in the brim, within an inch and a half of the edge, and fastened two hooks in the holes; these hooks were tied by a long cord to the harness, and thus my hat was dragged along for above half an English mile. But the ground in that country being extremely smooth and level, it received less damage than I expected.

Two days after this adventure, the Emperor having ordered that part of his army which quarters in and about his metropolis to be in a readiness, took a fancy of diverting himself in a very singular manner. He desired I would stand like a Colossus, with my legs as far asunder as I conveniently could. He then commanded his General (who was an old experienced leader, and a great patron of mine) to draw up the troops in close order, and march them under me, the foot by twenty-four in a breast, and the horse by sixteen, with drums beating, colors flying, and pikes advanced.

This body consisted of three thousand foot, and a thousand horse.

I had sent so many memorials and petitions for my liberty, that his Majesty at length mentioned the matter, first in the cabinet, and then in a full council; where it was opposed by none, except Skyresh Bolgolam, who was pleased, without any provocation, to be my mortal enemy. But it was carried against him by the whole board, and confirmed by the Emperor. That minister was *Galbet*, or Admiral of the Realm, very much in his master's confidence, and a person well versed in affairs, but of a morose and sour complexion. However, he was at length persuaded to comply; but prevailed that the articles and conditions upon which I should be set free, and to which I must swear, should be drawn up by himself. These articles were brought to me by Skyresh Bolgolam in person, attended by two under-secretaries, and several persons of distinction. After they were read, I was demanded to swear to the performance of them; first in the manner of my own country, and afterwards in the method prescribed by their laws; which was to hold my right foot in my left hand, to place the middle finger of my right hand on the crown of my head, and my thumb on the tip of my right ear. But because the reader may perhaps be curious to have some idea of the style and manner of expression peculiar to that people, as well as to know the articles upon which I recovered my liberty, I have made a translation of the whole instrument word for word, as near as I was able, which I here offer to the public.

GOLBASTO MOMAREN EVLAME GURDILO SHEFIN MULLY ULLY GUE, most mighty Emperor of Lilliput, delight and terror of the universe, whose dominions extend five thousand *blustrugs* (about twelve miles in circumference) to the extremities of the globe; monarch of all monarchs, taller than the sons of men; whose feet press down to the center, and whose head strikes against the sun; at whose nod the princes of the earth shake their knees; pleasant as the spring, comfortable as the summer, fruitful as autumn, dreadful as winter. His most sublime Majesty proposes to the Man-Mountain, lately arrived to our celestial dominions, the following articles, which by a solemn oath he shall be obliged to perform.

First, The Man-Mountain shall not depart from our dominions, without our license under our great seal.

2nd, He shall not presume to come into our metropolis, without our express order; at which time the inhabitants shall have two hours warning to keep within their doors.

3rd, The said Man-Mountain shall confine his walks to our principal high roads, and not offer to walk or lie down in a meadow or field of corn.

4th, As he walks the said roads, he shall take the utmost care not to trample upon the bodies of any of our loving subjects, their horses, or carriages, nor take any of our said subjects into his hands, without their own consent.

5th, If an express requires extraordinary dispatch, the Man-Mountain shall be obliged to carry in his pocket the messenger and horse a six days journey once in every moon, and return the said messenger back (if so required) safe to our Imperial Presence.

6th, He shall be our ally against our enemies in the Island of Blefuscu, and do his utmost to destroy their fleet, which is now preparing to invade us.

7th, That the said Man-Mountain shall, at his times of leisure, be aiding and assisting to our workmen, in helping to raise certain great stones, towards covering the wall of the principal park, and other of our royal buildings.

8th, That the said Man-Mountain shall, in two moons' time, deliver in an exact survey of the circumference of our dominions by a computation of his own paces round the coast.

Lastly, That upon his solemn oath to observe all the above articles, the said Man-Mountain shall have a daily allowance of meat and drink sufficient for the support of 1,728 of our subjects, with free access to our Royal Person, and other marks of our favor. Given at our Palace at Belfaborac the twelfth day of the ninety-first moon of our reign.

I swore and subscribed to these articles with great cheerfulness and content, although some of them were not so honorable as I could have wished; which proceeded wholly from the malice of Skyresh Bolgolam the High Admiral. Whereupon my chains were immediately unlocked, and I was at full liberty; the Emperor himself in person did me the honor to be by at the whole ceremony. I made my acknowledgments by prostrating myself at his Majesty's feet: but he commanded me to rise; and after many gracious expressions, which, to avoid the censure of vanity, I shall not repeat, he added, that he hoped I should prove a useful servant, and well deserve all the favors he had already conferred upon me, or might do for the future.

The reader may please to observe, that in the last article for the recovery of my liberty the Emperor stipulates to allow me a quantity of meat and drink sufficient for the support of 1,728 Lilliputians. Some time after, asking a friend at court how they came to fix on that determinate number, he told me that his Majesty's mathematicians, having taken the height of my body by the help of a quadrant, and finding it to exceed theirs in the proportion of twelve to one, they concluded from the similarity of their bodies, that mine must contain at least 1,728 of theirs, and consequently would require as much food as was necessary to support that number of Lilliputians. By which the reader may conceive an idea of the ingenuity of that people, as well as the prudent and exact economy of so great a prince.

The Adventures of Odysseus

THE CAVE OF THE CYCLOPS
ADAPTED FROM HOMER'S ODYSSEY
by PADRAIC COLUM

Homer's great epic poem, The Odyssey, *is probably the most famous tale of adventure that has come down to us from ancient times. It records what happened to Odysseus (Ulysses) on his long journey home from Troy, and is based partly on historical facts of the war between Greece and Troy. This incident about the giant Cyclops is told by Odysseus, the hero of the story, who was especially renowned for his great wisdom. It was he who thought up the plan of the Wooden Horse by means of which the Greeks at last captured the city of Troy after a ten-year siege. The curse that Polyphemus calls down on the Greek hero comes true. For after he escapes from the Cyclops, Odysseus still has to endure ten more years of innumerable hardships and adventures before he finally reaches his homeland in Ithaca.*

Later we came to the land of the Cyclôpes, a giant people. There is a waste island outside the harbour of their land, and on it there is a well of bright water that has poplars growing round it. We came to that empty island, and we beached our ships and took down our sails.

As soon as the dawn came we went through the empty island, starting the wild goats that were there in flocks, and shooting them with our arrows. We killed so many wild goats there that we had nine for each ship. Afterwards we looked across to the land of the Cyclôpes, and we heard the sound of voices and saw the smoke of fires and heard the bleating of flocks of sheep and goats.

I called my companions together and I said, "It would be well for some of us to go to that other island. With my own ship and with the company that is on it I shall go there. The rest of you abide here. I will find out what manner of men live there, and whether they will treat us kindly and give us gifts that are due to strangers—gifts of provisions for our voyage."

We embarked and we came to the land. There was a cave near the sea, and round the cave there were mighty flocks of sheep and goats. I took twelve men with me and I left the rest to guard the ship. We went into the cave and found no man there. There were baskets filled with cheeses, and vessels of whey, and pails and bowls of milk. My men wanted me to take some of the cheeses and drive off some of the lambs and kids and come away. But this I would not do, for I would rather that he who owned the stores would give us of his own free will the offerings that were due to strangers.

While we were in the cave, he whose dwelling it was, returned to it. He carried on his shoulder a great pile of wood for his fire. Never in our lives did we see a creature so frightful as this Cyclops was. He was a giant in size, and, what made him terrible to behold, he had but one eye, and that single eye was in his forehead. He cast down on the ground the pile of wood that he carried, making such a din that we fled in terror into the corners and recesses of the cave. Next he drove his flocks into the cave and began to milk his ewes and goats. And when he had the flocks within, he took up a stone that not all our strengths could move and set it as a door to the mouth of the cave.

The Cyclops kindled his fire, and when it blazed up he saw us in the corners and recesses. He spoke to us. We knew not what he said, but our hearts were shaken with terror at the sound of his deep voice.

I spoke to him saying that we were Agamemnon's men on our way home from the taking of Priam's City, and I begged him to deal with us kindly, for the sake of Zeus who is ever in the company of strangers and suppliants. But he answered me saying, "We Cyclôpes pay no heed to Zeus, nor to any of thy gods. In our strength and our power we deem that we are mightier than they. I will not spare thee, neither will I give thee aught for the sake of Zeus, but only as my own spirit bids me. And first I would have thee tell me how you came to our land."

I knew it would be better not to let the Cyclops know that my ship and my companions were at the harbour of the island. Therefore I spoke to him guilefully, telling him that my ship had been broken on the rocks, and that I and the men with me were the only ones who had escaped utter doom.

I begged again that he would deal with us as just men deal with strangers and suppliants, but he, without saying a word, laid hands upon two of my men, and swinging them by the legs, dashed their brains out on the earth. He cut them to pieces and ate them before our very eyes. We wept and we prayed to Zeus as we witnessed a deed so terrible.

Next the Cyclops stretched himself amongst his sheep and went to sleep beside the fire. Then I debated whether I should take my sharp sword in my hand, and feeling where his heart was, stab him there. But second thoughts held me back from doing this. I might be able to kill him as he slept, but not even with my companions could I roll away the great stone that closed the mouth of the cave.

Dawn came, and the Cyclops awakened, kindled his fire and milked his flocks. Then he seized two others of my men and made ready for his mid-day meal. And now he rolled away the great stone and drove his flocks out of the cave.

I had pondered on a way of escape, and I had thought of something that might be done to baffle the Cyclops. I had with me a great skin of sweet wine, and I thought that if I could make him drunken with wine I and my companions might be able for him. But there were other preparations to be made first. On the floor of the cave there was a great beam of olive wood which the Cyclops had cut to make a club when the wood should be seasoned. It was yet green. I and my companions went and cut off a fathom's length of the wood, and sharpened it to a point and took it to the fire and hardened it in the glow. Then I hid the beam in a recess of the cave.

The Cyclops came back in the evening, and opening up the cave drove in his flocks. Then he closed the cave again with the stone and went and milked his ewes and his goats. Again he seized two of my companions. I went to the terrible creature with a bowl of wine in my hands. He took it and drank it and cried out, "Give me another bowl of this, and tell me thy name that I may give thee gifts for bringing me this honey-tasting drink."

Again I spoke to him guilefully and said, "Noman is my name. Noman my father and my mother call me."

"Give me more of the drink, Noman," he shouted. "And the gift that I shall give to thee is that I shall make thee the last of thy fellows to be eaten."

I gave him wine again, and when he had taken the third bowl he sank backwards with his face upturned, and sleep came upon him. Then I, with four companions, took that beam of olive wood, now made into a hard and pointed stake, and thrust it into the ashes of the fire. When the pointed end began to glow we drew it out of the flame. Then I and my companions laid hold on the great stake and, dashing at the Cyclops, thrust it into his eye. He raised a terrible cry that made the rocks ring and we dashed away into the recesses of the cave.

His cries brought other Cyclôpes to the mouth of the cave, and they, naming him as Polyphemus, called out and asked him what ailed him to cry. "Noman," he shrieked out, "Noman is slaying me by guile." They answered him saying, "If no man is slaying thee, there is nothing we can do for thee, Polyphemus. What ails thee has been sent to thee by the gods." Saying this, they went away from the mouth of the cave without attempting to move away the stone.

Polyphemus then, groaning with pain, rolled away the stone and sat before the mouth of the cave with his hands outstretched, thinking that he would catch us as we dashed out. I showed my companions how we might pass by him. I laid hands on certain rams of the flock and I lashed three of them together with supple rods. Then on the middle ram I put a man of my company. Thus every three rams carried a man. As soon as the dawn had come the rams hastened out to the pasture, and, as they passed, Polyphemus laid hands on the first and the third of each three that went by. They passed out and Polyphemus did not guess that a ram that he did not touch carried out a man.

For myself, I took a ram that was the strongest and fleeciest of the whole flock and I placed myself under him, clinging to the wool of his belly. As this ram, the best of all his flock, went by, Polyphemus, laying his hands upon him, said, "Would that you, the best of my flock, were endowed with speech, so that you might tell me where Noman, who has blinded me, has hidden himself." The ram went by him, and when he had gone a little way from the cave I loosed myself from him and went and set my companions free.

We gathered together many of Polyphemus' sheep and we drove them down to our ship. The men we had left behind would have wept when they heard what had happened to six of their companions. But I bade them take on board the sheep we had brought and pull the ship away from that land. Then when we had drawn a certain distance from the shore I could not forbear to shout my taunts into the cave of Polyphemus. "Cyclops," I cried, "you thought that you had the company of a fool and a weakling to eat. But you have been worsted by me, and your evil deeds have been punished."

So I shouted, and Polyphemus came to the mouth of the cave with great anger in his heart. He took up rocks and cast them at the ship and they fell before the prow. The men bent to the oars and pulled the ship away or it would have been broken by the rocks he cast. And when we were further away I shouted to him:

"Cyclops, if any man should ask who it was set his mark upon you, say that he was Odysseus, the son of Laertes."

Then I heard Polyphemus cry out, "I call upon Poseidon, the god of the sea, whose son I am, to avenge me upon you, Odysseus. I call upon Poseidon to grant that you, Odysseus, may never come

to your home, or if the gods have ordained your return, that you come to it after much toil and suffering, in an evil plight and in a stranger's ship, to find sorrow in your home."

So Polyphemus prayed, and, to my evil fortune, Poseidon heard his prayer. But we went on in our ship rejoicing at our escape. We came to the waste island where my other ships were. All the company rejoiced to see us, although they had to mourn for their six companions slain by Polyphemus. We divided amongst the ships the sheep we had taken from Polyphemus' flock and we sacrificed to the gods. At the dawn of the next day we raised the sails on each ship and we sailed away.

Treasure Island

*These opening chapters are not perhaps the most exciting in
the book, but they do set the atmosphere of fear and mystery
about the events to come. And Treasure Island is so tightly knit,
the narrative mounts so steadily in suspense from chapter to
chapter, that it should not be begun except at the beginning.
Reading condensations or seeing it in the movies is not the same
thing; this is one book that needs to be read in its entirety to
appreciate the full flavor. The heroes and villains—young Jim
Hawkins, Billy Bones, the scarred buccaneer, one-legged Long
John Silver, blind Old Pew tapping down the road—emerge so
vividly and awaken such a strong emotional response in the reader,
that it is hard not to think of them as real people. Treasure Island
is that unusual book, a tale of pure adventure, written for the sake
of the story, yet written with such skill that it becomes a work of
art. It was the first story ever written about pirates and it is still
the best.*

Squire Trelawney, Dr. Livesey, and the rest of these gentlemen
having asked me to write down the whole particulars about Treasure Island, from the beginning to the end, keeping nothing back
but the bearings of the island, and that only because there is
still treasure not yet lifted, I take up my pen in the year of grace
17—, and go back to the time when my father kept the "Admiral

Benbow" inn, and the brown old seaman, with the saber cut, first took up his lodging under our roof.

I remember him as if it were yesterday, as he came plodding to the inn door, his sea-chest following behind him in a hand-barrow; a tall, strong, heavy, nut-brown man; his tarry pigtail falling over the shoulders of his soiled blue coat; his hands ragged and scarred, with black, broken nails; and the saber cut across one cheek, a dirty livid white. I remember him looking round the cove and whistling to himself as he did so, and then breaking out in that old sea-song that he sang so often afterward:

> "Fifteen men on the dead man's chest—
> Yo-ho-ho, and a bottle of rum!"

in the high, old tottering voice that seemed to have been tuned and broken at the capstan bars. Then he rapped on the door with a bit of stick like a hand-spike that he carried, and when my father appeared, called roughly for a glass of rum. This, when it was brought to him, he drank slowly, like a connoisseur, lingering on the taste, and still looking about him at the cliffs and up at our signboard.

"This is a handy cove," says he, at length; "and a pleasant sittyated grog-shop. Much company, mate?"

My father told him no, very little company, the more was the pity.

"Well, then," said he, "this is the berth for me. Here you, matey," he cried to the man who trundled the barrow; "bring up alongside and help up my chest. I'll stay here a bit," he continued. "I'm a plain man; rum and bacon and eggs is what I want, and that head up there for to watch ships off. What you mought call me? You mought call me captain. Oh, I see what you're at—there;" and he threw down three or four gold pieces on the threshold. "You can tell me when I've worked through that," says he, looking as fierce as a commander.

And, indeed, bad as his clothes were, and coarsely as he spoke, he had none of the appearance of a man who sailed before the mast; but seemed like a mate or skipper, accustomed to be obeyed or to strike. The man who came with the barrow told us the mail had set him down the morning before at the "Royal George;" that he had inquired what inns there were along the coast, and hearing ours well spoken of, I suppose, and described as lonely, had chosen it from the others for his place of residence. And that was all we could learn of our guest.

He was a very silent man by custom. All day he hung round the cove, or upon the cliffs, with a brass telescope; all evening he sat in a corner of the parlor next the fire, and drank rum and water very strong. Mostly he would not speak when spoken to; only look up sudden and fierce, and blow through his nose like a fog horn; and we and the people who came about our house soon learned to let him be. Every day, when he came back from his stroll, he would ask if any seafaring men had gone by along the road. At first we thought it was the want of company of his own kind that made him ask this question; but at last we began to see he was desirous to avoid them. When a seaman put up at the "Admiral Benbow" (as now and then some did, making by the coast road from Bristol), he would look in at him through the curtained door before he entered the parlor; and he was always sure to be as silent as a mouse when any such was present. For me, at least, there was no secret about the matter; for I was, in a way, a sharer in his alarms. He had taken me aside one day, and promised me a silver fourpenny on the first of every month if I would only keep my "weather-eye open for a seafaring man with one leg," and let him know the moment he appeared. Often enough, when the first of the month came round, and I applied to him for my wage, he would only blow through his nose at me, and stare me down; but before the week was out he was sure to think better of it, bring me my fourpenny piece, and repeat his former orders to look out for "the seafaring man with one leg."

How that personage haunted my dreams, I need scarcely tell you. On stormy nights, when the wind shook the four corners of the house, and the surf roared along the cove and up the cliffs, I would see him in a thousand forms, and with a thousand diabolical expressions. Now the leg would be cut off at the knee, now at the hip; now he was a monstrous kind of a creature who had never had but the one leg, and that in the middle of his body. To see him leap and run and pursue me over hedge and ditch was the worst of nightmares. And altogether I paid pretty dear for my monthly fourpenny piece, in the shape of these abominable fancies.

But though I was so terrified by the idea of the seafaring man with one leg, I was far less terrified of the captain himself than anybody else who knew him. There were nights when he took a deal more rum and water than his head would carry; and then he would sometimes sit and sing his wicked, old, wild sea-songs, minding nobody; but sometimes he would call for glasses round, and force all the trembling company to listen to his stories or bear a chorus to his singing. Often I have heard the house shaking with "Yo-ho-ho, and a bottle of rum;" all the neighbors joining in for dear life, with the fear of death upon them, and each singing louder than the other, to avoid remark. For in these fits he was the most overriding companion ever known; he would slap his hand on the table for silence all round; he would fly up in a passion of anger at a question, or sometimes because none was put, and so he judged the company was not following his story. Nor would he allow any one to leave the inn till he had drunk himself sleepy and reeled off to bed.

His stories were what frightened people worst of all. Dreadful stories they were; about hanging, and walking the plank, and storms at sea, and the Dry Tortugas, and wild deeds and places on the Spanish Main. By his own account he must have lived his life among some of the wickedest men that God ever allowed upon the sea; and the language in which he told these stories shocked our plain country people almost as much as the crimes that he described. My father was always saying the inn would be ruined, for people would soon cease coming there to be tyrannized over and put down, and sent shivering to their beds; but I really believe his presence did us good. People were frightened at the time, but on looking back they rather liked it; it was a fine excitement in a quiet country life; and there was even a party of the younger men who pretended to admire him, calling him a "true sea-dog," and a "real old salt," and such like names, and saying there was the sort of man that made England terrible at sea.

In one way, indeed, he bade fair to ruin us; for he kept on staying week after week, and at last month after month, so that all the money had been long exhausted, and still my father never plucked up the heart to insist on having more. If ever he mentioned it, the captain blew through his nose so loudly, that you might say he roared, and stared my poor father out of the room. I have seen him wringing his hands after such a rebuff, and I am sure the annoyance and the terror he lived in must have greatly hastened his early and unhappy death.

All the time he lived with us the captain made no change whatever in his dress but to buy some stockings from a hawker. One of the cocks of his hat having fallen down, he let it hang from that day forth, though it was a great annoyance when it blew. I remember the appearance of his coat, which he patched himself upstairs in his room, and which, before the end, was nothing but patches. He never wrote or received a letter, and he never spoke with any, but the neighbors, and with these, for the most part, only when drunk on rum. The great sea-chest none of us had ever seen open.

He was only once crossed, and that was toward the end, when my poor father was far gone in a decline that took him off. Dr. Livesey came late one afternoon to see the patient, took a bit of dinner from my mother, and went into the parlor to smoke a pipe until his horse should come down from the hamlet, for we had no stabling at the old "Benbow." I followed him in, and I remember observing the contrast the neat, bright doctor, with his powder as white as snow, and his bright, black eyes and pleasant manners, made with the coltish country folk, and above all, with that filthy, heavy, bleared scarecrow of a pirate of ours, sitting far gone in rum, with his arms on the table. Suddenly he—the captain, that is—began to pipe up his eternal song:

"Fifteen men on the dead man's chest—
Yo-ho-ho, and a bottle of rum!
Drink and the devil had done for the rest—
Yo-ho-ho, and a bottle of rum!"

At first I had supposed "the dead man's chest" to be that identical big box of his upstairs in the front room, and the thought had been mingled in my nightmares with that of the one-legged seafaring man. But by this time we had all long ceased to pay any particular notice to the song; it was new, that night, to nobody but Dr. Livesey, and on him I observed it did not produce an agreeable effect, for he looked up for a moment quite angrily before he went on with his talk to old Taylor, the gardener, on a new cure for the rheumatics. In the meantime, the captain gradually brightened up at his own music, and at last flapped his hand upon the table before him in a way we all knew to mean—silence. The voices stopped at once, all but Dr. Livesey's; he went on as before, speaking clear and kind, and drawing briskly at his pipe between every word or two. The captain glared at him for awhile, flapped his hand again, glared still harder, and at last broke out with a villainous, low oath: "Silence, there, between decks!"

"Were you addressing me, sir?" says the doctor; and when the ruffian had told him, with another oath, that this was so, "I have only one thing to say to you, sir," replies the doctor, "that if you keep on drinking rum, the world will soon be quit of a very dirty scoundrel!"

The old fellow's fury was awful. He sprang to his feet, drew and opened a sailor's clasp knife, and, balancing it open on the palm of his hand, threatened to pin the doctor to the wall.

The doctor never so much as moved. He spoke to him, as before, over his shoulder, and in the same tone of voice; rather high, so that all the room might hear, but perfectly calm and steady:

"If you do not put that knife this instant in your pocket, I promise, upon my honor, you shall hang at the next assizes."

Then followed a battle of looks between them; but the captain

soon knuckled under, put up his weapon, and resumed his seat, grumbling like a beaten dog.

"And now, sir," continued the doctor, "since I now know there's such a fellow in my district, you may count I'll have an eye upon you day and night. I'm not a doctor only; I'm a magistrate; and if I catch a breath of complaint against you, if it's only for a piece of incivility like to-night's, I'll take effectual means to have you hunted down and routed out of this. Let that suffice."

Soon after Dr. Livesey's horse came to the door, and he rode away; but the captain held his peace that evening, and for many evenings to come.

BLACK DOG APPEARS AND DISAPPEARS

It was not very long after this that there occurred the first of the mysterious events that rid us at last of the captain, though not, as you will see, of his affairs. It was a bitter cold winter, with long, hard frosts and heavy gales; and it was plain from the first that my poor father was little likely to see the spring. He sank daily, and my mother and I had all the inn upon our hands; and were kept busy enough, without paying much regard to our unpleasant guest.

It was one January morning, very early—a pinching, frosty morning—the cove all gray with hoarfrost, the ripple lapping softly on the stones, the sun still low and only touching the hilltops and shining far to seaward. The captain had risen earlier than usual, and set out down the beach, his cutlass swinging under the broad skirts of the old blue coat, his brass telescope under his arm, his hat tilted back upon his head. I remember his breath hanging like smoke in his wake as he strode off, and the last sound of him, as he turned the big rock, was a loud snort of indignation, as though his mind was still running upon Dr. Livesey.

Well, mother was upstairs with father; and I was laying the breakfast-table against the captain's return, when the parlor door opened, and a man stepped in on whom I had never set my eyes before. He was a pale, tallowy creature, wanting two fingers on the left hand; and, though he wore a cutlass, he did not look much like a fighter. I had always my eye open for seafaring men, with one leg or two, and I remember this one puzzled me. He was not sailorly, and yet he had a smack of the sea about him too.

I asked him what was for his service, and he said he would take rum; but as I was going out of the room to fetch it he sat down upon a table, and motioned me to draw near. I paused where I was with my napkin in my hand.

"Come here, sonny," says he. "Come nearer here."

I took a step nearer.

"Is this here table for my mate Bill?" he asked, with a kind of leer.

I told him I did not know his mate Bill; and this was for a person who stayed in our house, whom we called the captain.

"Well," said he, "my mate Bill would be called the captain, as like as not. He has a cut on one cheek, and a mighty pleasant way with him, particularly in drink, has my mate Bill. We'll put it, for argument like, that your captain has a cut on one cheek—and we'll put it, if you like, that that cheek's the right one. Ah, well! I told you. Now, is my mate Bill in this here house?"

I told him he was out walking.

"Which way, sonny? Which way is he gone?"

And when I had pointed out the rock and told him how the captain was likely to return, and how soon, and answered a few other questions, "Ah," said he, "this'll be as good as drink to my mate Bill."

The expression of his face as he said these words was not at all pleasant, and I had my own reasons for thinking that the stranger was mistaken, even supposing he meant what he said. But it was no affair of mine, I thought; and, besides, it was difficult to know what to do. The stranger kept hanging about just inside the inn door, peering round the corner like a cat waiting for a mouse. Once I stepped out myself into the road, but he immediately called me back, and, as I did not obey quick enough for his fancy, a most horrible change came over his tallowy face, and he ordered me in, with an oath that made me jump. As soon as I was back again he returned to his former manner, half fawning, half sneering, patted me on the shoulder, told me I was a good boy, and he had taken quite a fancy to me. "I have a son of my own," said he, "as like you as two blocks, and he's all the pride of my 'art. But the great thing for boys is discipline, sonny—discipline. Now, if you had sailed along of Bill, you wouldn't have stood there to be spoke to twice—not you. That was never Bill's way, nor the way of sich as sailed with him. And here, sure enough, is my mate Bill, with a spyglass under his arm, bless his old 'art, to be sure. You and me'll just go back into the parlor, sonny, and get behind the door, and we'll give Bill a little surprise—bless his 'art, I say again."

So saying, the stranger backed along with me into the parlor, and put me behind him in the corner, so that we were both hidden by the open door. I was very uneasy and alarmed, as you may fancy, and it rather added to my fears to observe that the stranger was certainly frightened himself. He cleared the hilt of his cutlass and loosened the blade in his sheath; and all the time we were waiting there he kept swallowing as if he felt what we used to call a lump in the throat.

At last in strode the captain, slammed the door behind him, without looking to the right or left, and marched straight across the room to where his breakfast awaited him.

"Bill," said the stranger, in a voice that I thought he had tried to make bold and big.

The captain spun round on his heel and fronted us; all the brown had gone out of his face, and even his nose was blue; he had the look of a man who sees a ghost, or the evil one, or something worse, if anything can be; and, upon my word, I felt sorry to see him, all in a moment, turn so old and sick.

"Come, Bill, you know me; you know an old shipmate, Bill, surely," said the stranger.

The captain made a sort of gasp.

"Black Dog!" said he.

"And who else?" returned the other, getting more at his ease. "Black Dog as ever was, come for to see his old shipmate Billy, at the 'Admiral Benbow' inn. Ah, Bill, Bill, we have seen a sight of times, us two, since I lost them two talons," holding up his mutilated hand.

"Now, look here," said the captain; "you've run me down; here I am; well, then, speak up: what is it?"

"That's you, Bill," returned Black Dog, "you're in the right of it, Billy. I'll have a glass of rum from this dear child here, as I've took such a liking to; and we'll sit down, if you please, and talk square, like old shipmates."

When I returned with the rum, they were already seated on either side of the captain's breakfast-table—Black Dog next to the door, and sitting sideways, so as to have one eye on his old shipmate, and one, as I thought, on his retreat.

He bade me go, and leave the door wide open. "None of your keyholes for me, sonny," he said; and I left them together, and retired into the bar.

For a long time, though I certainly did my best to listen, I could hear nothing but a low gabbling; but at last the voices began to grow higher, and I could pick up a word or two, mostly oaths, from the captain.

"No, no, no, no; and an end of it!" he cried once. And again, "If it comes to swinging, swing all, say I."

Then all of a sudden there was a tremendous explosion of oaths and other noises—the chair and table went over in a lump, a clash of steel followed, and then a cry of pain, and the next instant I saw Black Dog in full flight, and the captain hotly pursuing, both with drawn cutlasses, and the former streaming blood from the left shoulder. Just at the door, the captain aimed at the fugitive one last tremendous cut, which would certainly have split him to the chin had it not been intercepted by our big signboard of Admiral Benbow. You may see the notch on the lower side of the frame to this day.

That blow was the last of the battle. Once out upon the road, Black Dog, in spite of his wound, showed a wonderful clean pair of heels, and disappeared over the edge of the hill in half a minute. The captain, for his part, stood staring at the signboard like a bewildered man. Then he passed his hand over his eyes several times, and at last turned back into the house.

"Jim," says he, "rum;" and as he spoke, he reeled a little, and caught himself with one hand against the wall.

"Are you hurt?" cried I.

"Rum," he repeated. "I must get away from here. Rum! rum!"

I ran to fetch it; but I was quite unsteadied by all that had fallen out, and I broke one glass and fouled the tap, and while I was still getting in my own way, I heard a loud fall in the parlor, and, running in, beheld the captain lying full length upon the floor. At the same instant my mother, alarmed by the cries and fighting, came running downstairs to help me. Between us we raised his head. He was breathing very loud, and hard; but his eyes were closed, and his face a horrible color.

"Dear, deary me," cried my mother, "what a disgrace upon the house! And your poor father sick!"

In the meantime, we had no idea what to do to help the captain, nor any other thought but that he had got his death-hurt in the scuffle with the stranger. I got the rum, to be sure, and tried to put it down his throat; but his teeth were tightly shut, and his jaws as strong as iron. It was a happy relief for us when the door opened and Dr. Livesey came in, on his visit to my father.

"Oh, doctor," we cried, "what shall we do? Where is he wounded?"

"Wounded? A fiddlestick's end!" said the doctor. "No more wounded than you or I. The man has had a stroke, as I warned him. Now, Mrs. Hawkins, just you run upstairs to your husband and tell him, if possible, nothing about it. For my part, I must do my best to save this fellow's trebly worthless life; and Jim, you get me a basin."

When I got back with the basin, the doctor had already ripped up the captain's sleeve, and exposed his great sinewy arm. It was tattooed in several places. "Here's luck," "A fair wind," and "Billy Bones his fancy," were very neatly and clearly executed on the forearm; and up near the shoulder there was a sketch of a gallows and a man hanging from it—done, as I thought, with great spirit.

"Prophetic," said the doctor, touching this picture with his finger. "And now, Master Billy Bones, if that be your name, we'll have a look at the color of your blood. Jim," he said, "are you afraid of blood?"

"No sir," said I.

"Well, then," said he, "you hold the basin;" and with that he took his lancet from his case and opened a vein.

A great deal of blood was taken before the captain opened his eyes and looked mistily about him. First he recognized the doctor with an unmistakable frown; then his glance fell upon me, and he looked relieved. But suddenly his color changed, and he tried to raise himself, crying:

"Where's Black Dog?"

"There is no Black Dog here," said the doctor, "except what you have on your own back. You have been drinking rum; you have had a stroke, precisely as I told you; and I have just, very much against my own will, dragged you headforemost out of the grave. Now, Mr. Bones——"

"That's not my name," he interrupted.

"Much I care," returned the doctor. "It's the name of a buccaneer of my acquaintance; and I call you by it for the sake of shortness, and what I have to say to you is this: one glass of rum won't kill you, but if you take one you'll take another and another, and I stake my wig if you don't break off short, you'll die—do you understand that?—die, and go to your own place, like the man in the Bible. Come, now, make an effort. I'll help you to your bed for once."

Between us, with much trouble, we managed to hoist him upstairs, and laid him on his bed, where his head fell back on the pillow, as if he were almost fainting.

"Now, mind you," said the doctor, "I clear my conscience—the name of rum for you is death."

And with that he went off to see my father, taking me with him by the arm.

"This is nothing," he said, as soon as he had closed the door. "I have drawn blood enough to keep him quiet awhile; he should lie for a week where he is—that is the best thing for him and you; but another stroke will settle him."

THE BLACK SPOT

About noon I stopped at the captain's door with some cooling drinks and medicines. He was lying very much as we had left him, only a little higher, and he seemed both weak and excited.

"Jim," he said, "you're the only one here that's worth anything; and you know I've been always good to you. Never a month but I've given you a silver fourpenny for yourself. And now you see, mate, I'm pretty low, and deserted by all; and Jim, you'll bring me one noggin of rum, now, won't you, matey?"

"The doctor——" I began.

But he broke in cursing the doctor, in a feeble voice, but heartily. "Doctors is all swabs," he said; "and that doctor there, why, what do he know about seafaring men? I been in places hot as pitch, and mates dropping round with Yellow Jack, and the blessed land a-heaving like the sea with earthquakes—what do the doctor know of lands like that?—and I lived on rum, I tell you. It's been meat and drink, and man and wife, to me; and if I'm not to have my rum now I'm a poor old hulk on a lee shore, my blood'll be on you, Jim, and that doctor swab;" and he ran on again for awhile with curses. "Look, Jim, how my fingers fidges," he continued in the pleading tone. "I can't keep 'em still, not I. I haven't had a drop this blessed day. That doctor's a fool, I tell you. If I don't have a drain o' rum, Jim, I'll have the horrors; I seen some on 'em already. I seen old Flint in the corner there, behind you; as plain as print, I seen him; and if I get the horrors, I'm a man that has lived rough, and I'll raise Cain. Your doctor hisself said one glass wouldn't hurt me. I'll give you a golden guinea for a noggin, Jim."

He was growing more and more excited, and this alarmed me for my father, who was very low that day, and needed quiet; besides, I was reassured by the doctor's words, now quoted to me, and rather offended by the offer of a bribe.

"I want none of your money," said I, "but what you owe my father. I'll get you one glass, and no more."

When I brought it to him he seized it greedily, and drank it out.

"Aye, aye," said he, "that's some better, sure enough. And now, matey, did that doctor say how long I was to lie here in this old berth?"

"A week at least," said I.

"Thunder!" he cried. "A week! I can't do that; they'd have the black spot on me by then. The lubbers is going about to get the wind of me this blessed moment; lubbers as couldn't keep what they got, and want to nail what is another's. Is that seamanly behavior, now, I want to know? But I'm a saving soul. I never wasted good money of mine, nor lost it neither; and I'll trick 'em again. I'm not afraid on 'em. I'll shake out another reef, matey, and daddle 'em again."

As he was thus speaking, he had risen from bed with great difficulty, holding to my shoulder with a grip that almost made me cry out, and moving his legs like so much dead weight. His words, spirited as they were in meaning, contrasted sadly with the weakness of the voice in which they were uttered. He paused when he had got into a sitting position on the edge.

"That doctor's done me," he murmured. "My ears is singing. Lay me back."

Before I could do much to help him he had fallen back again to his former place, where he lay for a while silent.

"Jim," he said, at length, "you saw that seafaring man to-day!"

"Black Dog?" I asked.

"Ah! Black Dog," says he. "*He's* a bad 'un; but there's worse that put him on. Now, if I can't get away nohow, and they tip me the black spot, mind you, it's my old seachest they're after; you get on a horse—you can, can't you? Well, then, you get on a horse, and go to—well, yes, I will!—to that eternal doctor swab, and tell him to pipe all hands—magistrates and sich—and he'll lay 'em aboard at the 'Admiral Benbow'—all old Flint's crew, man and boy, all on 'em that's left. I was first mate, I was, old Flint's first mate, and I'm the on'y one as knows the place. He gave it me at Savannah, when he lay a-dying, like as if I was to now, you see. But you won't peach unless they get the black spot on me, or unless you see that Black Dog again, or a seafaring man with one leg, Jim—him above all."

"But what is the black spot, captain?" I asked.

"That's a summons, mate. I'll tell you if they get that. But you keep your weather-eye open, Jim, and I'll share with you equals, upon my honor."

He wandered a little longer, his voice growing weaker; but soon after I had given him his medicine, which he took like a child, with the remark, "If ever a seaman wanted drugs, it's me," he fell at last into a heavy, swoon-like sleep, in which I left him. What I should have done had all gone well I do not know. Probably I should have told the whole story to the doctor; for I was in mortal fear lest the captain should repent of his confessions and make an end of me. But as things fell out, my poor father died quite suddenly that evening, which put all other matters on one side. Our natural distress, the visits of the neighbors, the arranging of the funeral, and all the work of the inn to be carried on in the meanwhile, kept me so busy that I had scarcely time to think of the captain, far less to be afraid of him.

He got downstairs next morning, to be sure, and had his meals as usual, though he ate little, and had more, I am afraid, than his usual supply of rum, for he helped himself out of the bar, scowling and blowing through his nose, and no one dared to cross him. On the night before the funeral he was as drunk as ever; and it was shocking, in that house of mourning to hear him singing away at his ugly old sea-song; but, weak as he was, we were all in fear of death for him, and the doctor was suddenly taken up with a case many miles away, and was never near the house after my father's death. I have said the captain was weak; and indeed he seemed rather to grow weaker than regain his strength. He clambered up and downstairs, and went from the parlor to the bar and back again, and sometimes put his nose out of doors to smell the sea, holding on to the walls as he went for support, and breathing hard and fast like a man on a steep mountain. He never particularly addressed me, and it is my belief he had as good as forgotten his confidences; but his temper was more flighty, and, allowing for his bodily weakness, more violent than ever. He had an alarming way now when he was drunk, of drawing his cutlass and laying it bare before him on the table. But, with all that, he minded people less, and seemed shut up in his own thoughts and rather wandering. Once, for instance, to our extreme wonder, he piped up to a different air, a kind of country love-song, that he must have learned in his youth before he had begun to follow the sea.

So things passed until, the day after the funeral, and about three o'clock of a bitter, foggy, frosty afternoon, I was standing at the door for a moment, full of sad thoughts about my father, when I saw some one drawing slowly near along the road. He was plainly blind, for he tapped before him with a stick, and wore a great green shade over his eyes and nose; and he was hunched, as if with age or weakness, and wore a huge old tattered sea-cloak with a hood, that made him appear positively deformed. I never saw in my life a more dreadful-looking figure.

He stopped a little distance from the inn, and, raising his voice in an odd sing-song, addressed the air in front of him:

"Will any kind friend inform a poor blind man, who has lost the precious sight of his eyes in the gracious defense of his native country, England, and God Bless King George!—where or in what part of this country he may now be?"

"You are at the 'Admiral Benbow,' Black Hill Cove, my good man," said I.

"I hear a voice," said he—"a young voice. Will you give me your hand, my kind young friend, and lead me in?"

I held out my hand, and the horrible, soft-spoken, eyeless creature gripped it in a moment like a vise. I was so much startled that I struggled to withdraw; but the blind man pulled me close up to him with a single action of his arm.

"Now, boy," he said, "take me in to the captain."

"Sir," said I, "upon my word I dare not."

"Oh," he sneered, "that's it! Take me in straight or I'll break your arm."

And he gave it, as he spoke, a wrench that made me cry out.

"Sir," said I, "it is for yourself I mean. The captain is not what he used to be. He sits with a drawn cutlass. Another gentle-man——"

"Come, now, march," interrupted he; and I never heard a voice so cruel, and cold, and ugly as that blind man's. It cowed me more than the pain; and I began to obey him at once, walking straight in at the door and toward the parlor, where our sick old buccaneer was sitting, dazed with rum. The blind man clung close to me, holding me in one iron fist, and leaning almost more of his weight on me than I could carry. "Lead me straight up to him, and when I'm in view, cry out, 'Here's a friend for you, Bill.' If you don't I'll do this;" and with that he gave me a twitch that I thought would have made me faint. Between this and that, I was so ut-terly terrified of the blind beggar that I forgot my terror of the captain, and as I opened the parlor door, cried out the words he had ordered in a trembling voice.

The poor captain raised his eyes, and at one look the rum went out of him, and left him staring sober. The expression of his face was not so much of terror as of mortal sickness. He made a movement to rise, but I do not believe he had enough force left in his body.

"Now, Bill, sit where you are," said the beggar. "If I can't see, I can hear a finger stirring. Business is business. Hold out your left hand. Boy, take his left hand by the wrist, and bring it near to my right."

We both obeyed him to the letter, and I saw him pass something from the hollow of the hand that held his stick, into the palm of the captain's, which closed upon it instantly.

"And now that's done," said the blind man; and at the words he suddenly left hold of me, and, with incredible accuracy and nimbleness, skipped out of the parlor and into the road, where, as I still stood motionless, I could hear his stick go tap-tap-tapping into the distance.

It was some time before either I or the captain seemed to gather our senses; but at length, and about at the same moment, I released his wrist, which I was still holding, and he drew in his hand and looked sharply into the palm.

"Ten o'clock!" he cried. "Six hours. We'll do them yet;" and he sprang to his feet.

Even as he did so, he reeled, put his hand to his throat, stood swaying for a moment, and then, with a peculiar sound, fell from his whole height face foremost to the floor.

I ran to him at once, calling to my mother. But haste was all in vain. The captain had been struck dead by thundering apoplexy. It is a curious thing to understand, for I had certainly never liked the man, though of late I had begun to pity him, but as soon as I saw that he was dead, I burst into a flood of tears. It was the second death I had known, and the sorrow of the first was still fresh in my heart.

Twenty Thousand Leagues Under the Sea

THE SOUL OF THE NAUTILUS

by JULES VERNE

Jules Verne invented the scientific adventure story and this was just as popular toward the end of the nineteenth century as science fiction stories are today. In fact, after Captain Nemo had been killed off, there was such a wave of protest from the public that the author had to have him brought back to life. The Nautilus, as described in Twenty Thousand Leagues Under the Sea, *is certainly the most marvelous boat ever put together by human hands; it foretold the modern submarine with amazing accuracy. And long before they were invented, Jules Verne also predicted the airplane, the automobile, the telephone, the air-brake, and hundreds of other devices which opened up a new universe of scientific miracles to his readers.* Twenty Thousand Leagues Under the Sea *contains not only one of the most thrilling plots of all of Verne's scientific romances, but also descriptions of the undersea world that have never been surpassed.*

With a wave of the hand my host indicated the instruments that hung on the walls of his room. "Here," he began, "are the contrivances which control the navigation of the submarine. I have them always under my eyes, and they tell me my position and exact direction in the middle of the ocean. Which ones are known to you?"

"The thermometer, of course, which gives us the internal tem-

perature; and the barometer, which marks the weight of the air and foretells changes in the weather."

"To the left is the hygrometer."

"Which, if its name be any clue, must measure the dryness of the atmosphere. Oh, yes, and next to it is the storm-glass, the contents of which, by decomposing, announce the approach of tempests. And here is the compass which guides your course. But what is the next object?"

"A sextant, one of a different shape, perhaps, from what you are used to seeing."

"I was stupid indeed not to know it, anyhow. Well, that shows you the latitude by the altitude of the sun. There are the chronometers by which you calculate the longitude. And beside them the day and night glasses, through which you examine the points of the horizon whenever the 'Nautilus' rises to the surface of the waves. These are the usual nautical instruments. But the others which I do not know? In what way do they answer the particular requirements of your ship?"

"This dial with the movable needle is a manometer," said Captain Nemo. "By communication with the water, whose external pressure it registers, it gives us our depth at the same time. But really, Professor, there is a much better way for me to explain things to you than by discussing one by one and separately the various technical tools which you do not understand. Suppose I give you a basic explanation of the soul of the 'Nautilus.' Will you listen?"

"Like a good child to his father's words."

"Very well, then. There is a powerful agent which is obedient, rapid, easy, and conformable to every use. It reigns supreme on board my vessel. Every blessed thing is done by means of it. This agent warms it, lights it, and is the heart and soul of my mechanical apparatus. Its name is electricity."

"You don't mean it!" I cried in surprise.

"I do mean it," said the captain.

"But, my dear sir, your ship has an extreme rapidity of movement which does not at all agree with the function of electrical energy as I understand it. Until now its dynamic force has remained under restraint and has been able to produce only a small amount of power."

"Ah," said Captain Nemo, "but, you see, my electricity is not everybody's. You know what sea water is composed of. In a thousand grams of it are found 96½ per cent of water and about 2 per cent of chloride of sodium; small quantities of chlorides of magnesium and potassium, bromide of magnesium, sulphate of magnesia, sulphate and carbonate of lime. Chloride of sodium thus forms a large part of the separable ingredients, and it is this that I extract from sea water and of which in combination I compose my formula. I owe all to the ocean. It produces electricity, and from this I derive heat, light, motion—in a word, the very life of the 'Nautilus.'"

"But surely not the air you breathe?"

"I could manufacture the air for my consumption, but where is the use when I rise to the surface of the sea at will? And yet, even if electricity does not furnish me with air to breathe, it at least operates the powerful pumps that are stored in spacious reservoirs and which enable me to prolong as long as I care to my stay in the depths of the sea. This marvelous agent gives a uniform and unintermittent light, which the sun does not."

"Can you tell time by it, as well as by the sun?"

"Ho-ho! Far better, my friend. Look at yonder clock—it is electrical and runs with a regularity that defies the best chronometers. You notice that I have divided the dial into twenty-four hours, like the Italian clocks. For with me there is neither night nor day, but only that factitious light that I take with me to the bottom of the ocean. See? Just now it is ten o'clock in the morning."

"Exactly. That ends, I presume, the uses to which you put your willing agent?"

"By no manner of means! Here's another application of electricity: the dial hanging straight in front of you indicates the speed of our ship. An electric thread puts it in communication with the screw, and the needle registers the actual rate we are traveling.

Look! We are now spinning along at a uniform speed of fifteen miles an hour."

"Will wonders never cease? You were inspired when you made a servant of a power that replaced wind, water, and steam."

"But we are still far from through, M. Aronnax," said my host, rising. "If you are willing, we'll look over the stern quarters of the 'Nautilus.'"

In reality, I already knew the anterior part of this submarine boat, of which this is the exact division, starting from the ship's head: the dining room, five yards long, separated from the library by a water-tight partition; the library, five yards long; the large drawing room, ten yards long, separated from the captain's room by a second water-tight partition; the said room, five yards in length; mine, two and a half yards; and lastly, a reservoir of air, seven and a half yards, that extended to the bows—total length thirty-five yards, or one hundred and five feet. The partitions had doors that were closed hermetically by means of India rubber instruments, and that insured the safety of the "Nautilus" in case of a leak.

I followed Captain Nemo through the waist and arrived at the center of the boat. Here a sort of well opened between two partitions. An iron ladder, fastened with an iron hook to the partition, led to the upper end. I asked the captain what the ladder was used for.

"It leads to the small boat," he said.

"Ye gods and little fishes! Have you a boat?" I asked in much surprise.

"There's nothing remarkable about that. And it's an excellent sailer, too—light and insubmersible. It serves me as a fishing craft or as a pleasure boat."

"But surely, when you wish to embark in it, you must first come to the surface of the water?"

"Not at all. It is attached to the upper part of the hull of the 'Nautilus' and occupies a cavity specially made for it. It is decked over, entirely water-tight, and held together by solid bolts."

"Describe to me the process of embarking in it when undersea."

"Most willingly. This ladder leads to a manhole made in our submarine's hull, which corresponds to a similar hole in the side of the small boat. By this double opening I enter. They shut the one belonging to the 'Nautilus,' I close the other by means of screw pressure, I undo the bolts, and the little craft shoots up to the surface of the sea with prodigious speed. I then open the panel of the bridge which till then has been carefully shut. I mast it, hoist my sail, take up my oars—and I'm off!"

"Off you are, Captain, I see that. But how, in the name of mystery, do you get on, or rather in, again?"

"Oh, I don't come back, M. Aronnax. The 'Nautilus' comes and gets me when I order it to."

"And they know where to find you?"

"Why not? An electric thread connects us. I simply telegraph what I wish to. It is quite simple."

"All things are simple," I said, astonished at these marvels, "when you know how to do them."

After we had passed by the cage of the staircase that led to the platform, I saw a cabin six feet long in which Conseil and Ned Land, enchanted with their repast, were devouring it with avidity. Then a door opened into a kitchen nine feet long, which was situated between the large storerooms. Electricity did the cooking here better than gas itself. The streams of current under the furnaces lent to the sponges of platina a heat that was regularly maintained and distributed. The flow of current also heated a distilling apparatus which, by evaporation, furnished excellent water for drinking. Near this kitchen was a bathroom comfortably furnished and fitted with hot and cold water taps.

Next was the berth room of the vessel, sixteen feet long. But the door was shut, and I could not see the arrangement of it, which might have given me an idea of the number of men employed on the "Nautilus."

Beyond was a fourth partition, that separated off the engine room. A door opened, and I found myself in the compartment in which Captain Nemo—who must be an engineer of a very high order—had installed his locomotive machinery. This engine room, clearly lighted, did not measure less than sixty-five feet in length. It was divided into two sections. The first part contained the apparatus for producing electricity, and the second the machinery that connected it with the screw. I studied it with great interest in order, if possible, to understand the engines of the "Nautilus."

"You note," said the captain, "that I use Bunsen's contrivances and not Ruhmkorff's. The latter would not have been powerful enough. Bunsen's units are fewer in number, but large and strong, which experience proves to be the most satisfactory. The electricity produced passes forward, where through electromagnets of huge size it works on a system of levers and cogwheels that transmit the rotary movement to the axle of the screw. This one, the diameter of which is nineteen feet and the thread twenty-three feet, performs about one hundred and twenty revolutions a second."

"And you get thereby?"

"A speed of fifty miles an hour."

"I saw the 'Nautilus' maneuver before the 'Abraham Lincoln,' and I already had my own ideas as to its speed. But speed is not the only, and often not the chief requisite. You must see where you go. You must be able to direct your ship to the right, to the left, above, below. How do you get to the depths, where you find an increasing resistance which is rated by hundreds of atmospheres? How do you return to the surface of the ocean? And how do you maintain yourselves in the requisite medium? Am I asking too much, Captain?"

"Not at all, Professor," replied my courteous host, but only after a slight hesitation. "You may as well know, seeing that you are never going to leave this submarine. Come into the saloon which usually serves us for a study, and there you will learn all you wish to know about the 'Nautilus.'"

More Good Reading

For Younger Readers

HOMER THE TORTOISE by Margaret J. Baker. Illus. by Leo Bates. Whittlesey House. A charming and witty tale about Homer, a scholarly tortoise who nonchalantly speaks Greek as well as English, plays chess expertly, and becomes the adviser to some delightful English schoolgirls.

PETER PAN by Sir James M. Barrie. Illus. by Nora Unwin. Scribner. A new edition with fine illustrations of this famous whimsical story of the boy who never grew up.

FREDDY, THE DETECTIVE by Walter R. Brooks. Illus. by Kurt Wiese. Knopf. When Freddy, a pig, decides to become a detective, some pretty funny things happen to the farmyard animals on Mr. Bean's farm. (Among the dozen other popular *Freddy* stories are *Freddy Goes to Florida*, *Freddy, the Cowboy*, and *Freddy and the Space Ship*.)

POO-POO AND THE DRAGONS by C. S. Forester. Illus. by Robert Lawson. Little, Brown. A delicious fantasy of how some well-behaved dragons make themselves useful and welcome in an English home. Grownups enjoy the sly humor too. By the author of the famous *Captain Hornblower*.

MR. POPPER'S PENGUINS by Richard and Florence Atwater. Little Brown. Hilarious things happen in the Popper household when father gets a penguin for a pet. A most enjoyable nonsense story.

THE WIZARD OF OZ by L. Frank Baum. Bobbs Merrill. The first book is the most famous, and by far the best, of a long series of original tales about the land of Oz. Once children start on these Oz books, it is hard to stop them from going through the more than 20 other volumes.

HONK THE MOOSE by Phil Stong. Illus. by Kurt Wiese. Dodd, Mead. A most amusing story about a sad-eyed, hungry moose who wanders into a small-town livery stable, and how a group of boys struggles to get rid of him. Funny pictures too.

MARY POPPINS by Pamela L. Travers. Illus. by Mary Shepard. Harcourt. A most astonishing nursemaid, Mary Poppins is severely matter-of-fact as she performs fantastic magic for her young charges. A wonderful modern classic, not to be missed. (Also *Mary Poppins Comes Back* —"This time at the end of a kite string,"—and *Mary Poppins in the Park*.)

For Older Readers

THE JUNGLE BOOKS by Rudyard Kipling. Illus. by Kurt Wiese. Doubleday. Contains all the Mowgli stories, unique tales about a boy who learns the laws of the jungle when he is adopted by a family of wolves. Also other wonderful jungle stories like *Rikki-Tikki-Tavi*.

THE STORY OF SERAPINA by Anne H. White. Illus. by Tony Palazzo. Viking. A delightfully humorous fantasy about Serapina, the cat who could carry milk bottles with her tail, mind the children, and entertain them too.

THE HOBBIT, OR THERE AND BACK AGAIN by J. R. R. Tolkien. Houghton Mifflin. The adventures of a mythical creature called a hobbit, as he goes on a search with some dwarf friends, to rescue gold from the dragons who had stolen it. The plot can give you no idea of the completely original charm of this tale, the author's brilliant narrative skill and sly humor. A modern classic.

CHARLOTTE'S WEB by E. B. White. Illus. by Garth Williams. Harper. A girl, a pig, and a spider form an odd threesome which makes a humorous and beautifully written fantasy.

THE TWENTY-ONE BALLOONS by William Pène du Bois. Viking. An account of a fabulous balloon voyage around the world based partly on science and partly on nonsense. An enchanting combination of adventure, fantasy, and satire about science fiction.

THE WONDERFUL ADVENTURES OF NILS by Selma Sagerlof. Illus. by H. Baumhauer. Pantheon. A beautiful new edition of the well-loved fantasy about a mischievous boy who gets reduced to the size of an elf and flies over Sweden with the wild geese. Written by the famous Swedish novelist with a special savor of its own.

THROUGH THE LOOKING GLASS by Lewis Carroll. Illus. by John Tenniel. Continuing the extraordinary happenings that begin in *Alice's Adventures in Wonderland* when Alice follows the white rabbit down the hole into the looking glass world. These two stories usually appear together in one volume and there are many editions of this ageless classic. Some boys and girls can't see the special charm of its satire and fantasy if *Alice* is given to them too early, but all (including grownups) come to love it, later if not sooner, and appreciate why it has become the most famous of all fantasies ever written for children.

THE MYSTERIOUS ISLAND by Jules Verne. An exciting imaginative tale about scientific adventures in strange worlds. By the author of *Twenty*

Thousand Leagues Under the Sea who was the grand-daddy of all modern science fiction writers. Written at the end of the 19th century, his fantasies foretold modern inventions with astonishing accuracy, and they are still fascinating today.

FARMER IN THE SKY by Robert A. Heinlein. Scribner. An exciting science fiction story about a boy's adventures in interplanetary travel at the end of the 20th century. By an author who has written some of the best stories on space travel, a subject so tremendously interesting to modern youngsters, especially boys.

SEVEN SCIENCE FICTION NOVELS by H. G. Wells. Dover. Pioneer fascinating stories in this field by a famous English writer.

BEST OF SCIENCE FICTION edited by Groff Conklin. Crown. A large and well-selected anthology of science fiction stories. (Also *Treasury of Science Fiction.*)

THE THURBER CARNIVAL by James Thurber. Harper. Wonderfully humorous stories, much admired by grownups for their fine writing and wit, but equally appealing to boys and girls over eleven or so for their sheer fun. With the authors own clever cartoons.

CHUCKLEBAIT selected by Margaret C. Scroggin. Knopf. A fine collection of really funny stories by a librarian who knows what young readers like. (Also *More Chucklebait.*)

TIME TO LAUGH by Phyllis Fenner. Knopf. Amusing folk stories as well as modern ones are included in this excellent collection.

MYTHS, LEGENDS AND HERO TALES

MIGHTY MEN FROM ACHILLES TO JULIUS CAESAR by Eleanor Farjeon. Illus. by Hugh Clusterman. Appleton. Well-told short tales about heroes of the ancient world and legends such as that of the founding of Rome by Romulus and Remus. Excellent for reading aloud. (Also *Mighty Men from Beowulf to William the Conqueror.*)

IN THE DAYS OF THE GIANTS by Abby Farwell Brown. Illus. by E. B. Smith. Houghton Mifflin. A good first book about Norse mythology.

THE HEROES by Charles Kingsley. Macmillan. A fine cycle of 30 Greek myths. The vigorous adventure stories such as those of Perseus, Jason, and other Greek heroes appeal especially to boys and girls.

THE GOLDEN FLEECE AND THE HEROES WHO LIVED BEFORE ACHILLES by Padraic Colum. Illus. by Willy Pogany. Macmillan. A companion volume to the author's *The Children's Homer* and distinguished retelling of the famous Greek myths by a poet who manages to recapture the feeling of the period beautifully.

PAUL BUNYAN SWINGS HIS AXE by Dell J. McCormick. Caxton. Simpli-

fied tall tales about the legendary American lumberjack well arranged to
tell the story of his life.

JOHN HENRY AND HIS HAMMER by Harold W. Felton. Illus. by Aldren A.
Watson. Knopf. A dramatic and effective account of the Negro super-
man who has become part of the epic of the building of the railroads in
America.

PECOS BILL, GREATEST COWBOY OF THEM ALL by James C. Bowman.
Illus. by Laura Bannon. Whitman. Tall tales about the wonderful exploits of a legendary cowboy. Interesting background of American frontier
life.

STORIES OF THE GODS AND HEROES edited by Sally Benson. Illus. by Steele
Savage. Dial. Based on Bulfinch's *Age of Fable* the better known of the
Greek myths are retold with vigor and distinction. Fine illustrations.

MYTHOLOGY by Edith Hamilton. Illus. by Steele Savage. Little, Brown.
A distinguished book, valuable both for general reading and as a reference
for all the characters in Greek mythology. Contains excellent introduc-
tions and notes about the stories.

STORIES OF ADVENTURE

BUSH HOLIDAY by Stephen Fennimore. Doubleday. An American boy has
some adventurous brushes with the strange wild life in the bush country of
Australia.

FUJIO by Raymond Creekmore. Macmillan. A boy's thrilling adventure
on the lofty volcano of Fujiyama. True Japanese background and handsome lithographs.

STORIES OF THE SEA selected by Phyllis Fenner. Illus. by Kurt Worth.
Knopf. Exciting sea stories collected from the writings of famous authors.

THE LINE OF DANGER: True adventure stories compiled and edited by
Margaret C. Scoggin. Knopf. A good and varied collection of true-life adventures of mountain climbers, deep-sea divers, hunters, and others who
have done the kind of exciting things boys and girls like to read about.
(Also *The Edge of Danger*.)

ESKIMO BOY by Pipaluk Freuchen. Illus. by Ingrid V. Nyman. Lothrop.
This heroic tale of a boy's fight to save his family from starvation is absorbing and almost too realistic for comfort. Told by the daughter of the
famous Arctic explorer Peter Freuchen, the Eskimo life is described authentically and feelingly.

SMOKY, THE COWHORSE by Will James. Scribner. The life story of a
western pony told by a cowboy in his own vivid colloquial speech. One of
the best stories of the great West. (Also *Lone Cowboy: My Life Story*.)

THE YEARLING by Margaret Kinnar Rawlings. Illus. by N. C. Wyeth.

Scribner. No youngster, or adult either, who has any feeling for animals can resist this lovely story of Jody Baxter and his pet fawn. Set dramatically in the backwoods of Florida.

CAPTAINS COURAGEOUS by Rudyard Kipling. Doubleday. How the spoiled son of a rich man is thrown by accident among some hardworking fishermen, and how he learns some fine lessons about real life from them. Not preachy, but a thoroughly interesting narrative.

A CONNECTICUT YANKEE IN KING ARTHUR'S COURT by Mark Twain. American boy cast back to the days of chivalry has some hilarious adventures among the knights of old. The satire is broad and delightful and not wasted on youngsters.

THE THREE MUSKETEERS by Alexandre Dumas. Any youngster who passes the age of 13 or 14 without having shared the high adventures of the three dashing and romantic swordsmen in this famous historical novel has missed something special. (Also *The Count of Monte Cristo.*)

MUTINY ON THE BOUNTY by Charles S. Nordhoff and James Norman Hall. Little, Brown. A gripping sea story based on a famous mutiny that actually happened in English naval history. (Also *Pitcairn's Island* and *Hurricane.*)

CAPTAIN HORATIO HORNBLOWER by C. S. Forester. Little, Brown. Exciting naval adventures of a brave British captain during the Napoleonic wars.

ANNAPURNA by Maurice Herzog. Dutton. The true and absorbing story of the terrific struggle of men against the heights of Annapurna. Told with modesty and deep feeling by the man who climbed to the top.

THE SPIRIT OF ST. LOUIS by Charles A. Lindbergh. Scribner. A thrilling and extraordinarily well written account of the famous solo flight across the Atlantic, particularly interesting for its wealth of personal details. With maps, charts, and photographs of the flight.

WIDE WONDERFUL WORLD

CHILDREN OF THE SEA by Wilfred S. Bronson. Illus. by the author. Harcourt. A delightful account of the activities of one of nature's most charming creatures, the dolphin. Told with a fine blend of accuracy and humor.

PADDLE-TO-THE-SEA by Holling C. Holling. Illus. by the author. Houghton Mifflin. The story of a toy Indian canoe's travels through the Great Lakes makes geography seem fresh and fascinating. (Also *Tree in the Trail.*)

THE EARTH FOR SAM by W. Maxwell Reed. Illus. by Karl Moseley. Harcourt. The story of mountains, rivers, dinosaurs and early men told in a dramatic way that links the evolution of earth and man clearly. (Also *The Stars for Sam.*)

THE BOY'S BOOK OF INSECTS by Edwin Way Teale. Dutton. Stimulating descriptions of all the common insects by a naturalist who writes with rare distinction. Many photographs and diagrams. By the author of the delightful *North With the Spring*, an adult book about the rebirth of nature—trees, flowers, birds, insects—as spring moves northward that would fascinate any boy or girl interested in these things.

ANIMALS ON THE MARCH by Jannette Lucas and W. Maxwell Reed. Harcourt. How all the animals of the earth descended from prehistoric animals, presented in a remarkable book with fine explanatory drawings.

ANIMALS NOBODY KNOWS by Ivan T. Sanderson. Illus. by the author. Viking. Lively descriptions of unusual and interesting animals by a well-known explorer.

WIND, SAND AND STARS by Antoine de Saint-Exupéry. Harcourt. An account of the early days of aviation by the heroic French flyer who was also a distinguished writer. An adult book, but older boys will thrill to the excitement of the author's struggles with the clumsy early planes.

HUNTERS OF THE GREAT NORTH by Vilhjálmur Stefansson. Harcourt. Fascinating true story of how the author became an explorer, and an account of his first thrilling expedition to the Arctic.

THE WONDERFUL WORLD OF MATHEMATICS by Lancelot Hogben. Illus. by André, Charles Keeping, and Kenneth Symonds. Garden City. A truly remarkable book describing how the growth of science went along with the course of civilization. With outstanding illustrations. An excellent eye-opener for youngsters who think they "hate math", as well as those interested in science.

ONE GOD: THE WAYS WE WORSHIP HIM by Florence M. Fitch. Lothrop. An outstanding book for parents to read to younger children or for children over 10 to read themselves. Thoughtful, accurate and reverent explanations of the great religions in America—Jewish, Catholic and Protestant. Illustrated with fine photographs. (Also *Ways of Worship in the Orient*.)

THE BIBLE DESIGNED TO BE READ AS LIVING LITERATURE: The Old and The New Testaments in the King James Version. Arranged and Edited by Ernest Sutherland Bates. Simon and Schuster. An outstanding editing job in which well-considered omissions and re-arrangements have been made to make the Bible more readable for modern people and to bring out its poetic beauty and dramatic qualities.

FAMOUS PEOPLE AND FAMOUS EVENTS

Historical Fiction

THE LITTLE HOUSE IN THE BIG WOODS by Laura Ingalls Wilder. Illus. by Helen Sewell. Harcourt. This and six successive books in a series about the ups and downs of a brave and intensely human pioneer family have been written from the author's childhood remembrances and have become modern classics. Should be part of every American child's heritage.

MEN OF IRON by Howard Pyle. Illus. by the author. Harper. One of the best of this well-loved author's stories (*The Merry Adventures of Robin Hood*, etc.) with fine historical background. This one is about how knights of old were trained, and the clanging battles of the days of chivalry in England. (Also *Otto of the Silver Hand*.)

HITTY—HER FIRST HUNDRED YEARS by Rachel Field. Illus. by Dorothy Lathrop. Macmillan. The exciting autobiography of a New England doll which delights girls long past the doll age and gives them a better feeling for the meaning of the times than most history books.

JOHNNY TREMAINE by Esther Forbes. Houghton Mifflin. One of the best of all the stories about Revolutionary days. Gives the young reader real insight into the troubled feelings in New England at the time of the Boston Tea Party by sharing the emotions of a brave boy who goes through many dangerous exploits at that time. (Also *America's Paul Revere*.)

DRUMS by James Boyd. Scribner. A delightful and deeply felt novel about Revolutionary days, this time with a Southern background.

WAGONS WESTWARD by Armstrong Sperry. Winston. Gives a vigorous and unforgettable picture of the American pioneers' movement westward. Strong and realistic writing.

THE RED BADGE OF COURAGE: An Episode of the Civil War by Stephen Crane. A beautifully written and dramatic story of the fears and feelings of a young soldier in the Civil War.

Great Lives and Events

LANDMARK BOOKS. Random House. There are now about 80 titles in this distinguished series of books, about events and people that have become turning points in American and world history. They are all written by good authors, in a vigorous and dramatic style to appeal to young people of about 10 to 14. Among the finest of them are the following:

THE PONY EXPRESS by Samuel Hopkins Adams
DANIEL BOONE by John Mason Brown
THE LANDING OF THE PILGRIMS by James Daugherty
PAUL REVERE AND THE MINUTE MEN by Dorothy Canfield Fisher
WILD BILL HICKOCK TAMES THE WEST by Stewart Holbrook
THE VIKINGS by Elizabeth Janeway
GETTYSBURG by Mackinlay Kantor
THE MONITOR AND THE MERRIMAC by Fletcher Pratt
CUSTER'S LAST STAND by Quentin Reynolds
THE VOYAGES OF COLUMBUS by Armstrong Perry

TEN SAINTS by Eleanor Farjeon. Illus. by Helen Sewell. Oxford. The beautifully told stories of the lives of famous saints like St. Francis, St. Christopher, St. Patrick.

GEORGE WASHINGTON'S WORLD by Genevieve Foster. Illus. by the author. Scribner. An original book that links together and vividly interprets all that was going on in the world at the time, making history doubly real. Companion volumes, and equally distinguished are *Abraham Lincoln's World* and *Augustus Caesar's World*.

Poetry Collections

THE COMPLETE NONSENSE BOOK by Edward Lear. Wonderful limericks and nonsense jingles that children of all ages enjoy. Lear's own inimitable drawings add to the fun.

THE HOME BOOK OF VERSE FOR YOUNG FOLKS edited by Burton E. Stevenson. Illus. by Willy Pagány. Holt. Youngsters of any age can find things they enjoy while browsing through this large and varied collection.

JUNIOR ANTHOLOGY OF WORLD POETRY edited by Mark Van Doren and Garibaldi Lapolla. Boni. A distinguished collection of poetry from all over the world, arranged according to countries. Includes especially good translations. For children over 10.

THE WINGED HORSE ANTHOLOGY edited by Joseph Auslander and Frank Ernest Hill. Doubleday. A fine collection, particularly rich in modern poetry. Good for boys and girls over 11.

Index